A GIFT
FOR ALL AGES

CLIFFORD & JOYCE PENNER

A GIFT
FOR ALL AGES

WORD PUBLISHING

Word (UK) Ltd
Milton Keynes, England

WORD BOOKS
WACO, TEXAS, USA
WORD AUSTRALIA
Heathmont, Victoria, Australia
SUNDAY SCHOOL CENTRE WHOLESALE
Salt River, South Africa
ALBY COMMERCIAL ENTERPRISES PTE LTD
Scotts Road, Singapore
CONCORDE DISTRIBUTORS LTD
Havelock North, New Zealand
CROSS (HK) CO
Hong Kong

A GIFT FOR ALL AGES

ISBN 0–85009–151–9

Reproduced, printed and bound in Great Britain for Word (UK) Ltd by Cox and Wyman Ltd, Reading.

We dedicate this to our family

Julene Maree
Gregory Boyd
Kristine Renée

Contents

Introduction: Sexuality   ix

I. Family Planning   1

   1. To Baby or Not to Baby   3
   2. Choosing and Using Birth Control   16
   3. Sex and Infertility   30
   4. Childlessness, Adoption, and Sex   44
   5. Sex during and after Pregnancy   55

II. Children Impact the Sexual Life   73

   6. Mommy, What Are You and Daddy Doing in There?   75

III. Teaching Our Children about Sex   87

   7. Modeling and Communicating Healthy Sexual
      Attitudes   89
   8. Affirming Sexuality in the Infant and Toddler   101
   9. The Curious Years—Preschool to Puberty   107
   10. The Squirrelly Years—Junior High   115
   11. The Decision-Making Years—Senior High   122
   12. Sex Education with Values   136

IV. Single Sexuality   151

   13. Single, Sexual, and Sanctified   153

V. Handling Adult Sexuality in Special Situations 171

14. Sex and the Unconsummated Marriage 173
15. Sex and the In-laws 185
16. Sex and Illness 190
17. Sex and Aging 206

VI. Tough Sexual Issues 221

18. Sexual Molestation and Abuse 223
19. Sexual Infections 242
20. Sexual Addictions 253

Index 267

Introduction: Sexuality

Sex is powerful! It gets our attention. It is a vital part of who we are as human beings created in the image of God. It grabs our total being. It is that intense dimension of us that makes us male and female. In the act of sex two people become one. We most lose ourselves to one another. Sex can take us to the highest peaks of ecstasy or to the deepest pits of despair and degradation. Sex is part of God's design for us. Sex is good!

Our sexuality is much broader than mere sexual intercourse. It refers to our whole person. Our sexuality is with us for life—from before birth until death. It includes all the characteristics and feelings that make us male and female. We associate our sexuality with the roles we play as boys and girls, or men and women. How we relate with the same sex and how we relate to the opposite sex are part of our sexuality. The feelings and thoughts that stir inside us are part of those relationships. Our vitality, our sexual drive energy, is the basis for getting things done in life and the basis for sexual arousal and release. In addition, our sexuality includes all sexual behavior from hand-holding and kissing to sexual intercourse. And all of this is in God's image!

Even though our sexuality is so basic to who we are as human beings, many times issues of sexuality are harbored inside of us. They are our most private secrets. How easily we feel ashamed and embarrassed! We have difficulty sharing what we really think and feel. We lack knowledge, feel inadequate, and are unsure.

Every family sends messages about sexuality. Some are spoken, but the loudest are lived. They are silently communicated through our attitudes and actions. There are sexual issues that concern and confront all families. They can be avoided or distorted, but they won't go away.

Our culture saturates us with sex. The media is a prime source of the overexposure. But our conversations, jokes, dramas, and literature all contribute. Sex is woven into the very fabric of our existence. There is no escape. We cannot protect our children from it, and we cannot pretend that it doesn't exist. So the only choice is to be knowledgeable. We need to have the best information to help ourselves and to help our children. Knowledge can make a positive difference in our lives and influence the development and adjustment of our children. That is what this book, *A Gift for All Ages,* is all about. This is its intention and purpose.

In 1975 we joined our professional lives. Until that time, Joyce had been teaching nursing at California State University in Los Angeles and had coordinated the development of the curriculum for the new school of nursing at Azusa Pacific University in Azusa, California. Cliff had a private practice as a Clinical Psychologist. He had trained lay counselors in churches and trained and supervised volunteers for a Volunteer Los Angeles Hotline.

At that time Cliff was asked to teach a ten-week class on sexuality to seminary wives. Confronted by the topic of sex and sixty women, he coerced Joyce into joining him. So we combined Cliff's psychological and theological expertise with Joyce's physiological-psychosomatic awareness, studied diligently, and presented ten two-hour sessions on sexuality. Being clinicians, we never expected knowledge to make a difference in people's sexual experience, but to our delight it did! The success of that experience led us to teaching seminars on sexual adjustment for couples in churches throughout the country. The content of the seminars developed into our first book, *The Gift of Sex.*

Becoming known as experts on the subject of sex, we began teaching sexuality to all age groups. Joyce developed a sex education program for our own school district. We began giving Human Sexuality lectures on college campuses and teaching sex education to junior highers, high schoolers, singles, and premarital couples. Joyce was asked to teach nurses and nursing students to deal with sex and illness. Cliff started groups for women who had been sexually abused as children. And thus, *A Gift for All Ages* evolved.

In our home, sex is such a common topic that we sometimes worry that we will miss some developmentally necessary communication with our children. It's easy to take for granted that they will be well informed because of our familiarity with the topic.

We will be referring to our children throughout this book. They have taught us much of what we know about teaching kids about sex. We are convinced that as parents we can learn what we need to know about parenting our children if we take time to listen to them.

Julene is our college-aged young adult. She has always been a question-asker, has dated throughout her adolescence, and has been very open with us in the process of learning about her sexuality. Having her out in the world on her own is sometimes frightening.

Greg is a high school adolescent, who is very serious about his life decisions while keeping us in stitches with his wry humor. He reads avidly and thinks through who he wants to be and how he is going to behave. His deliberateness is comforting. His solitude often makes us wonder what's going on inside.

Kristine is our twerp. She is school age and is quickly becoming prepubescent. Being nine (seven years younger than our other two), she has always seemed like a little adult. She is the one who has grown up with sex being so familiar that she has not asked the typical age-appropriate questions, so we sometimes wonder what all she has assimilated in that alert mind of hers.

We tend to be very involved parents, loving and giving but with high expectations, probably even a little overanxious. Our family is a vital part of who we are. We thank God for them. We have been very blessed.

A Gift for All Ages is a family handbook on sexuality. It deals with all *informative* issues on sexuality. Our information is not geared to the resolution of theoretical issues. It is practically oriented to the needs of the family. Every home needs some portion of this book. It is designed to be a resource book, a family's first-aid kit for sexual issues. Parents may want to read some chapters with their children. Other chapters will give them guidance in dealing with their children, and still others are for the parents themselves. Adults will find some sections beneficial in making major life decisions, or for helping a friend in trouble. Adolescents will benefit from reading several of the chapters. There is information for the single person, children of all ages, the childless couple, parents, and the elderly. Since our sexuality is with us from birth to death, it is indeed *A Gift for All Ages*.

For Further Study

Katchadourian, Herant A., M.D. and Donald T. Lunde. *Fundamentals of Human Sexuality,* 3rd Edition. New York: Holt, Rinehart, and Winston, 1975.

Masters, William H., Virginia E. Johnson, and Robert C. Kolodny. *Masters and Johnson on Sex and Human Loving.* Boston: Little, Brown and Company, 1986.

Penner, Clifford L. and Joyce J. Penner. *The Gift of Sex,* Waco, Texas, Word, Inc., 1981.

1

Family Planning

To Baby or Not to Baby

When we consider all the forces at work in the world—the rising nuclear threat, the threat of overpopulation, the high divorce rate, the increase in single parent families, the uncertain inflation level and cost of living, the millions of uncared for and unwanted children— the importance of the decision to have a child becomes obvious. Children deserve the right to be born into a world where they are wanted, where they will be loved and cherished. Not only do they have basic physical needs, but they have emotional and spiritual needs as well. They need a home where they will receive loving care and warm acceptance.

A Critical Decision

The only absolutely irreversible relationship decision you will ever make is the choice to bring a life into this world. That may sound dramatic. It may tie your stomach in knots or leave you in a real quandary about how to reach this decision. But it remains a fact. If we buy a house, choose a career, even choose a husband or wife, those decisions are reversible—as difficult, unpleasant, or immoral as we may find them to be. But with the decision regarding a child, we have no recourse. Isn't it marvelous that millions of children are born each year, when the decision is this fateful? And it is even more surprising that many modern, educated, enlightened couples never give a thought as to whether or not they want children.

Not only is it an irreversible decision, but it also involves long-term commitment. The initial commitment to parenting is from birth through adolescence. But many times there are financial and certainly emotional commitments that go far beyond the exciting yet turbulent years of adolescence. Many parents whose children have long ago left home report that the sense of being the concerned parent never leaves them. So not only is it impossible to reverse the decision, but we are left to live with the consequences throughout life. Death and adoption are the only forces that can really break that commitment and responsibility. Giving a child up for adoption may free the parent technically, but many times not emotionally.

So the awesomeness of this decision, its irreversibility and the long-term commitment, all increase the significance of the choice to have children. To bring a life into the world is a serious responsibility. We take on the feeding, clothing, and sheltering of the *life*—and then the shaping, the influencing, and the educating of the *person* involved. Our children come to us with what they inherit through their genes, but their lives are, as it were, empty slates. We as parents bear the responsibility for filling that slate. We help to shape these undeveloped beings into persons of special uniqueness and worth in society.

Let's look at the other side of the coin: the rewards of having children. The decision to have a child is the decision to bring into our lives that wonderful, soft, dependent bundle of joy who can fulfill us as parents. Babies evoke an instinctive response in their parents. The decision to become parents seems like a natural one. A child offers us the opportunity to give ourselves totally to someone else. We can share our values and our faith more completely with our children than with anyone. In addition to the dependence of an infant, and the joy of all the stages of development, some parents have children so that they will be cared for in their old age. There are many specific rewards that push us to have children, besides the unexplainable, indefinable urge toward procreation. Probably it is the drive for self-perpetuation—that is, making sure we have offspring to survive us, a part of us that will live on.

Most of us have the capacity to procreate. To make a decision *against* what is our potential, against what or how we were created to be, takes a great deal of struggle and conscious effort.

Everybody Expects You to Have a Baby

The process goes something like this: fun comments are made during the engagement time about children, and relatively little pressure is felt. After the couple gets back from the honeymoon, however, they may notice the comments are increasing both in frequency and expectation. "Well, now that you are married and all that's over with, when should we be expecting our first grandchild?" Or a few months later, "How is everything going between you and Steve?"

The pressure may be even more demanding. The first time the wife experiences the flu or nausea the expectation is that she is pregnant. It isn't as if anyone is asking what the couple wants. They assume what the couple wants and send a message, "You will not live up to our expectations if you do not have a child and don't have one soon!" For the couple who is planning on having children this can easily become a mild irritant. Parents or friends are not letting you do what you want to do when you want to do it. But for those couples who are not planning on having children (or are unsure or unable), this pressure can be incredible.

If several years pass and still there are no children, the pressure may become unbearable. When the woman reaches her thirtieth birthday or gets a raise or promotion on the job, the nervousness of her "directors" heightens. As time goes on, the pressure can increase to the point of being obnoxious.

We have known couples who received letters from out-of-town relatives with suggestions for assuring fertility. Others have told couples they were praying for their pregnancy when the couple wasn't even trying to conceive (and, in fact, were using birth control). The message is, "What is the matter with you? Have you been checked out by a doctor? There are all kinds of modern ways that you can be helped these days." All this may occur before the couple has even decided they want to have a child.

There is innate expectation or anticipation that the choice for children will be made. Some people think that society is violated if a couple chooses not to have children. Having a family is not considered an option but an expectation. The assumption is, *"Of course* you'll be having children!" It's as expected as, *"Of course,* now that you're married, you'll be living together."

At the same time that couples are experiencing the pressure to have children, they may be observing a most contradictory message regarding children. Before you have children you get this message: "Children are wonderful. They fulfill your life; they provide you with one of life's happiest experiences. If you don't have children you will be missing out on something vitally important." It is a clear and strong message that says "to have children is wonderful."

Once you have children, the wonderfulness seems to disappear. The new message is that one should get this parenting business over with as quickly as possible. Being a parent is a real drag. Parenting is not held in high esteem as a full-time job. Mothers often express their frustration with their children, rather than their delight and pride. When delight and pride *are* expressed, parents are made to feel that they are being inappropriately boastful. So babies are something you should look forward to in your life, but then not expect to enjoy them.

He Wants a Baby But I Don't

A major source of stress in a marriage relationship can be disagreement between husband and wife about when or whether to have a baby.

There are many reasons why either the husband or wife might not be ready for a child: A woman may feel she needs more security in her career. She may have difficulty interrupting her career to start a family. Emotionally she may feel she is not ready to give herself so totally to another person. Her relationship with her husband may not be stable enough to warrant bringing a child into the family. Finances can be a major issue. She may fear that without her income the family could not survive. In such a situation a child would cause severe stress or a major change in lifestyle. She may not be ready for the stress of these changes.

From the man's perspective, the reasons could be very similar. He may have financial concerns, anxiety about timing, or conflict in the marriage relationship. Most frequently, when the man is resistant, he is not ready to take on the role of being the responsible father. He senses that this new role is going to dramatically alter his lifestyle. He is right! Bringing a baby into the family will change life drastically! It is most reasonable that a husband consider those issues *before* deciding to become a parent.

For both parties, there may be the fear of the unknown. Even as marriage brings about radical changes and requires adjustments, so does having a child. It is never completely predictable what the effects of these changes will be. For some, it is surprisingly jarring. For others, parenthood is a natural, easy adjustment. The couple falls into their roles as if they had always been parents.

Mary and Fred had been married for five years. He was just completing an advanced degree. She had already completed her education. Both had strong professional careers. They were very responsible people who had every reason to believe that life with a child would flow smoothly because of how they had adjusted to other changes.

In spite of their positive history together, Fred had a deep-seated fear that even though he was twenty-six years old, he was not competent to become a father. This new role was going to demand more from him than he could deliver. Nevertheless, he decided to go along with his wife's desire to have children. Fortunately, once he became a father, he naturally accepted his role and has functioned most adequately as a parent with all three of his children.

Diane and Jerry started having children early in their married life, mainly because Diane wanted them. While Jerry was hesitant, Diane had been trained in child care and was eager for the children to be born. The unpredictable happened. Diane found being a mother extremely stressful. Often she became overwhelmed with the care of the children and left them in day care as long as possible each day. Jerry, on the other hand, gave of himself in a free and loving way. He was able to be a most involved father, quite in contrast to what he had expected.

So far we have been discussing husband-wife uncertainty in regard to having children. What if one of the spouses doesn't want a child at all? This is a real dilemma. Such a conflict should obviously have been discussed before the marriage and usually is if the couple has had premarital counseling. What sometimes happens is this: the man tells his bride-to-be that he doesn't think he ever wants to have children, but she assumes that she can talk him into it. She thinks she can change his mind and then is severely disappointed and distraught when she discovers two or three years later that he's even more adamant about not having children than he was before. It is always dangerous to go into a marriage assuming that you can change a person's viewpoint on a major issue. There are good reasons why some people might not want to have children. The passage of time or a new relationship does not necessarily reverse those reasons.

Should you find that the two of you cannot come to an agreement on whether or not you want children, we would strongly encourage you first to talk about it as openly as you can.

Second, do some reading on the subject. One book written for this exact purpose is *A Baby? Maybe: A Guide to the Most Fateful Decision in Your Life* (Whelan, Elizabeth M. New York: Bobbs-Merrill, 1976). This book is designed to help you think through all the reasons why you are struggling with this issue and what the ramifications are. It gives some good pointers on how to go about making this decision.

Children: To Have or Not Have—A Guide to Making and Living with Your Decision (Elvenstar, Diane C. San Francisco: Harbor Publishing, 1982) is a workbook with many different forms for a couple to complete. Its evaluation questionnaires can help you determine whether children are for you or not.

If the two of you cannot reach agreement regarding parenthood, it will be necessary for you to seek professional help. It is important that you not expect someone else to make your decision for you. Rather, seek someone who can help you define your differences and search out the right path to follow.

Some marriages end in divorce because the issue of whether or not to have children is irreconcilable.

Do Babies Make a Marriage?

If there is stress in a marriage, the couple may expect that having children will somehow resolve that problem. Psychologists used to think that this expectation was unfounded. As we have interacted with various couples, we discover that for some this is, in fact, a valid experience. A certain kind of bond or connection begins when a child is born. Up until that point the marriage may have been in jeopardy. But having a child together may be the "cement" that binds some couples together. Unfortunately, there are many more cases where the opposite happens. Couples who counted on children saving their marriage end up getting a divorce. Their children did not help resolve their marital difficulties; instead, the stress of the new responsibilities accentuated the conflict that was already present.

Eric and Nancy were just that kind of couple. At the time of their marriage, Nancy's parents had been strongly against the relationship. They had gone through continual stress in their dating, breaking up and getting back together many times. Finally, somewhat on an impulse, they decided to marry. When they found that married life was not really much better than the dating life had been, they agreed that perhaps they needed children. So they brought two children into the world. Two and a half years later they separated and were finally divorced. In this situation, having children only made a bad situation worse.

Sometimes just the opposite happens. Glen and Linda had been married about four years. Linda married Glen on the rebound. The man she really wanted to marry had broken off their engagement. Throughout the first four years of their married life, Linda's mind continually returned to her first love and the joy she believed would have been hers in that marriage. Glen didn't offer the warmth, intensity, and excitement she had known with her previous boyfriend.

Linda became pregnant without really planning for it, and a change began immediately. Glen became much more involved in the relationship. His care for Linda was intense as they anticipated the arrival of their first child. When the baby arrived, Glen became a most caring, loving, and devoted husband and father. It was almost as if something new had happened to him as a result of his child being born.

We tell these real-life, actual stories to illustrate that there is no easy way to predict a couple's response to having a child. We can say this very emphatically, however: it should never be assumed that a child is going to improve a relationship. That may be the outcome, but it should not be the expectation. Many children are brought into the world because they are desired for the purpose of improving a marriage. That is a most inadequate and potentially dangerous basis for having children.

Eyes Wide Open to the Delights and the Dilemmas

In choosing to have children, it is crucial to get a realistic perspective. Spend time with couples who have children of all ages. Babysit for children of various ages. Read about children.

We are struck by the fact that as a couple prepares for their first child, all of their energy seems to be going toward preparing a room oriented around a baby. All of the investment goes toward what is needed for the first twelve months. Many of us come to parenting with this attitude. We see ourselves parenting this wonderful, warm, soft, cuddly little baby.

We disregard the fact that we are going to be up nights, that the baby is going to have messy diapers and at some stage is going to smear that mess all over the lovely, newly decorated walls. The baby is going to have croup, and not only will it keep us up at night but have us worried about whether he or she is going to survive.

Once babies reach that first stage of independence, they are going to want their own way. They are going to enjoy taking a dish of rice and turning it upside down on their heads. It's fun to have those little granules go showering down all around their heads. Often the fun is accentuated by watching mother come off the wall. This provides a great deal of entertainment for the little one- or two-year-old.

Some babies are going to want to be rocked, while others just prefer to be put into the crib, so we won't get to hold them as much as we want.

They are going to grow and change. At each stage of development, we will need to flex and adjust to their ever-changing need for us as parents. We are going to have to be ready to give and give and give.

On the other hand, there is nothing that can compare with the joy of watching a growing child. Our own little children running after us and calling us "Mommy" or "Daddy," asking to be comforted when there has been a scratch or a fall, and wanting to be held when they are sick are all examples of the incredible warmth children bring. They love to play games. They run to hide as we walk into the room or they make some new discovery about the world around them. Nothing can compare with the rewards of these experiences.

As we move toward the decision to have children, it is absolutely crucial that we face realistically the joys on the one hand and the burdens and stress on the other. It is important that we know ourselves and our reactions to the responsibility of children. The more we have to give, the more we receive. Loved children are clearly easier to parent than deprived children.

Stewardship and Responsibility

We hear much about stewardship, about the need for us to be good stewards of that with which we have been entrusted. In society, we talk about being stewards of the natural resources, not wasting water or trees, and not polluting the air, soil or rivers. Stewardship is important. But we hear relatively little about being good stewards of children who have been entrusted to us.

Parenting is society's way of perpetuating itself. We are entrusted with the full responsibility to nurture the development of our children's potential as long as they are totally in our care. So much human potential is wasted because it was never developed by those who were responsible for nurturing it. The responsibility of being good stewards of the natural resources that are present in our children includes training them to be good members of society, assisting them in learning effective decision-making skills, and helping them to fully develop their natural gifts. We are also responsible to teach them to respect themselves and those around them, to help them recognize their dependence on God, the Creator and Giver of Life.

It is our strong feeling that society's encouragement to have children must be accompanied with the encouragement to accept the serious responsibilities of parenting. We see this as the only way to break into the dilemma of negative or inadequate parenting being passed from one generation to the next. Parenting education and consultation can break into this pattern, but that is really a subject for another book (now in the planning stages).

Can We Choose to Be Childless?

Most of us grew up assuming that we would be parents. Parents usually want their children to have children. We can count on it that all of our friends who are having children will want us to have children. So to make the decision to be childless is a daring move. It counters the natural expectations.

If we choose not to have children, the most automatic response from others is to label this as a selfish decision. Yet whether you are a couple who is thinking about that choice for yourselves, or have friends who are thinking about remaining childless, it is vital that you hear and understand why that choice is being made.

There are many reasons why couples decide not to have children. The most common reason for deciding against having children is age. Either one or both spouses feel they are emotionally or physically too old or inadequate. This is especially true for second marriages where one partner already has a child. In some instances, it may be that a couple fears they have experienced too much stress in their relationship. Bringing children into their world would only add to that stress, and they don't think their relationship could survive. This seems like a mature, head-out-of-the-sand kind of decision. We've known people who were so committed to serving others they felt a child would be an interruption of that fulfillment. In still other instances, some have chosen to be childless for medical reasons, or concern about one or the other partner not being able to be a responsible parent.

A couple from the Midwest wrote to us. They were struggling with whether or not to have children. The wife wrote saying that her husband had had a severe problem with impulsively exhibiting himself. He still struggled with this at times. They had reached the decision that with his sexual insecurities and a very unstable employment history, it was important not to bring a child into their home. The mother would be in constant fear of both sexual exploitation and financial insecurity.

Even though childlessness is an option in today's world, it is important to note that only about two or three percent of the population ever make the choice to remain childless. Couples choosing to remain childless are clearly in the minority. We need to be very gentle with couples who are making the choice to be childless. It is their personal choice and they must be free to make it.

A word from the authors might be in order right here. We are both delighted with the fact that we have three children. They are an *important* part of our lives. The whole experience of parenting has been very positive for us. So our stressing both sides of parenting should not be construed as an indication that somehow we think to choose to be parents is a bad idea. We do believe it is a serious decision that is often taken too lightly, so we are emphasizing the seriousness of bringing children into the world.

There is naturally the question, "Is it not my Christian responsibility, my moral responsibility to have children? Did not God command Adam and Eve to subdue and replenish the earth? Was it not part of the Hebrew culture to perpetuate life? Is it not a natural God-given instinct to be a parent?" It seems that all those questions can be answered in the affirmative. However, we must remember that we have not chosen to live our lives in most natural, creative way. If we did, then we would begin producing children at age thirteen, fourteen, or whenever we are physically capable. And we would keep on having children until menopause, which might be ten, twenty, or thirty children later!

Once we have made the decision that we will not have as many children as we can possibly have, then we have made the decision to go against what is natural. The obvious option is available to us. We can choose to have one child, or two, or five, or none at all. Let us repeat again—we are not advocating that couples choose not to have children. We are advocating that people make a conscious choice.

Getting Pregnant: A New Reason for Love-making

In most of us there seems to be the urge to show that we can impregnate or be impregnated and bear children. It is part of being a man or a woman. When we have decided we want children, our sexual experience may be filled with a special meaning.

When the decision has been reached, and you are ready to conceive, we'd recommend that you make it a very special time, somewhat like your wedding night. The attitude with which we start a life will, at least subtly, be transmitted to our child. If at some point we can say to our child, "You know, when we decided that we wanted to have you, we went off to the seashore for a weekend and we spent our time talking and walking and loving one another in a most special and close way, and that's where you came from. You are the product of love. We didn't get pregnant that weekend, but a few months later we were pregnant and you were starting to grow. That beginning time of love and closeness is really what brought you to us. You are very special!"

Some couples find a new freedom in their love-making as a result of not having the concern about birth control. If the woman was on the Pill there may have been anxiety about its effect on her. If the couple was using a barrier method such as a condom or a diaphragm, there may have been an ongoing concern as to whether it would do its work. If they were using some variation of the rhythm method, there may have been concern as to whether they were making love on a safe day. So now, without the fears about pregnancy, in fact, with the desire for pregnancy, it brings new freedom. This can be especially true for the woman, when she finds herself able to let go and be intensely sexual, because she has the great urge to become pregnant. For the husband, there may be a new feeling of potency that says, "Now I am able to make love for all of the right reasons. Not only for the joy and pleasure but also for the possibility of impregnation." When these feelings are shared, they can serve to bring the two of you closer to one another.

Timing the Arrival of Children

The question is often asked, "When is the right time to get pregnant?" There rarely is a perfect time. For most couples it is best to wait until they have connected deeply with each other. But beyond this point, there are so many variables that it is hard to say when is the right time.

Even though many women are successfully producing and enjoying their first baby in their late thirties or early forties, we do know that physically the twenties are the best child-bearing years for a woman. But there are other issues: how it fits into your education and career goals, your finances, and other family responsibilities. If you wait to reach perfection at your jobs, in your marriage or finances, you will likely never have children, so forget that goal! You can plan for parenthood, choose wisely, and set goals. If there are fears or hesitations, they should be confronted. Sometimes we find that one or both spouses keep delaying because of some anxiety about the possibility of having a child. When that is the case, it is important to face it, and define the fears.

We have a seven-year gap between our second and third child because of such a delay. Joyce had German measles during the twelfth week of her second pregnancy with a 90 percent chance of having a defective child. Without the technology of today, there was no way to know until he was born that Greg would be totally normal and healthy. So we lived with five months of concern. From that point we connected pregnancy with anxiety about producing a normal child. Since we already had a healthy girl and boy, we were hesitant to go for a third. We finally had the courage six years and three months later, and what a special treat Kristine has been.

In conclusion, to baby or not to baby is a decision every couple will face. In the complexity of today's world, to have children is not as natural an outcome of marriage as was true during the past, when lifestyles were simpler and more family-oriented. This is a decision that needs to be made between you and with the sense of God's blessing.

For parents of married but childless children, we encourage you to "set them free"! Give them a copy of *A Baby? Maybe* and let them make their own decision in their own time. Nothing is a greater delight to parents or grandparents than the arrival of a child freely chosen. Those who choose to be without children need your ongoing love and support, even though you may be disappointed in their decision. Those unable to conceive need your most special love and care.

For Further Study

Elvenstar, Diane C. *Children: To Have or Not Have. A Guide to Making and Living with your Decision.* San Francisco: Harbor Publishing, 1982.
Whelan, Elizabeth M. *A Baby? Maybe: A Guide to the Most Fateful Decision in Your Life.* New York: Bobbs-Merrill, 1976.

2

Choosing and Using Birth Control

Family planning is the process of setting up a reproductive life program. It is thinking, praying, and talking with each other about whether or not to have children, when to have children, and how to regulate those choices with an effective birth control measure.

Once a couple decides that they are not going to allow themselves to get pregnant any time that would happen naturally, they have chosen to use birth control. It is estimated that if women decided to let nature take its course for their reproductive lifespan, most women would produce between ten and thirty babies! That would not only create an incredible personal and financial burden, but also a world overpopulation problem of monumental dimensions! The command God gave to be fruitful, multiply, and fill the earth has already been completed. The current world concern is how we are going to responsibly care for the children already in the world. This has led to couples approaching reproduction by choice, rather than by chance. When choice fails, either because of inability to reproduce (see Chapter 4) or because of an unwanted pregnancy, both individuals and the family unit are strongly impacted.

Moral and Religious Issues

Over the years the church has struggled with the issue of birth control. The concern has been that to take reproduction into our own hands is interfering with God's plan for our lives. In other words, we are in some way interrupting the work of the Master Creator. The Mormon church takes a position of not interfering with reproduction in any way. In fact, the more children the better!

Other religious leaders recommend that responsible choices need to be made, but that no "unnatural" methods of controlling conception be used. In 1984, Pope John Paul II took a bold stand on birth control. He proclaimed that the practice and attitude of contraception were "harmful to man's interior spiritual culture" (*Time,* Dec. 3, 1984, page 66). The challenge from Pope John Paul II, to the members of the Roman Catholic Church was to be available for motherhood and fatherhood. The Roman Catholic Church has held that abstinence during the woman's fertile time is the only acceptable means of preventing conception. The belief is that sexual union and procreation are inseparable in the plan of God. These pronouncements are based on "natural law" rather than direct biblical teaching. Natural law promotes the concept of a moral order or reasonable principle of humanity that fits with creation as determined by the Roman Catholic Church.

The third camp would put no restrictions on birth control, but rather see it as a personal choice. The belief is that God created us as intelligent human beings. He gave us dominion over the earth. His primary message is how He wants to relate to us as His people—how we can come to Him, be forgiven by Him, and become a member of His family. He gave us free choice and expects us to use that freedom wisely. The primary goals for His people are that we love Him and each other.

We believe that each person must come to grips with the religious and moral issues of birth control. Next, those issues have to be worked through within the marriage relationship. It is best if the birth control issue is settled before marriage. Ask yourselves, "How does our reproductive plan fit with our religious beliefs? Would we like to have children? How old would we like to be when we have children? How would we feel if we couldn't have children? How would we feel if we got pregnant without planning for it? What are our life goals? How do children fit into those goals?"

Each of us comes to marriage with attitudes regarding childbearing. The purpose of birth control is to conceive only when that is desired and planned. Our attitudes about childbearing will affect our feelings about using birth control. These need to be cleared with each other before the couple decides to marry.

We have an acquaintance who married a man older than she. *After* marriage she discovered that he was violently opposed to having children. They are now divorced. The opposite situation could happen: one spouse could be totally against using birth control, and the other not ready to allow babies to arrive at random.

Agreement concerning the attitude and feeling toward the issue of birth control is vital to family planning. If a choice is made that birth control will be used, then the method needs to be selected.

Birth Control Methods

Birth control includes all methods of limiting the birth of children. Contraception is one of these. Contraception prevents the man's sperm from uniting with the egg cell from the woman. Contraception is used to prevent pregnancy, not to interrupt once conception has taken place. That is an important moral and religious distinction. We are not talking about *taking* life, we are talking about *preventing* a new life from beginning. Even though many texts include abortion in the chapter with birth control, and many times abortion is the method used to prevent childbearing, we believe in prevention of conception, not interruption once conception has occurred.

There is no perfect method of contraception. There are many that work, but what works well for one couple may not work well for another. All methods currently practiced have both advantages and disadvantages. The method of choice will be as effective as the couple using it.

Even though the rhythm method of avoiding intercourse during the woman's fertile time and the withdrawal method of Onan in the Old Testament have always been with us, contraceptives have been used since the 1500s. Crude forms of condoms were used at that time. Rubber condoms and diaphragms were first used in the 1840s. Providing barriers between the sperm and the egg were the only methods of birth control until the 1930s. About that time Dr. Graffenburg, the discoverer of the G-spot in the woman's vagina, developed the first IUD from silkworm gut. The oral contraceptive, the Pill, came onto the scene in the late 1950s. It actually resulted from the search for a method to increase fertility.

Today a variety of reliable methods are available. However, there is no one perfect method. Choosing a proper birth control method is a serious matter. It is not the woman's decision. It is a couple's decision that needs to be made with thought and care. Help is available to make that decision.

In choosing a birth control method there are four issues that need to be considered: safety, effectiveness, convenience, and personal preference. Personal preference may be based on safety, effectiveness, or convenience. Or it may be connected with choices that have nothing to do with the facts. It may be based on something you've heard or some past experience. If a method is not going to be used faithfully because of who you are, it will not be effective even if it is safe, effective, and convenient. How it interferes with your sexual relations will influence your personal preference. Personal preference needs to be discussed between the two of you. We will provide information on the other three considerations.

Abstinence: Refraining totally from sexual intercourse as a method of birth control is 100 percent effective. Even though it may seem to be convenient and risk-free as well, it certainly isn't much fun. Divorce would be the risk. We believe abstinence is the method of choice before marriage, but clearly against biblical teaching after marriage. First Corinthians 7:3–5 says that we are not to withhold ourselves from one another except by agreement for a season of prayer and then come together again quickly lest we be tempted.

Withdrawal: Having intercourse (entry of the penis into the vagina), but removing the penis from the vagina before the man ejaculates (releases seminal fluid containing sperm) is a frequently practiced method of birth control. It has many drawbacks. First, it can be emotionally and physically upsetting. Two people have united themselves intensely, then (and at the height of openness and vulnerability) they pull apart. Second, many men do not have fine control over when they ejaculate, so accidents are most likely to happen. A man has five to ten seconds warning before he is about to ejaculate. Once he is about to ejaculate, he cannot stop it. He may not get out and far enough away from the vagina in those five to ten seconds. Also, the higher the degree of arousal, the less self-control he has. So even if he started with the best intentions of withdrawing, at the peak of arousal he may not do so. Third, for many men, seminal fluid containing sperm is released before ejaculation. There is enough sperm released to impregnate a woman without an ejaculation.

Douching: Using some means to flush the seminal fluid containing sperm out of the vagina has been attempted for ages. Unfortunately, this method is neither effective nor safe. The ineffectiveness stems from the fact that those tenacious little sperm are fast and determined. They get into the uterus and go looking for the egg in the uterine tube long before the woman can get to her douche bag and solution. In addition to being ineffective, douching is not recommended because it upsets the natural environment of the vagina and makes a woman more susceptible to infection. The current popular use of colas by teenagers is extremely dangerous. Yes, the colas are spermicidal, so they kill any sperm that haven't already found their way into the uterus. However, the bubbles of the pressurized carbonated soda pop may be forced into the uterus, be absorbed into the bloodstream as an embolus, and cause sudden death.

Barrier Method: The barrier contraceptives we will discuss are condoms, the sponge, diaphragms, cervical caps, and vaginal spermicidals.

A condom is commonly referred to as a rubber, prophylactic, safety, or sheath. It is a rubber device shaped like the finger of a glove and is placed over the erect penis before entry into the vagina. For people who are allergic to rubber products, natural animal skin condoms can be purchased. Condoms are one of the most commonly used contraceptives in the United States. They have the advantage of being easy to purchase and not requiring a physician's prescription. They also provide a barrier to protect against sexually transmitted diseases. There are no side effects from the use of condoms so they are safe. Their effectiveness depends on how they are used.

Out of one hundred couples using condoms for one year, ten pregnancies will occur. In using condoms successfully you must be certain the condom is new and free of holes or tears. It is important that the condom be rolled over the erect penis leaving one-half inch slack to catch semen. The woman's vagina needs to be lubricated before entry with a condom. A dry vagina may cause the condom to be removed during thrusting. If vaginal lubricant is not adequate, saliva or other water-based lubricants can be used. Petroleum products should not be used with rubber condoms. After the man ejaculates, he must hold the condom in place as he withdraws from the vagina so that no seminal fluid containing sperm will seep out as he withdraws.

Condoms are sexually inconvenient: love play must be interrupted to put them on and the man must keep an erection until withdrawal from the vagina. That can cause considerable anxiety for some men and, thus, interfere with their sexual response. For others, it is just a nuisance.

The sponge has been referred to as the female condom. This is because of its easy availability and use. It can be purchased by anyone without prescription and does not require a fitting. It is a two-inch round, soft polyurethane sponge that is permeated with spermicide. An advantage over the condom is that it is inserted before sexual play. While the manufacturers claim it can be left in place for twenty-four hours with equal effectiveness for repeated intercourse, recent findings are questioning that. It is 77 percent effective in preventing pregnancy but must be left in place for at least six hours after intercourse. Insertion is easy. After wetting it, it is folded and placed in the vagina with a finger. The pressure of the vaginal wall holds the sponge in place against the opening of the cervix.

Although there is no evidence of significant health risks for women using the sponge, allergic reactions to the spermicide and chronic vaginal irritation have been reported. Toxic Shock Syndrome has occurred in a few cases when the sponge was forgotten and left in for more than thirty hours. Even though a woman can purchase and use a sponge without professional assistance, it is recommended that she seek help to learn to find her cervix and properly place and remove the sponge. The position of her uterus may be such that the sponge cannot adequately protect her cervix.

The diaphragm has been used effectively for well over one hundred years. The vaginal diaphragm is made of soft rubber, shaped like a bowl, with a flexible spring at the outer edge. A spermicidal jelly or cream must be used with a diaphragm to insure effectiveness, since the diaphragm itself cannot prevent all sperm from reaching the cervix. To insert the diaphragm, the woman puts a small amount of spermicidal jelly or cream in the bowl and around the edge of the diaphragm. She then pinches the opposite sides of the rim together so that the diaphragm folds in the middle. The flattened shape can now be inserted into the vagina. Once inserted, the flexible rim resumes its original shape. She can then properly position the diaphragm to completely cover the cervix. It should fit securely and comfortably between the rear wall of the vagina and the upper edge of the pubic bone.

Thirteen out of one hundred women per year using the diaphragm get pregnant. That risk can be reduced to about 2.4 with experienced insertion and 100 percent usage. The diaphragm has the advantage of having no side effects. Also it is usually inserted before intercourse, and thus does not interfere with scheduled love-play. The diaphragm must be prescribed and fitted by a physician. The fit will need to be checked after pregnancy, pelvic surgery, or a weight change of ten pounds or more. The position of the diaphragm should be checked every time you have intercourse.

Some women cannot use a diaphragm because of poor vaginal muscle tone, sagging uterus, or vaginal obstructions. The diaphragm will not stay in place for women with these conditions, so an arcing, or bow-bend diaphragm may be needed. For all women, the diaphragm must be left in place for at least six hours after intercourse and the woman should not douche during this time. After removal, the diaphragm is to be washed with soap and water, rinsed, dried carefully, checked for holes by holding up against the light, powdered lightly with corn or potato flour, and placed in its special container. When using a rubber diaphragm it is important not to use petroleum-based vaginal lubricants because they interfere with the effectiveness.

The cervical cap is similar to the diaphragm with a slightly higher effectiveness. Made of thick rubber or plastic, it is thimble-shaped, has a rim, and fits over the cervix. Just like the diaphragm, the cap needs to be fitted by a professional on a healthy cervix. The cap is inserted in a similar way as is the vaginal diaphragm.

Insertion can be difficult. The cap is pressed together and pushed along the back wall of the vagina until it comes to rest against the back of the cervix. Then the cap is allowed to open and is pushed up to cover the cervix. Its placement over the cervix needs to be checked.

The same guidelines for use of spermicidal gel or cream apply to the cervical cap as to the vaginal diaphragm.

Two other caps, the vault cap which covers the cervix and the roof of the vagina, and the vimule cap for women with gynecological problems, may be available. Caps have the advantage of staying in place for several days. Once in place, they are less likely to dislodge than the diaphragm. The disadvantage is their lack of availability in the United States. You have to persist to find one!

Vaginal Spermicides: Foams, creams, jellies, and tablets inserted into the vagina block the cervical opening, immobilize and kill the sperm. They need to be inserted at designated times before intercourse.

Foam is the most effective of this group, but all increase their effectiveness when used in combination with another barrier method.

IUD (Intrauterine Device): Since the IUD has been removed from the market in the United States due to its health hazards, we will not discuss it.

Hormonal Pregnancy Prevention: Various forms of the pill have been researched and debated since their arrival on the market in the late 1950s. Their convenience and effectiveness make them more desirable. Yet, the possibility of health complications for pill users has alerted everyone's attention. When the pill is taken consistently, it has a track record of 99.7–100 percent effectiveness.

The pill is a combination of synthetic estrogen and progesterone hormones that, when given to a woman, shut off the natural production of these hormones so that she no longer ovulates (produces an egg). There are various types and brands of pills. The ratio and amount of the chemical replacement of progesterone and estrogen vary with different pills. Each person's body has to be evaluated to determine which pill will be most effective with the fewest side effects. Unfortunately, some women try one pill, have side effects, and decide that the pill is not for them. They may need to change to a lower level dosage or a pill that has a different proportion of progesterone to estrogen.

Even though there are about twenty-eight different pills available in the United States, they all fit into one of three types:

1. The combined pill is the most common and is taken daily for twenty-one days, starting with the fifth day of the cycle. It is discontinued, and then bleeding starts on the twenty-eighth day.

2. The triphasic pill contains a higher dose of estrogen, yet the total amount of hormones is lower than the combined pill. Twenty-one pills are taken but there are three different pills with varying levels of estrogen and progesterone in each phase to try to reproduce more directly the normal female hormonal cycle. There are six of one kind, five of another, and ten of another. They need to be taken in the order prescribed to be effective. Side effects are reduced with this system.

3. The mini-pill comes with progesterone only. It is taken daily without a break. Unlike the other oral contraceptives, it prevents the sperm from getting through rather than stopping ovulation. It is not as effective as the other two types of pills.

All pills contain powerful chemicals that are absorbed into the circulation and affect the total body. One report suggests that there are over fifty metabolic side effects associated with taking oral contraceptives. So even though there are women who tolerate the pill very well, their body chemistry is being affected.

Since liver function and metabolism of carbohydrates, fats, and proteins are all affected, vitamin and mineral absorption is reduced. Therefore, women on the pill should take a vitamin-mineral supplement that is high in Vitamin B6, Folic Acid, Vitamin C, Calcium, Phosphorus, Magnesium, and Zinc. High doses of Vitamin A should not be taken because it is fat soluble, and fat metabolism is not as effective when on the pill.

Increase in body weight occurs for some women because of retention of fluid. An increase of ten pounds or more would be a sign that birth control pills should be changed or discontinued.

Some women experience minor discomfort when they first start taking the pill. These symptoms of breast tenderness, nausea, vomiting, and spotting between periods, usually go away after two to three months of use.

Cancer, heart problems, circulatory disease, and liver impairment have all been scares associated with taking the pill. Couples deciding whether or not to use the pill need to know if the woman's health will be jeopardized. Although there are conflicting reports, there is also consistent evidence available. The risk of serious problems increases greatly for women who are over thirty-five years of age, who smoke more than fifteen cigarettes per day, who have high blood pressure, who are diabetic or have high blood fat levels, or who are a third above their ideal weight. Long-term, steady use of oral contraceptives for more than five years *may* increase the risk of circulatory disease.

What does this mean? Young women in their twenties and thirties who have had regular periods for at least one year, who are not smokers, overweight, diabetic, or do not have high blood pressure, jaundice, mononucleosis, or other liver disorders will probably be able to take the pill without complication. They are usually advised to periodically get off the pill and use another method. Pill use is ruled out for women who have had blood clots, inflammation in the veins, serious liver disease, unexplained bleeding from the vagina, or suspicion or history of cancer. Young girls who are still growing and whose hormonal functioning is not yet mature, should not take the pill because it will slow or stop normal growth and development.

Women should be aware that certain medications will interfere with the effectiveness of the pill. Some antibiotics, antihistamines, sedatives, tranquilizers, Dilatin, Phenobarbital, and others may interfere with the pill's purpose of preventing pregnancy. A Granny-to-be wrote "Dear Abby" telling her that her son and daughter-in-law were about to have their first baby. She blamed the pregnancy on a short term treatment for an ear infection with antibiotics, while the daughter-in-law was trusting the pill for pregnancy protection. Check with your physician about any medication you are to take. Ask how it interacts with and changes the effectiveness of your hormonal contraceptives.

There are benefits from using the pill. Premenstrual tension lessens, cramps at the time of menstruation decrease, the number of days and the amount of blood loss is lessened, the time of menstruation is totally predictable, and sometimes acne declines.

The pill can affect a woman's sexuality. Some find the physical changes with their periods and removal of acne enhances their sexuality and body image. About an equal number of women report an increase in sexual desire as report a decrease. Just as some experience positive side effects, others report negative changes like actual increase in acne, chronic vaginitis, breast tenderness, and so on. These complications lead to decreased sexual desire and responsiveness. Many women using oral contraceptives do not experience any significant change in sexual behavior, sexual interest, or sexual enjoyment.

What about the morning-after-pill or postcoital contraception? Large doses of progestrone have traditionally been given within twelve to twenty-four hours after rape or unintended intercourse to prevent impregnation by triggering a menstrual flow. There is current legitimate concern that the result may actually be an abortion of a fetus. What are the facts? The sperm can live in the uterus up to five days after ejaculation. For impregnation to occur the egg must unite with the sperm within twelve to twenty-four hours after it is released from the ovary. Thus the union of the egg and sperm could occur inside the woman anytime from minutes to five days after intercourse. When the egg unites with the sperm it is a mass of cells until implantation which occurs four to seven days after the sperm and egg have found each other. At the time of implantation the sperm penetrates the egg, which attaches itself to the uterine wall, and the fetus begins to grow.

In a real-life situation there is no way to absolutely know when each of these events is occurring. Therefore, postcoital contraception has the danger of causing abortion rather than preventing impregnation. With that risk, the morning-after pill moves out of the contraceptive category.

Are there hormonal contraceptives for men? No, there are not.

Hormonal methods of birth control are constantly being researched. The family planning services and your physician usually have up-to-date reports. Keep yourself informed, so that your choice is based on fact rather than fear.

Natural Methods: More and more couples today are considering "natural" methods of birth control because they fear the potential risks of many contraceptives. The various natural methods are based on the principle of avoiding sexual intercourse during the woman's fertile phase of the menstrual cycle. The "rhythm" or "Billings method" may be the terms you've heard in reference to natural family planning. The Roman Catholic Church has helpers trained to teach natural methods.

Most family services offer a thorough program of training. Ingrid Trobisch and Elizabeth Roetzer have written a book, *An Experience of Love* (Fleming H. Revell: Old Tappan, New Jersey, 1981), which details every dimension of planning pregnancies without using contraceptives or sterilization. There are other excellent resources available. We will not provide enough detail here to train you to be able to effectively practice natural family planning. We will summarize the key ingredients to help you determine if this is the method you would prefer to use.

The traditional "rhythm" method is based purely on calculation which always offers an element of risk, because a woman's cycle can vary. Effective natural family planning requires mucus charting, tabulating the temperature of the body at rest upon awakening, and inspection of the cervix to determine the woman's fertile days. There are four days of the menstrual cycle, during menstruation, when the woman is absolutely infertile. Then she is considered 97–99 percent infertile until she sees that her vaginal mucus is stretchy, thicker, and yellower. At this time, the checking of her cervix will indicate a change.

After menstruation, the cervix feels hard and the opening into the vagina is closed. As the cycle moves toward ovulation, the cervix loosens up and softens, so that at about the time of ovulation it feels soft and the opening actually gapes slightly. After ovulation it returns to its firm, closed state. So, total abstinence is necessary from the time of seeing the mucus and noting the softened, open cervix until the woman's temperature has been elevated for three days.

Elevation of the temperature for three days will insure that the egg is no longer fertilizable. The egg lives twelve to twenty-four hours, but sperm live three to five days. This is the process that will need to be learned. Much more training is required than what we have given you here, so do not expect to safely use natural family planning by following this information alone.

For disciplined, determined, well-trained couples, natural family planning has been successful and enjoyable. Couples can enhance their sexual relationship by exploring total body pleasure without intercourse during their fertile or questionable days.

Surgical Methods: The opposite extreme of natural family planning is sterilization. Sterilization is a final form of birth control. It ends the ability of the man or woman to reproduce. Even though a man's sterilization may be reversed in many cases (75 percent), it needs to be thought of as a final, not temporary, method of birth control.

For the woman, sterilization is referred to as tubal ligation. Simple tubal ligation, the tying of the fallopian tubes to prevent the sperm and egg from meeting, is rarely done today because of its ineffectiveness. In addition to the tubes being tied, they need to be either crushed, divided and buried, have a section removed, or a combination of the last two procedures. These procedures do not require major abdominal surgery. An instrument can be used that passes through the abdominal wall, the vagina, or the uterus. Many times hospitalization is not necessary.

Since the above procedures can rarely be effectively reversed to allow pregnancy, reversible methods are being explored with some success. Clips or bands have been used to shut the tubes, plugs have been inserted to block the end of the tubes, and an Italian gynecologist, Igno Tergi, M.D., has moved the tubes. He detaches the tubes from the ovary, makes incisions into the peritoneum (the lining of the abdominal cavity), and sews the fallopian tubes into this lining. When the woman wants to get pregnant, he surgically disconnects the tubes and moves them back to their original position.

When tubal methods fail, which is only one percent of the time, it is because the procedure itself failed due to misjudgment. There are some surgical risks involved. Even though reversibility has been successfully performed, women should think of the tubal methods as permanent. If you are a woman pursuing sterilization, gather all the data you can about the specific method your physician will use, the success rate, any complications and possible after-effects. Some methods are thought to interfere with pelvic blood flow and produce symptoms of Premenstrual Tension. Ask questions. It's your body!

Vasectomy for the man is the simplest and safest form of surgical sterilization. The live sperm are prevented from reaching the penis. The sperm normally travel from the testes, where they are produced, through the vas deferens, a tube that leads through the prostate gland to the urethra. During a vasectomy, a small portion of the vas deferens is removed and the cut ends are tied off and sometimes cauterized. This procedure interrupts the sperm's journey, so that sperm will not be released when a man ejaculates during a sexual experience. He will still produce seminal fluid, since some of that is produced in the portion of the duct system above the cut. One caution—a man may have to ejaculate twenty-five times or more before all live sperm (that were in the duct system above the cut) will have been cleared. Several seminal fluid specimens will need to be taken to the laboratory for confirmation of the finalization of the sterilization process.

Sterilization should not be taken lightly. Even though the results bring incredible freedom to the couple or individual who is definitely finished with child-bearing, the unforeseen can happen. A child may die, a spouse can be lost through death or divorce, or other great tragedies can wipe out a total family except for the one parent. That is why we recommend that the person who is absolutely certain he/ she does not want any more children, no matter what the circumstances, be the one to be sterilized. If both spouses are certain, then the vasectomy is the recommendation of choice because of its ease and safety.

Neither male nor female sterilization changes the sexuality of the person in any way. The woman will still produce eggs and the man will still produce sperm. These disintegrate and are absorbed. The woman continues to menstruate. Hormonal production remains normal for both. Sexual responsiveness and behavior are unaffected. More freedom may result.

Birth control is a very personal matter. Personal feelings, as well as the technical facts, are an important part of the couple's choice of birth control. It is not an easy decision, because there is no method perfect in both effectiveness and safety.

For Further Study

Carrera, Michael. *Sex: The Facts, the Acts, and Your Feelings.* New York: Crown Publishers, 1981. "Birth Control."

Close, Sylvia. *Sex During Pregnancy and After Childbirth.* Wellingborough: Thorson's Publishers Limited, 1984.

Hatcher, Robert A., M.D., Gary K. Stewart, M.D., Felicia Stewart, M.D., Felicia Guest, Nancy Josephs, and James Dale. *Contraceptive Technology, 1982–83.* New York: Irvington Publishers, Inc., 1982.

Keith, Louis G., ed. *The Safety of Fertility Control.* New York: Springer Publishing Company, 1980.

Kolodny, Robert C., William H. Masters, Virginia E. Johnson, Mae A. Biggs. *Textbook of Human Sexuality for Nurses.* Boston: Little, Brown, and Company, 1979. Chapter 12: "Sex and Family Planning."

Kolodny, Robert C., William H. Masters, Virginia E. Johnson. *Textbook of Sexual Medicine.* Boston: Little, Brown, and Company, 1979, Chapter 15: "Sex and Family Planning."

Trobisch, Ingrid, and Elizabeth Roetzer. *An Experience of Love, Understanding Natural Family Planning.* Old Tappan: Fleming H. Revell Company, 1977.

3

Sex and Infertility

A True Story

Paul and Gail, an attractive young couple in their late twenties, came to our office for help. Sexually, they were having a difficult time. As their story unfolded, we discovered that their problems had begun when they decided it was time to begin their family. Let's back up a little and tell you what happened to them. We tell it because their experience incorporated almost all the potential barriers to fertility we have encountered in our practice.

Paul and Gail were a handsome couple who had come from wealthy families. By the normal social expectations, one would think their life together would be ideal. Paul had graduated from an eminent university with a major in business administration and was rising rapidly in his corporation. Gail had been teaching school until they began trying to conceive, and now she functioned as a homemaker and community volunteer.

In spite of all the right external conditions, they struggled with a problem that affects about ten to fifteen percent of all couples during their reproductive years. Before they had attempted to conceive, their sexual life together had been fun and fulfilling. Both were vitally interested, highly arousable, orgasmic, and enjoyed their sexual life together. Yes, they had their share of the normal stresses of life. But as far as the sexual department went, they were both finding fulfillment and joy.

After they moved into a new home in a fine community and decorated their home, they decided it was time to start their family. Gail left her teaching job. Their sexual experience took on new meaning as they were eager to conceive. The edge of eagerness disappeared as slight disappointment crept in. Each month when the menstrual period began there was the letdown that "it hadn't happened yet." But, as is true for most couples, they began each month with new hope.

As time went on, that small feeling of doubt and concern built almost to the point of panic. At first neither of them said anything to the other about it. They only thought, *What if we're unable to have kids?* and then tried to push the thought away. (A couple is not considered to be experiencing a fertility problem until they have attempted to conceive for at least a year. On the average, most couples conceive in about six months, with about 25 percent conceiving after one month of trying, around 60 percent by the end of six months, and about 80 to 85 percent after one year.)

After a year, Paul and Gail talked to their family doctor about the problem. He asked them many questions as he began the exploration. As is true with most couples, they wondered who to blame for their failure to conceive. It is natural to want to blame one another or at least to pinpoint who is responsible. In our society, there is still a tendency to blame the woman. But it doesn't really matter whose fault it is since the couple shares the problem.

Infertility balances out rather evenly between men and women. About two-fifths of the time it is the woman's problem and about two-fifths of the time it is the man's problem. About one-fifth of the time it is impossible to diagnose whose problem it is—or both partners contribute to the cause. Included in the last group are those situations where it is impossible for the doctor to determine any physical basis for the lack of conception. It is always important when a couple has some doubts about their ability to conceive, that both seek help from a physician. It is never predictable as to whether it will be the man or the woman who is hindering impregnation.

The first thing the doctor wanted to know from Paul was whether he was in fact able to ejaculate inside the vagina during intercourse. Some men experience what is called "retarded ejaculation." They find themselves fully aroused with a complete erection, able to experience intercourse, but unable to ejaculate when inside the woman. This is an emotional rather than a physical dilemma which can be reversed through sexual therapy.

Next the doctor wanted to know whether ejaculation was occurring so prematurely that it was taking place outside the vagina. If this were the case, the sperm would have less opportunity to travel through the vagina into the cervix and on up to meet the ovum (egg) inside the fallopian tubes. By the time these questions had been answered it was becoming clear that Paul's difficulty was not a mechanical one of depositing the sperm where it needed to be.

We should mention other possible mechanical difficulties. Sexual functioning always needs to be evaluated. Several couples with whom we have worked have experienced difficulties with impregnation because of either severe impotence or vaginismus.

Impotence has to do with the inability to achieve or maintain an erection. When there is an inability to maintain an erection long enough for vaginal entry, impregnation is highly unlikely. A couple may not have been able to culminate their marriage in sexual intercourse because of impotence on the part of the man.

This inability to have sexual intercourse can also be caused by vaginismus, that is, an involuntary closing of the vagina, on the part of the woman (see Chapter 14). Unconsummated marriages are treatable situations. In dealing with either of these conditions, a couple should seek help first from a physician and then from a sexual therapist.

The more superficial, technical possibilities needed to be eliminated. The doctor wanted to know whether Gail was using any kind of lubricant that might be killing the sperm (spermicidal). He also wanted to know whether she was douching, and, thus, altering the natural vaginal environment. This could be making it difficult for the sperm to survive.

The positions used during intercourse were questioned. When the doctor discovered that part of the dilemma was Paul's low sperm count, he suggested a position that would bring the ejaculate in direct contact with the opening of the cervix. This was to increase the likelihood of a healthy sperm traveling into and surviving within the uterine passage. The suggested position was with Gail on her back, buttocks slightly elevated with a pillow and knees pulled up toward the chest, allowing Paul to penetrate as deeply as possible (an exaggerated missionary position).

When the difficulty in conceiving is due to the position of the cervix and uterus, the woman will need to lie in a certain position for an extended period of time after intercourse. With some problems, it is necessary for the woman to stay on her back with her buttocks slightly elevated by a pillow and her legs up to help the sperm arrive right at the opening of the cervix.

If the gynecologist discovers that the woman has a retroverted or tipped uterus, he/she may suggest entry from the rear with the woman staying in what is called the "knee-chest position," that is, on her knees with her chest on the bed for an extended period after ejaculation. This is an uncomfortable position to maintain for a long period of time, and yet it can certainly help with conception.

Frequency of sexual intercourse was evaluated. A balance was suggested. If the block of time between experiences is too long, then the chance of intercourse occurring at the fertile time is lowered and the sperm are less lively. This reduces the possibility of impregnation. If intercourse is too frequent, for example on a daily basis, that will negatively affect the sperm count and decrease the possibility of conception. To create the most ideal conditions for impregnation, most physicians recommend that a couple wait one to three days between ejaculations.

Recent stress in the couple's life together could also hinder conception by blocking ovulation. Severe illness, death, financial trauma, vocational upheaval, or marital difficulties are all stresses that could hinder conception.

After these technical, mechanical reasons for infertility have been eliminated, the doctor will explore possible physical reasons. The man's sperm count will be checked. It takes a certain number of sperm per cubic centimeter of ejaculate for impregnation to take place. When the count gets down to 20 or 30 million per cubic centimeter there is a much lower chance of impregnation than if there is a high count. A high count would be 50 or 60 live sperm per cubic centimeter. The active sperm count is compared with the sluggish sperm count.

If the man contracted mumps in adulthood, with subsequent damage to the testicles, he may have a low sperm count. A varicocele or varicose vein on the testicle increases the temperature in the testicles and thus reduces the number of vigorous sperm produced. Sometimes an underdeveloped testicle condition has lasted throughout puberty causing damage to the part of the testicles that produces the sperm. There are other temporary and long-term causes for low sperm count. Whatever the source of the difficulty if there are not enough active, healthy sperm, the likelihood of pregnancy is lessened. In Paul's situation, it was discovered that he did have a varicocele which was lowering his sperm count.

Gail had physical interruptions of her reproductive cycle that contributed to their infertility as well. She was not ovulating on a regular basis. This seems to have been the result of high dosage birth control pills taken continuously during the early years of their marriage. Gail had chosen the pill to stop her ovulation, but she had never regained a consistent ovulation cycle after going off the pill. After medical treatment to "fire" the ovaries, Gail and Paul succeeded in conceiving. Then Gail experienced a miscarriage, a huge disappointment!

After Gail recovered from the miscarriage, they resumed their efforts to conceive. The monthly expectation for pregnancy returned. Yet at the end of each month they discovered that she had not even ovulated. There was incredible disappointment! For eight months they were taking temperatures, checking vaginal mucus, ingesting medication to induce ovulation, and calling Paul home in the middle of the day for intercourse. The physician recommended frequent sexual activity around the time of ovulation and then little the rest of the month. Sex was by prescription, not desire.

Finally, after this eight-month period, there was an ovulation. Gail did become pregnant and a healthy baby boy was born. Eager to have another child, they shortened the breast-feeding period to allow ovulation to resume.

Again, they struggled. Gail went in for minor exploratory surgery—a laparascopy, to examine the reproductive system. Paul had his varicocele repaired, which helped raise his sperm count. He had every other part of him reviewed, evaluated, and repaired.

Getting pregnant the second time was even more difficult than the first. Artificial insemination was attempted at Gail's peak ovulation time. Paul would hurry home, ejaculate into a bottle, and Gail would then rush across town on a forty-five-minute drive to their doctor. The doctor would artificially implant the sperm at the ideal spot for impregnation. After six monthly attempts, they conceived and Gail gave birth to a beautiful little girl.

By this time, sex had become associated with such a demand to produce at a certain time and in a certain way that they no longer desired each other for the purpose of sexual pleasure. With Paul running home when she called, ejaculating into a bottle, the artificial insemination, the focus on temperatures, mucus, and sperm counts, they had become so clinically oriented that they no longer had a capacity to connect with feeling. All romance was gone from their relationship.

For the first nine months after their second child was born, they had no sexual experience whatsoever. They avoided each other. Sex felt like a burden, rather than a joy. By this time, Paul was thinking, *There's something wrong with me. I'm not interested anymore. I couldn't care less about this. Life is fine without sex. If I'm a sexual being I certainly don't know where that part of me is. I probably couldn't even function if I tried.*

Gail was having many of the same thoughts. It was at this point that they sought our counsel. They were excited about their two children. But now they lacked desire for one another sexually and it seemed impossible to imagine getting back together.

Whether the problem is low sperm count or some kind of testicular problem for the man, ovulation problems, cervical problems, endometriosis, or the position of the uterus for the woman, it is likely to bring emotional stress and distance to the relationship.

Sexual Problems That Occur As a Result of Infertility

By now it is obvious why a couple might have difficulty maintaining sexual intimacy through all the gyrations of trying to conceive. Infertility produces a state of crisis. In addition, many of the necessary procedures interfere with free sexual closeness. The possibility for intimacy is obviously decreased if the woman is on her knees and chest for an hour after the sexual experience or if the man is having to run home at 11:42 in the morning to ejaculate into a bottle. These "command performances" do little to enhance sexual pleasure and enjoyment.

Only an unusual couple can avoid the negative impact of an extended effort at conception. When sexual intercourse becomes a means to an end, even the very natural goal of conceiving a child, it is likely to lose the spontaneity, the joy, and the enthusiasm that may have been there previously. In fact, this is true any time we find ourselves focused on sexual goals rather than on sexual pleasure. We deal with this problem extensively in our book, *The Gift of Sex*.

Let's review the scene. The couple begins by anticipating that pregnancy will be easy and natural. After an extended period of trying, the internal pressure and anxiety build as the external pressure from friends or grandparents increases dramatically. It's at this point that the first blaming begins and the desperate mood sets in. By now, it is almost impossible for the couple to have a natural sex life because sex has become an effort to produce a result. The natural flow of pleasure and intimacy diminishes. The man will wonder about himself and whether he is "really a man"—and the woman will be sure that there is something wrong with her.

We have opposite forces in action. On the one hand is the drive to conceive which brings a couple together. On the opposite side is the sexual demand that produces a noticeable decrease in sexual desire as pressure reduces sexual enjoyment. A chronic depression may set in—not the depression that would send a person to a hospital ward, but an ongoing state of despondency. Spontaneity is lost. Hopelessness overwhelms expectancy. The demanding, programmed sexual performances destroy the romantic dimension.

The procedures the couple goes through elevate the stress. The continual pelvic examinations by the physician have a detrimental effect. The woman repeatedly experiences her genitals as "the doctor's" to examine, rather than her and her husband's source of sexual pleasure. Producing sperm samples into a bottle leaves the husband with little desire for normal sexual arousal and release. This is especially true if he has to produce at the physician's office. The artificial insemination leaves the woman feeling that she is on the soft end of a probing test tube. The man may feel he is inadequate because he can't even impregnate his own wife. He feels he can't be much of a man if he's "shooting blanks."

All of these factors reduce the couple's self-esteem and naturally affect their sexual life. It should also be noted that many times, as in the case of Paul and Gail, the whole procedure (from starting to conceive to coming to our office) can be a five-year process. Through all of this, high levels of anger, frustration, and tension can cause other marital difficulties.

Any time a sexual experience becomes goal-oriented rather than pleasure-oriented, any time sex is by demand rather than by desire, any time sexual experience is directed outside of us rather than in response to our inner urges, it will significantly disrupt the sexual relationship. The woman's orgasmic response will inevitably diminish. The husband may have difficulty getting or keeping an erection because he has become anxious about having to produce at a certain time under unarousing conditions. Both may have lost their desire for sexual intimacy.

Fulfillment in Spite of Pressure

Togetherness can be maintained when both spouses are committed and helped to focus on the intimacy of love-making. Whether the consequences of trying brings about loss of orgasm for the woman, impotence for the man, or diminished sexual desire, there are certain steps that couples can take to help reduce the negative consequences of the infertility. We suggest six areas for your attention. These steps are not to be taken in order, but should happen simultaneously.

1. *Know that you are not the first couple to go through this experience.* Be reassured that in most cases, help is available for you to have the child you so dearly desire. Faced with the problems of infertility, couples often feel terribly alone in their experience. They ask the questions, "Why me? Is God punishing me? Is it because I was sexually involved before we were married? What is wrong with us?" It helps to be aware that infertility is experienced by ten to fifteen percent of couples. In most cases the problems are treatable and can be remedied. Sometimes just knowing that you are not alone helps. Part of the problem is that most people don't talk about their infertility difficulties because it makes them feel less adequate than others. Hence you may not have heard from your friends about their own struggle with infertility.

2. *Continue living as much of a normal life as possible.* Just because you are struggling to get pregnant doesn't mean you need to withdraw

from society, stop being engaged in your hobby, stop participating in the community or church activities, or quit playing on the local softball team. It is crucial to continue to be involved with those activities that have brought joy into your individual lives. In your marital life, pay close attention to doing those special things you have always done. By all means, continue to get away for weekends, whether you enjoy camping or staying at the downtown Sheraton hotel. Keep up those positive aspects of life.

3. *Communication must take place on at least three levels.* First of all, it is vital that the patterns of communication which you have found to be important for your relationship be continued or even increased during this stressful time. When self-esteem is being tested, hope fading, and depression setting in, pay special attention to the effective communication skills that have maintained your healthy marriage. If you have not established an ongoing system for communication, with time set aside for this, the present moment would be an important time to begin the habit.

A second absolutely essential focus of communication is the sharing of the thoughts, feelings, and reactions to the problem of infertility. Much benefit can come from expressing those anxieties as they occur: the hopelessness as it creeps in, the despair as it is felt, the fluctuations in the feelings that are inevitable, the impact on the masculinity and femininity as it is experienced, and the way one's attitude toward the future is altered. Anything that can get your feelings out in the open will help you survive.

Recognize that this is a dilemma you share. You are in it together. If you have never learned to talk openly in your relationship, this would be an ideal time for the two of you to get into a learning experience that helps you increase your communication skills and develop more intimacy in your relationship. Marriage encounters or seminars, classes, or retreats that teach effective communication in marriage are beneficial. Find some way to keep sharing the feelings and reactions as they occur. These include the first feelings of surprise and anger, the sense of isolation or separateness that you may feel from all your friends who are conceiving, or the grief experienced as the waiting persists.

A third essential ingredient of communication is to have at least one place, apart from your doctor's office, where you can talk freely and openly about your dilemma. This may be with family members—

parents, brothers and sisters, aunts, uncles. It may be a special couple who are deep and close friends, where privacy can be assured. Or it may be that you would deal with this best in a professional situation. This can involve either a minister, a marriage and family counselor, or a psychologist.

There are organizations designed to provide help and support for those with fertility problems. One such organization which operates at a national level is called RESOLVE (National Headquarters in Boston: 617–484–2424) and should be listed in your local phone directory. Your physician may know of others. A crucial source of encouragement will be the knowledge that you have support and care, both from each other, and from a few important, concerned people.

4. *Educate yourselves.* Get as much information as possible so that you have clear knowledge of what is happening to you. Begin by asking your physician for information on the subject of infertility. Ask questions as they occur to you. Find an up-to-date book at your local bookstore or library that will enlighten you about the causes and remedies for infertility. Attend a lecture at the local hospital. Pay attention to magazine articles written by knowledgeable professionals who could let you know exactly what is the current understanding of infertility. There is much more information available on infertility than we can cover here. Our focus in this chapter has to do with helping you deal with your relationship and sexual effects of infertility rather than providing an exhaustive statement on the causes and treatments.

5. *Continue the pleasure and intimacy of the sexual experience even when trying to conceive.* This will not be possible for all sexual experiences. When there is a rushed event because the temperature charts or the mucous secretions indicate that this is the right time for impregnation, the sexual act will be more functional.

When possible, atmosphere can add spark to the rushed daytime experiences. For a noon attempt at conception, use your private patio in the summertime, a bedroom that you usually don't use for sleeping, a place with a view if the woman is going to have to stay in a certain position, or a cozy setup in front of the fireplace if this is the dead of winter. The newness of the atmosphere can distract from the demand to produce.

Make a plan for physical intimacy in your less rushed, scheduled times to conceive. Go the extra mile in setting up an atmosphere which will bring excitement. For example, if the experience is going to be at night, prepare the room by lighting candles or making a love nest on the floor. Turn on your favorite love-making music. Get out those satin sheets that you use for special occasions. Make the event special.

In addition to setting the atmosphere, a focus on bodily pleasure can make the sexual experiences special. Enjoying the pleasure of each other's bodies is affirming and brings connection for the couple. Many books have been written on this subject. We have outlined step-by-step experiences in *The Gift of Sex*. Find extended times for sexual enjoyment and pleasure by engaging in body caressing, thus heightening the arousal, and keeping some of the vitality present even if you are getting together on the doctor's schedule for the purpose of impregnation.

Another important ingredient for keeping intimacy and pleasure alive, during the months or years of pursuing impregnation, is to make a concerted effort to get together at times other than when you are striving to conceive. Have sex for fun and no other purpose! We are aware that you may need to limit sexual ejaculation to two or three times during ovulation. Even during these times sexual play without ejaculation adds fun and variety. During the rest of the month when sexual experiences are your choice, plan special times that are designed for relaxation without any demands. If sex has never been fun, this would be a good time to learn together. Read a book or attend a seminar on sexual enhancement and in this way add new variety to your experience.

6. *Maintain or develop ongoing nonsexual affection.* Not only are sharing feelings and sexual intimacy important, but also share with each other the closeness of affection, including the hugs and kisses. Take time to affirm each other. Remind yourselves of your love. Take time to go out to dinner, to a movie, for a walk. Plan time together that builds closeness. Spend time in mutual bodily pleasuring that is not designed to arouse but can provide enjoyment for both. Begin by learning to caress feet and face and hands, including the whole body except the genitals, as set out in *The Gift of Sex*.

Intimacy building can keep the two of you close while feeling the demands and failures of unsuccessful pregnancy attempts. Stress and tension have a way of wedging their way into a relationship and nudging people apart. The process is gradual. It is a result of not sharing the pain, and feeling badly about yourselves and each other at a time when you need all the support you can get from each other. Learn to laugh and cry together.

Maintain and develop all areas of intimacy. Aesthetic, literary, musical, athletic, or craft and hobby interests should be continued. Pay attention to your spiritual life. This is vital! At a time of helplessness, God's all-knowing power and care are available. Your times of corporate or personal worship, prayer, or Bible study may be a significant source of strength. This would be especially true as your helpless feelings find solace in your relationship with God.

These six steps are not magic. They are not going to make every sexual experience a honeymoon delight. There will still be a laborious quality to conception when fertility is a problem. But if the steps are applied in a steady, deliberate fashion, they can reduce the distance that too often develops for couples experiencing infertility. It will help maintain at least a vestige of the former relationship that can be resumed once the struggle is over.

After the Trying Stops

Whether you are no longer trying because you have reached a decision that pregnancy is an impossibility, or you have stopped trying because you have successfully conceived, a time of re-focusing and re-learning will be necessary for most couples. Paul and Gail spent five years working on this process. The difficulties they had in readjusting to sexual experiences that were self-directed and aimed at pleasure and sexual fulfillment are not an extreme.

There are specific steps to take to insure happier adjustment as you resume your ongoing sexual life. Let's look at this first from the perspective of the couple who has conceived as many children as they want.

(1) Plan your contraception between yourselves and with your physician, being sure that both of you feel comfortable and confident with the method chosen (refer to Chapter 2).

(2) Maintain some form of physical intimacy between the time of the birth of the child and the point when your physician says you are physically ready to resume sexual intercourse. This could be just

the normal day-to-day affection of hugging and kissing, giving each other body caresses and pleasuring, or some mutual stimulation, even to the point of orgasm.

(3) Plan very carefully for your first sexual intercourse after childbirth (refer to Chapter 5). This needs to be a special event.

(4) Plan and schedule physical times to be together that can grow into a sexual experience if both desire. There will be a natural resistance to scheduling, since that smacks of scheduling sex to conceive. Yet, if the two of you are going to come together in a way that brings fulfillment, active planning will be necessary. If you do not make touching a priority, you may end up in the same place as Paul and Gail, who found themselves never getting together. By planning we mean allowing blocks of time in your schedule where love-making is possible. Plan an evening meal together or an hour away that has the possibility of growing into a sensual time. Life is going to be different with children in the home. As the two of you recognize that difference, talk about it, and make plans to bring your worlds together. You can make the necessary adjustments to find happiness in your sexual lives.

For those who have to accept the fact that they will never bear children, their sexual adjustment is addressed in the next chapter on childlessness. Grieving the loss is painful. Most couples go through a clear-cut series of feelings upon the discovery of their unresolvable infertility.

With infertility on the increase, all of us need a new sensitivity to sharing the pain with those who struggle to get pregnant. They need our support. That will best happen as being open about infertility problems becomes acceptable in our culture. Learning to share with each other and close friends and relatives is the start.

For Further Study

Aral, Sevgi O., Ph.D., and Willard Cates, Jr., M.D., "The Increasing Concern With Fertility. Why Now?" *Journal of the American Medical Association.* November 1983, vol. 250, no. 17, 2327–2331.

Bernstein, Judith, R.N., and John H. Matton, M.D., "An Overview of Infertility." *Journal of Obstetrical and Gynecological Nursing.* September/October 1982, 309–314.

Carrera, Michael. *Sex: The Facts, the Acts, and Your Feelings.* New York: Crown Publishers, 1981. "Infertility."

Elstein Max. "Effects of Infertility on Psychosexual Function." *British Medical Journal,* August 1975, 2, 296–299.

Hatcher, Robert A., M.D., Gary K. Stewart, M.D., Felicia Stewart, M.D., Felicia Guest, Nancy Josephs, James Dale. *Contraceptive Technology,* 1982–83. New York: Irvington Publishers, Inc., 1982. "Infertility."

4

Childlessness, Adoption, and Sex

Every little girl who plays with dolls grows up knowing that someday she will have her own children. Playing house is practice for the real thing. This basic belief continues on through adolescence to the point of marriage. A couple expects that children will be a part of their life together. It usually isn't a question of "if" a couple can have children, but rather "when." There are, of course, those few couples who decide not to do so. But for most there is the decision to wait through the years of schooling, and the establishment of some financial stability. Then they are ready to have the children who are seen as an inevitable part of their lives.

Infertility comes as a real shock, leaving a sense of powerlessness, for those 10–15 percent (or about one-sixth of the population) who discover they may not be able to have children. Even though the infertility can usually be treated successfully, there still is a significant segment of the population who will remain childless.

Adoption is the quick answer, and yet 90 percent of single mothers are keeping their babies if they bring them to full-term. So the pool of couples looking for children is far greater than the pool of babies available. The wait will often be five or six years *if* the couple qualifies. Some are left looking for personal connections for adoptions, international adoptions, or resigning themselves to a life without children.

The frustration, anger, and anxiety of facing infertility are feelings most couples experience as they work with their physician in attempting to bring about pregnancy (see Chapter 3). For those who decide to remain childless or are unable to adopt, the adjustment is major. It is going to call for much internal strength and reliance on God. It requires you to readjust your view of yourselves as individuals and as a couple facing a future that is only going to include the two of you. There is the loss of realizing you will have no one to live on after you.

True, many opportunities will come your way as a result of this change in your life (experiences not available to those who have children). While you may be able to look at the benefits later, when first going through the pain of adjustment, it does not help to have the benefits recited. This time of readjustment, of accepting that your lives together will be without children, could seem very much like the period of adjustment right after marriage. Then you were working to become comfortable with one another. But you knew that some day you would have a family. Lifestyle patterns and plans both in terms of location and recreation will need to be processed one more time. You will need much support, understanding, and encouragement when you finally face the reality that children are absolutely not going to be a part of your future.

Facing childlessness is indeed one of life's major predicaments. The erosion of hope, it is a steady, gradual loss of a life's dream. It is a life crisis. What is crisis? When we face an event that threatens life as we now know it, we usually experience the stress of crisis. Crises are those situations which go beyond the usual day-to-day problems and require special kinds of solutions. A crisis usually threatens something that has become an expected part of our life, such as a job, your health, a marriage, a home, or life itself.

Most of the time when dealing with a crisis, we find that it is time-limited. That is, if a house burns down or we lose a job, the emotions are not dragged out over long periods of time. Infertility is more like a severe, long-term, perhaps fatal illness which moves us from crisis to crisis. Many times with infertility problems, the crisis is re-experienced every month as the woman again begins to menstruate. The failure to conceive is mourned each time. The hope continues to erode. Facing childlessness at the end of a fertility battle is much like facing death after long-term illness. It is the final and most intense crisis of loss.

When a couple is in crisis, they have little to give each other, and often they feel very alone—especially when their infertility has not been shared in a supportive setting. Most times they are receiving advice that encourages them to keep a stiff upper lip, keep faith, believe that it is God's will, to pray harder, be stronger. These are nonsupportive messages rather than caring that listens to their pain and responds to their hopelessness. They need a group that stands with them through the struggle and is there to cry with them when the emptiness of childlessness becomes a reality.

Personal Consequences

Since childbearing is a natural stage in our development, the inability to produce children has a deep and cutting impact on our self-esteem. Something is wrong with us. It radically alters our self-image and view of our own sexuality. Even though most of us accept the sexual part of us as having two purposes—one, the procreative purpose, and second, the purpose of pleasure—when we have difficulties with conception, pleasure is affected.

As we experience a decline in self-esteem, there is a direct impact on how we feel about our body and our body-image. It is as if we have discovered a defect in our bodies and hence we have lower worth. Our sense of wholeness suffers.

Social Consequences

Since the beginning of time, children have been the fruit of marriage. In the Old Testament, there was a stigma attached to childlessness. While we think of our present culture as more open and sophisticated, this viewpoint is still part of our thinking, both within and outside the church. We complete our manhood by fathering a child. Motherhood is the most total expression of a woman's femininity.

In the *American Journal of Obstetrics and Gynecology* (Vol. 135, No. 2, 1979, pp. 177–180) Rosenfeld and Mitchell suggest that many of our views on normal adult mental health are specifically connected with parenthood. "Maturity, unselfishness, social isolation, and loneliness" are seen as directly related to our capacity to be parents. We may argue about the rightness of these expectations, and promote individual wholeness without reproduction, yet most of us function with deeper feelings and beliefs that continue to connect marriage with childbearing. Children validate marriage.

Emotional Consequences

Barbara Eck Menning is the founder of RESOLVE Inc., a national nonprofit organization that offers help and support for couples experiencing infertility. She has outlined a series of feelings typical of those facing infertility and then childlessness ("The Emotional Needs of the Infertile Couple," *Fertility and Sterility,* Vol. 34, No. 4, October 1980, pp. 313–319). She notes that most couples respond with surprise, denial, anger, isolation, guilt, and grief.

It is the all-American way to believe that we are in control of our destiny. We marry, wait awhile using birth control, and then expect that when we stop using birth control, we will automatically become pregnant. No one is prepared for the surprise that comes when we discover that pregnancy is not possible. It leaves us in a state of shock.

Next comes denial: we believe that this can't happen to us. While denial may be helpful for a short time as we get adapted, it can have serious and detrimental effects if we allow it to persist. We may start rationalizing that we never really wanted kids anyway. Or we may keep believing that pregnancy is a possibility, even after the doctor has assured us that it is not. The denial continues when we protect ourselves from feeling the pain of anger, isolation, guilt, and grief that needs to follow. We do not want to believe or accept the reality of our inability to have children.

When we finally do accept the loss, we are most likely to experience a major bout of *anger.* The angry response is there because of the loss of control over our bodies and our future. Sometimes the anger comes out at people who have children, those who have "too many" children, or those who choose not to have children when they could. Anyone who represents a choice we don't have and makes a different choice than we would make could be the cause of our anger. This angry response is very normal because we feel a mixed sense of fear, loss of control, and helplessness.

Isolation is a very common part of the experience of infertility and childlessness. The ashamed, low self-worth feelings connected with infertility keep us from sharing our experience. We don't want people to feel sorry for us, nor do we want advice and home remedies, so we keep the problem a secret.

There are consequences to this isolation. The secrecy makes the couple bear the pain alone, rather than getting the support that would be available to them from their community. It may keep them from each other. There may be feelings of blame. How the final pain of childlessness is dealt with between them will depend on how they have handled the various infertility crises.

For example, if the man has kept all of the feelings inside himself while the woman has spilled out the frustration and concern, they may have distanced themselves from each other. If they have kept communication open, the sexual experience alive, and shared the painful process, the isolation from the rest of the world may bring them together.

Nevertheless, most of us, with our Western thought patterns, look for cause and effect. Why did this happen? Whose fault is it? If we had done this or not done that, would we now be happy parents? We look for all manner of explanations to find some way to understand our childlessness. We feel guilty. We may blame past guilt-producing behaviors such as masturbation, premarital sex, abortion, extramarital affairs, or homosexual preoccupation. Sometimes even birth control measures or sexual pleasure itself produces the guilt.

Many of us operate on a system which says that if we do good then God will reward us. The flip side of that is if we do evil, then God will punish us. Childlessness can be seen as a punishment for wrong-doing. Let us listen to Christ's answer to His disciples when He was asked why a man was blind. "Was it his sins or the sins of his parents?" they inquired. Christ's response was that it was neither, but rather that God would be glorified. We interpret that to mean, in the normal consequences of human life—sickness, illness, poverty— we cannot attempt to determine blame. It is humanly impossible for us ever to understand the total purposes of life and the universe.

Finally, when we have experienced the shock, denial, anger, isolation, and guilt, and are facing the reality that there will be no children, we are forced to deal with grief. Grief is a very normal and natural response to loss. In this instance, it is not a tangible loss, like a home or the death of a child, but rather it is the loss of a hope or a dream. It is a more ambiguous loss to deal with in that there is no one moment of actual crisis.

When we lose a job, there is a point at which the boss says, "You're fired." When we get a divorce, there is that moment when the judge says, "You are divorced." When someone has a terminal illness and dies, there is that point of death. When a child gets married and moves across the country, there is that point of saying "Good-bye" and then driving away. But with infertility there is no moment at which we can be declared absolutely infertile unless the reproductive organs are removed or totally unfunctional. Even then, the hope of adoption may linger. It is difficult to pinpoint the loss of a dream or hope. Hence it is difficult to pinpoint the moment at which one begins to grieve the loss of childbearing and accept the state of childlessness. Yet the grief pain needs to be worked through just as do the more tangible losses.

Close friends of ours have been through this agony. With their permission we share their experience. "The hardest part is not knowing. It is very lonely! Living for ten years with an unfulfilled expectation is exceedingly wearing on the emotions and the relationship. After a while it is as if you live life waiting to miss your next period. If it is a day or two late, the warm, tender feelings begin to build and then the crushing disappointment." This couple never did get a diagnosis of what was wrong. She finally had to have a hysterectomy because of endometriosis. This was thought to have been the cause of the infertility.

Facing the reality that all possibilities of bearing a child had been removed was a cutting blow. Then when several adoption attempts also fell through, the reality had to be faced. They would never have children! That was deeply painful!

We asked how it was possible to live life with this ongoing uncertainty. Their answer was, "Ultimately you have to get your peace from believing that God's will is being worked out in your life." This brings us to the last stage.

The final healing is the stage of acceptance or as Menning calls it, "resolution." You are past the steady pain and can move on with the business of life. You will make decisions about how you are going to proceed with the reality of no children.

At various times throughout your lives, the emptiness of not having children may bring deep sadness. These are grief pangs. They are the normal result of loss. Even when you have worked through the loss, readjusted to life, and found new fulfillment, there will be reminders that hurt. Allowing yourselves the pain, sharing it with someone, asking God to heal and fill your lives with meaningful outlets—all these help.

Some couples find that as they invest themselves in their careers and volunteer work, the rewards replace the loss. Taking care of other people's children for the weekend, teaching a Sunday school class, or coaching a Little League team, are avenues of finding the joys and benefits of children without all the hassles. The two of you will need to discover the source of fulfillment that works best for you. A short-term therapy process with a qualified counselor can be most helpful. Talking together is essential.

Childlessness and Sex

Sexually, you need to re-engage in a caring, loving, slow process that can help the two of you move toward a life of sexual satisfaction and fulfillment. This will take planning, scheduling, and learning to focus on the pleasure of each other's bodies.

You could follow some of the steps outlined in *The Gift of Sex*. These begin with foot, hand, and facial caresses. Then you can move on to total body pleasuring that doesn't include genitals. Then you can include genitals but without a great deal of stimulation, then with some arousal and stimulation, and finally moving on to intercourse. This process of rediscovering, of backing way up and moving through every step of sexual intimacy, is essential in recovering sexual fulfillment. We would also encourage reading some good books on sex out loud to each other. Besides *The Gift of Sex* we would recommend Dagmar O'Connor's book, *How to Make Love to the Same Person for the Rest of Your Life: And Still Love It* (Doubleday & Co., Inc.: New York, 1985). Both of these would revive the sexual stirrings. We would also recommend attending a human sexuality class, weekend seminar, or retreat. Make your sexual life a clear priority.

Birth control continues to be an issue. The two of you need to decide whether you want to leave the rare possibility open that conception could occur, even at age 40 or 45. Or do you want to permanently assure that conception is never going to happen so you can go ahead and plan your lives without any late-in-life surprises? Usually when the doctor has said that conception is an impossibility, it *is* an impossibility. But there are those situations when, miracle of miracles, suddenly the woman is pregnant, and you as a couple need to determine whether that surprise is something you can manage.

Adoption

When a spouse loses a partner by death, or a fiancee by rejection, it is important not to marry on the rebound. Frequently those "second-choice" mates don't work out on a long-term basis. This same thing is true with the rebound response of adoption when a couple faces infertility. When a couple has not emotionally worked through their inability to bear children, the adjustment to the adopted child may be difficult. The child may never quite measure up to what they think their own children would have been. So it is vital that before you move on to the process of adopting you resolve the loss of not bearing your own children.

It is not only important that you internally accept adoption, but also socially. Adoption may be seen as a sign or symbol of inadequacy, an announcement to the world of your infertility secret. Don't proceed with adoption until you are totally comfortable with it. The research has shown that how ready the parents are to give themselves to the newly adopted child is a much greater factor in how the child adjusts in the adoptive setting than the discovery later on that the child was adopted. How a child experiences love and acceptance from adoptive parents will be the most important issue for adjustment. This is why it is so crucial that a couple work through their loss of childbearing and their feelings about adoption.

Adoption or caring for foster children are choices that some couples who are unable to bear children find extremely fulfilling. Adopted children become *their* children. They feel that same deep sense of joy, excitement and completion as other couples do with the birth of a natural child. These children are experienced as very special gifts from God.

In adopting an infant, the process is long with many screenings and hurdles to be overcome. Specific information about when a baby will arrive may not be available. Even when there is a pregnant mother with a due date who is ready to give up the baby, the actual announcement is sudden and startling. Pregnancy has a way of preparing not only the mother, but also the father and the immediate community for the arrival of the baby.

Waiting for an adoptive child is not the same. There has not been the sensation of the child in the womb with the kicking and moving, the heartbeat, and the regular check-ups at the doctor—and many other experiences. So when the adoptive parents suddenly have the new baby in their arms, the infant can feel more like a stranger than might be true of the biological child.

Bonding has not occurred. Since it is so important that a special bonding happen between the parents and child, it might be wise to abstain from sexual involvement for a few weeks, to let those special mother-child and father-child connections occur.

When a baby is born into the family, there is the difficult healing and emotional adjustment that has to take place as a result of the process of childbirth. The mother is frequently breast-feeding. Usually there is a six-week recuperation and adjustment time. For the adoptive parents there are obviously some differences. Yet the process may be similar, since there is the adjustment to a new infant in the home.

The adoptive father may well experience the same kind of envy or jealousy of the child that would be true of a biological child. It is easy to experience a child as an intruder in the relationship and especially on the sexual life. The same time and fatigue adjustments will need to be made with adopted infants, as with newborn natural babies.

Fortunately, the mother's body has not suffered the stress of labor and delivery, so she will have more energy available. After the initial adjustment period, it would be important to follow much the same steps as recommended for sex after childbirth (see Chapter 5). If there has been the long-term infertility struggle, the steps outlined for sex after infertility would help you readjust to your sexual life together (Chapter 3).

Adopting Older Children

Most families go through four phases when they adopt an older child. These impact the sexual life. These four phases are: commitment, honeymoon, storm, and adaptation.

In the initial *commitment* phase, it is likely that your attention will be distracted from yourselves sexually with all your energy going into nurturing the new child. It would be unlikely that there would be much sexual activity at all during this first phase.

The *honeymoon* phase: everyone in the family, as well as the new child, will be striving to be on their best behavior and to present their best selves. During this time, the sexual life would likely take a positive jump.

But then the *storm* comes. The storm is that period during which the adoptive relationships are tested. The child may feel rejected and the parents inadequate. When parents are being tested in terms of their perseverance, discipline, power, and consistency, the sexual life will usually reflect that tension and either be purely functional or nonexistent.

But as with any crisis, we usually get through it. The adoption either "takes," the storm lasts forever, or the child may actually be given back to the court. If the two of you weather the adoption well, the good feelings will allow for a full sexual life. If, however, the storm has taken such a toll that it has been divisive between you as husband and wife, then some recommitment and reconnective work is going to be necessary—both in terms of communication and relationship, as well as the sexual experience.

Adopting a child will inevitably be an event that brings stress. Stress always affects the sexual relationship. It does not need to be the end— it can be the time for a new beginning where the two of you discover each other sexually in ways that have not been enjoyed before. You can use this as an opportunity for growth in your communication and in your sexual life.

Adoption and Hope

Many of us know women who became pregnant a month after they adopted a child. So there is the folklore that if the couple will just relax, children will be conceived and born. Statistics actually say something quite in contrast to this. The research has shown that after adoption, between 3 and 6 percent of the adoptive parents conceive— so this obviously is not a surefire method for dealing with infertility.

It is not fully understood why these few postadoptive pregnancies occur. It may be that in these instances, the reduction of stress brought about the pregnancy. Some authorities suspect that it could be due to some subtle biochemical changes in the woman's body that happen as a result of parenting. Even though the numbers are few, this small percentage does hold out a measure of hope. We would encourage you to talk about that hope if either of you feels it. Recognize it as an unlikely possibility, yet take birth control precautions if pregnancy after adoption would be negative.

Conclusion

For a few couples, their sexual relationship is unaffected by the infertility struggle, the process of adjustment to adoption, or the grief of accepting childlessness. In fact, sex is the glue that holds the relationship together. For most, however, deterioration of sexual fulfillment is likely when that is not counteracted with a conscious focus.

Whatever the outcome for the two of you, whatever the stress you go through in reaching that point, we trust that you will find peace with each other and with your situation. May God's strength and blessing be with you. May you find the fullness of life intended for you.

For Further Study

Menning, Barbara Eck. The Emotional Needs of Infertile Couples. *Fertility and Sterility.* October 1980, vol. 34, no. 4, 313–319.

Rosenfeld, David L., M.D., and Eileen Mitchell, B.S., Treating the Emotional Aspects of Infertility: Counseling Services in an Infertility Clinic. *American Journal of Obstetrics and Gynecology.* 1979, 135, 177–180.

Seibel, Machelle M., M.D., and Melvin L. Taymor, M.D., Emotional Aspects of Infertility. *Fertility and Sterility.* February, 1982, vol. 37, no. 2, 137–145.

Walker, Herbert E., Sexual Problems and Infertility. *Psychosomatics,* August 1978, vol. 19, no. 8, 477–484.

Sex during and after Pregnancy

Pregnancy and childbirth produce emotional and social changes, as well as the obvious physical changes. All of these changes affect the couple. The process of having a baby can add enough stress to disrupt a relationship, or it can pull a couple together and deepen their relationship.

How is the sexual life affected? Recent studies have examined the patterns of sexual relations both during and after pregnancy. Sexual desire, frequency of sexual intercourse, various sexual activities, and the effect on orgasm have all been analyzed.

When Joyce was studying nursing in the early 1960s, the cautious recommendations for sexual activity during and after pregnancy were unchallenged. Her maternity nursing textbook reads as follows:

"Sexual intercourse is usually permitted in moderation until the last six weeks of the pregnancy. However, many physicians advise against intercourse during the first three months of pregnancy or during the time of the regular menstrual periods because of the danger of abortion. If the patient has had previous abortions (miscarriages), coitus will probably be restricted until two weeks after the third missed menstrual period. Toward the end of pregnancy, marital relationships may cause premature labor or introduce infection. Relationships should not be resumed until after the six-week examination or until the doctor knows everything is normal" (Davis, M. Edward, M.D. and Reva Rubin, R.N., M.N., C.M., M.S.; *Obstetrics for Nurses,* Philadelphia: W. B. Saunders Co., 1962).

What do we know today? Are these sexual restrictions necessary during pregnancy? Researching sexual behaviors and responses has answered many of the concerns about sex during and after pregnancy. Some are still awaiting clearer answers.

SEX DURING PREGNANCY

We want to look, first, at how sexual activity is affected by pregnancy and, then, at how pregnancy is affected by sexual intercourse and/or orgasm.

Pregnancy Affects Sex

Surveys indicate that as the pregnancy lengthens in time, sexual activity decreases, with a sharp decrease for many couples during the last three months. Why is this?

Socially and culturally there is the attitude that pregnancy and sexuality don't go together. Historically, the pregnant woman has been regarded as an asexual being. One husband shared: "We haven't enjoyed each other sexually for a long time. Not the way we used to before Meg got pregnant. I guess we lost the momentum. Once we found out she was pregnant, we pretty much stopped having sex. We weren't sure if it was OK. It just didn't seem right to be sexual with her."

Even though it takes sexual intercourse to get pregnancy started, a pregnant woman may not be seen as sexual. She is seen as taking a hiatus from sexual desires and behaviors for the duration of the pregnancy and even after. She is now becoming a mother and all of us know that mothers are *not* sexual! She is in transition between being herself and being the mother of a child. Most societies have rules or rituals which govern transition times from one social identity to another, similar to puberty rights. Avoidance of sexual intercourse is a common ritual for a woman becoming a mother and even for a man becoming a father.

Some women don't *feel* as sexual during the early months of pregnancy. This decrease in desire is both emotionally and physically based. Although hormonal changes are not thought to *cause* decrease in sexual desire during early pregnancy, they do trigger the physical symptoms that may lead a woman not to feel sexual. Tenderness and enlargement of her breasts may elicit a pulling away from breast contact with her husband. Nausea and sleepiness may make her physically unavailable. The presence of medical complications will surely interrupt sexual activity. Closeness and reassurance of love continue to be very important for the woman who doesn't have the physical stamina for sexual intimacy. We encourage couples to increase the nonsexual physical closeness.

Emotional components also affect sexual desire. Difficulty accepting body changes creates a sexual guardedness in sharing freely in a sexual way. Or pulling away from sex may be a response to the feeling of connection with the new life inside. It is as if the woman's pregnant body belongs to the child so can't be enjoyed by her husband. Sometimes there is a sense of keeping the growing baby securely locked inside her as her exclusive property. She feels she must save herself for her baby. Even as it was believed that a male athlete should not ejaculate before a competitive event (since sex leaves us spent), so the woman needed to conserve her energy and vitality for the baby. Sometimes the desire to guard the pregnancy results from difficulty in conceiving.

Men also have emotional reactions to their wives' pregnancy that causes them to avoid sex. Some men believe that sex with a pregnant woman is immoral. Most often men's avoidance of sex during pregnancy has to do with the fear of hurting the mother or baby. What is interesting is that most women report that they think their husbands are avoiding them sexually because they are unattractive. Very few men react to pregnancy as a turnoff. This indicates a need to communicate. Whatever the feelings are during these early months of adjustment, talk about them. Harbored feelings grow, and then separate us. Shared feelings bring clarity and connection.

There are other emotional reasons for avoiding sex. When either the husband or wife does not feel love for the other, but has only been sexually active to get pregnant, pregnancy will abruptly interrupt the sexual relationship. If the relationship has not been satisfying, pregnancy becomes a good excuse for avoiding the disappointing sexual experience.

The sexual feelings in response to pregnancy can be just the opposite. Some women report an increase in their sexual drive during these early months. These are the women who feel a sense of relief at not having to worry about trying to get pregnant or avoid pregnancy. Others who experience more desire connect it with an improved self-esteem. Pregnancy enhances their view of themselves sexually. Instead of seeing themselves as asexual, some women get a new sense of self-worth from carrying a baby.

Men can have this same positive response to their wives' pregnancy. We have found this to be true for us. Cliff always found Joyce's pregnant state very attractive. Many men are proud to be responsible for their wives' pregnancies. Increased sexual desire may be an expression of a new joy and connection between the husband and wife. For other couples, particularly those who have been pregnant before, sexual desire doesn't change at all with the onset of pregnancy.

Some studies of sexual desire during the second trimester of pregnancy (4–6 months), report a gradual decline while others report that most women desire sex more frequently. Whatever is true for you is what you need to follow. Both husband and wife need to be free to listen to their feelings, share them with each other, and then make decisions about their sexual activity. In a normal, healthy pregnancy with both desiring sex, the act can bring relaxation and increased intimacy.

Lack of sexual interest, reduced sexual activity, and even some decreased frequency of orgasm seem to be quite common during the last three months of pregnancy. Physical changes are mostly responsible. Pregnant women become weary with carrying the extra burden of weight. They feel awkward. Moving and turning is an effort. As one woman so vividly described, "I walk like a duck, look like a cow, and feel like an elephant."

Because of the woman's large protruding abdomen, position for intercourse will need to be changed. This is a great time to experiment and break out of old patterns. A side-by-side or sitting position may be preferred. Probably the most frequently recommended position has the man kneeling or standing beside the bed with the woman's legs being held by his arms. This gives freedom of movement for him without putting pressure on the baby. Sometimes a rear entry position is most comfortable. The woman can either be on her knees or lying on her side with her back to her husband and her knees bent toward her abdomen. One author recommended that the most important action to improve sex life during the last trimester is to go out and buy more pillows—more than you think you will need.

How pregnancy affects couples' sexual lives varies greatly depending on their individuality, their relationship, the circumstances, as well as the stage of pregnancy. Decrease in sexual interest, activity, and responsiveness during pregnancy is usually connected with a lessening or absence of sexual stirrings, physical complaints, and fears of harming the baby or mother. Keeping physical closeness and sexual activity alive will enhance the couple's relationship, the woman's feelings about herself, and her general well-being. We would encourage couples to plan weekly touching times into their lives. The activity of these times can vary with the feelings of the moment. Talking and touching are always important for handling life's changes.

Sex Affects Pregnancy

We have looked at the effects of pregnancy on a couple's sexual life. What about the effects of sex on pregnancy? When sex is avoided during pregnancy because of fear, that fear has to do with the concern that sex will have a detrimental effect on the baby or mother. Can intercourse cause harm during pregnancy? Are there times when certain sexual activities or responses need to be restricted?

The three primary concerns about having sexual intercourse and/or orgasm for the woman are that she will abort the fetus during the first trimester, that she will deliver the baby prematurely, or that she and the fetus could be infected. Let us look at each of these fears.

When a woman has an orgasm her uterus contracts. Uterine contractions are what push the baby out of the uterus and vaginal passage during labor and delivery. So it is practical to wonder if allowing oneself to have an orgasm when pregnant might cause abortion or premature labor. Fortunately, we also know that the uterus undergoes contractions regularly during a pregnancy without triggering expulsion of the fetus. Much research has been conducted on this issue. It has been concluded from these studies that intercourse, orgasm, or both need *not* be restricted for the majority of pregnant women. Sexual activity appears to be safe throughout pregnancy for almost all women.

In a normal pregnancy, it is not easy to set off labor before the body is ready. If intercourse or orgasm could terminate a pregnancy easily, unwanted babies would be avoided that way. Love-making alone cannot set off labor before the cervix is ripe (soft and opening). But when the cervix is ripe, then anything can set off labor, including sexual intercourse or orgasm.

There are situations in which sexual intercourse and/or orgasm are prohibited. Sexual stimulation to orgasm should be avoided by women who habitually abort. When a woman has had difficulty keeping her pregnancy, for whatever reason, it is wise to avoid the uterine contractions of orgasm. Talk to your physician.

Similarly, this restriction of orgasm is also advised for women for whom premature labor is a threat. That would be true for women whose cervixes have dilated prematurely, who are bleeding, who have experienced previous threatened premature labor, or who are carrying a multiple pregnancy. Sometimes the physician will instruct the woman not to have intercourse because of one of these situations. Orgasm will not be mentioned, so the couple will continue other forms of sexual activity that brings the woman to orgasm. This happened for us before Greg, our second child, was born. At that time, we were unaware of what happens in our bodies during a sexual response cycle. Joyce started dilating six weeks before she was due to deliver. We were faithful patients, so stopped having intercourse, as instructed by the doctor, but continued closeness and caressing with orgasms for Joyce. Fortunately, the other treatments we were following postponed labor and delivery for three more weeks. Being only three weeks early, Greg was as healthy as a full-term newborn. When intercourse is restricted, assume that stimulation of the woman to orgasm is also a danger, unless that difference is clarified.

There are times when vaginal abstinence, the avoidance of intercourse, is indicated. During the first three months of pregnancy, threatened or inevitable abortion is a clear reason for avoidance of intercourse as well as orgasm. This is important to avoid infection. Once the sac or membranes have ruptured, vaginal abstinence is definitely a necessary restriction in order to avoid infection.

So intercourse and orgasm should be avoided in women with obstetric complications such as bleeding, ruptured membranes, premature dilation of the cervix, threatened abortion, or premature labor. However, there is no reason to restrict such activity for a normal pregnancy. Most studies have shown that there is no connection between intercourse, orgasm, and other sexual activity with the onset of labor. In fact, it has been found that pregnant women who were orgasmic had a lower percentage of premature deliveries than did nonorgasmic women. So intercourse and orgasm, per se, are not related to prematurity. It is just that these may be injurious when prematurity is already threatening.

Infections are an unlikely complication from intercourse, if the couple has a monogamous relationship. If either spouse has had other sexual partners, there is the risk of the mother acquiring a sexually transmitted disease. These can be a cause of death for the mother, the fetus, or the newborn. Since the baby is in the well-protected sac, it will not be infected unless the mother is infected with a blood-borne organism. Then it is passed through the placenta to the fetus.

One sexual activity that is highly dangerous during pregnancy is the blowing of air into the vagina. Oral sex itself is harmless, but deaths have resulted when air has been blown into the vagina. Death occurs within minutes if the air forced into the vagina happens to form an air bubble. The air is forced from the vagina into the uterus and into the bloodstream through the uterine lining. A bubble or air embolism forms and may travel to the lungs, brain, or heart causing sudden death. The same danger is present with vaginal douching during pregnancy.

It is important to be aware of these necessary restrictions. Nevertheless, since we have spent more time detailing the limitations than proclaiming the freedom to fully enjoy sex during pregnancy, you may feel that it is better to avoid sex just in case. That isn't true! If you are concerned about any of the special situations for yourself, check with your physician so you can relax and enjoy yourselves.

Unnecessary sexual inhibitions or restrictions during pregnancy can be a source of stress that is detrimental to a successful pregnancy. If there are no complications and the woman has no history of miscarriage or premature birth (and the couple wants it), they can safely enjoy sexual intercourse and orgasm from the onset of pregnancy until the beginning of labor (or the opening of the cervix).

SEX AFTER PREGNANCY

Whether the pregnancy ends with a miscarriage, stillbirth, or a newborn baby, the weeks after are a time of crises and adjustment for the couple. Sexual adjustment is one of the more critical emotional adjustments of this time period. With the loss of the pregnancy or expected baby, there is the pain and separation of grief, the doubt about oneself, and the feeling of sexual abnormality. When a baby enters the home, the changes in social and family relationships are tremendous. With the birth of each baby, the shape of the family changes. The relationships within both the nuclear and extended family are shifted. Sometimes these shifts are felt abruptly; sometimes they are almost unnoticed.

Miscarriage

The emotional effects of a miscarriage will have a more jarring impact on the sexual life of a couple than will the physical trauma—although physical recuperation is more serious than the couple expects. A miscarriage or spontaneous abortion is the natural termination of a pregnancy prior to the twentieth week of the pregnancy. Spontaneous abortions are estimated to occur in fifteen percent of all pregnancies.

There are various reasons why the woman loses a baby. Hormonal abnormalities, high blood pressure, anemia, diabetes, or severe emotional problems in the mother are known causes. Genetic defects, infection, and anatomical abnormalities in the fetus are other proven causes. Many times, however (about 50 percent of the time), the cause is unknown. It is important for the couple to be informed of the cause when that is known. Don't hesitate to ask!

Since the cause is often not known or not explained to couples, many women live with misconceptions. It is common for women to feel they caused the miscarriage. Sexual activity may be assumed to be the cause. This will affect the sexual relationship. Some women fear they will no longer be able to bear children. Such women feel less feminine for not fulfilling their reproductive role.

It is important for the couple to acknowledge the importance of the lost pregnancy. Each of them may experience the grief and loss differently. Sharing and accepting those differences can strengthen the marital relationship. Feeling guilt or blaming the other adds to the stress. It is highly unlikely that there was anything either the husband or wife did to cause the miscarriage, even though they may feel they did. Even when the pregnancy was unplanned, the experience remains emotionally upsetting. Feelings of sadness, anxiety, depression, and hostility are common. Often the woman is affected longer than the man. She may be weepy for several weeks and even experience loss of sexual interest, while he may have resolved the loss and be impatient to move on with life. If sexual intimacy is to be resumed with enjoyment, emotional needs and differences must be attended to. Take time to talk to each other and to other caring listeners.

Stillbirth

The grief of a stillbirth or the death of a newborn is amplified by the sense of having produced a "bad baby"—one who was defective or unable to live. All too often, there seems to be no place on the maternity ward for the mother without a baby. The staff doesn't know how to handle the loss. They are prepared to care for mothers with babies, not mothers without babies. Many times the mother is hastily sent home. She feels that she has lost her baby, her status as a mother, *and* her role as a patient. Yet she is a person who needs extra care and attention.

A medical journal reported a case of a woman who after delivering a stillborn was put in a room alone, and not even looked in on for twelve hours. She wasn't checked physically, or offered anything to drink.

A friend of Joyce's from nurses' training had a baby die in the hospital a few days after it was born. When the baby wasn't brought to her at its usual feeding time, Jan started calling the nurse. No one responded. After some time, she walked up to the nurses' station, but couldn't get anyone to talk to her. One of the nurses told her someone would be with her in a moment. Finally, a nurses' aide (who had no training), took her to a supply room, had her sit on a chair, told her that her baby had died, and walked out. Jan, feeling physically weak and totally dazed, had to find her way to a telephone to contact her husband. She had to manage this unexpected, saddening news without the support or care of the hospital staff.

These are extremes. Usually hospital personnel are better able to deal with loss than was true in these two situations. Yet it is not unusual for a woman who has lost her baby to feel like an outcast. Most of us are uncomfortable and don't know what to say, so we avoid the person. We treat her like she has the plague at a time when she needs us beside her, sharing her pain.

Whether or not to see the dead baby, what to do about funeral rituals, and choosing or not choosing a name are all issues that the couple needs to decide. The amount of information the couple is given and the amount of choice (with support) will help ease this difficult situation.

Mothers whose babies live even a few moments are better able to handle the tragedy than those whose babies are born dead. Mothers who deliver stillborns are better able to mourn when they can see their dead baby and know what will become of it. Even if the baby is grossly defective, it is recommended that the parents be given the choice of seeing their child. Cleaning and wrapping the baby in a receiving blanket lessens the shock of the defects. Then allow the parents to unwrap and examine the baby at their own pace if they desire. If you have experienced such a loss, you may have your own sense of what would have been best for you. The primary concern is that feelings of loss are taken seriously and that you as a couple are given the support you need.

If you are friends of a couple who has lost a baby, go to them. Give them a hug. Bring them a meal. Be with them. You don't have to say anything except that you are sorry, that you care, and that you want to be available in any way they need you.

Contrary to what is commonly believed, both parents will experience profound grief from the death of a baby they have never known or enjoyed. That grief may not be resolved for years. The grief begins with a sense of shock and disbelief and is followed by a time of confusion and pain. As the death becomes real, feelings of anger and guilt take over. The mother may mentally search through the pregnancy for evidence of something she did wrong or should have done better. Overwhelming sadness can naturally lead to depression. This is accompanied by a sense of loneliness which may last several months. During this time it is unlikely that the grieving couple will feel sexual. Yet, closeness and physical affirmation are extremely important. Holding each other and crying helps lighten the despair. As the despair lessens, "the light begins to appear at the end of the tunnel." Heaviness is relieved and life's functions are reestablished. Sexual joy may need to be rediscovered. Take time to find each other. Bodily pleasure lessens pain.

Bringing Baby Home

Most of the time couples face both the joy and stress of bringing home that wonderful new creation—the precious little person who will change their lives so dramatically. Sexual adjustment can go smoothly or be difficult.

Resuming Sexual Activity

The six to eight weeks following labor and delivery are known as the postpartum period. It is during this time that the woman's genital organs return to their previous condition. The uterus shrinks back to almost its pre-pregnancy state, shape, and position. It takes only two to three weeks for the cervix (opening of the uterus) to close and the vagina to return to normal. The breasts prepare to nurse the infant.

When is it possible to resume sexual intercourse? In the past, enforced abstinence was the rule during the six weeks following birth. All of the literature at this time indicates that there is no need to wait that long. No evidence has been found to indicate that having sexual intercourse early has an adverse effect on the healing. This is particularly true when there has not been an episiotomy (incision to enlarge the vaginal opening) or the episiotomy has been carefully repaired with little tissue damage.

Most couples prefer to resume comfortable intercourse in the second or third postpartum week. The only reason not to return to sexual intercourse would be pain or vaginal irritation or infection. Some women report having had intercourse five days after delivery without any complications. Any stitches should have healed within ten days. Provided the woman hasn't developed an infection and the couple are sure they are freshly washed and follow good hygienic practices, it is up to them to determine when to resume intercourse.

We encourage making the first love-making time after childbirth a special event. Plan very carefully. This would best be a scheduled rather than a spontaneous time. Make a decision that you are both ready for sex and then prepare for it. Plan a time when the baby has just eaten and is least likely to awaken. You may want to have someone close to you take the infant for an hour or two.

Many women think of this time in the same way they thought of their first intercourse. It is like being a virgin again. Use the same precautions to avoid pain. That is, take plenty of time to caress and enjoy the pleasure of each other's bodies. Proceed to entry slowly with the woman in control of guiding the penis into the vagina. Use a lubricant. Albolene (a facial cleanser) is one we like. Allercreme (non-lanolin), which is excellent to pleasure the total body, also works well as a lubricant. It would be helpful for the man to have ejaculated within twenty-four hours before this time together so that he will not ejaculate too quickly. This can be taken care of through self-stimulation or through manual caressing by the wife, if that is enjoyable for her.

Plan for some special romance as part of the setting of your enjoyment together. Joyce had experienced so much sexual pain after Julene was born that we went to see a romantic movie with plenty of "turn on" for our reinitiation after Greg was born. It worked well! Joyce had extensive stitching from a breech delivery (feet first) with Julene. Greg was an easier birth, so that helped also. To the best of your ability, see to it that the first sexual intercourse after childbirth occurs under ideal conditions in terms of setting, fatigue, preparation of your bodies, and time of day.

Take the necessary birth control precautions even if the mother is breast-feeding. Though many women do not ovulate (so cannot become pregnant) during the first few months of breast-feeding, some do. Some women ovulate before they have their first menstrual period. You may want to refer to Chapter 2 in deciding what birth control method would be your choice during this important time of reconnecting sexually.

How Sex Is Affected

Tiredness and fatigue are natural deterrents to sex. The woman's body has experienced a major blow. First of all, she has been carrying around this twelve-to fifty-pound basketball in her abdomen for nine months. Then she is recuperating from the physical trauma and emotional intensity of the birth process. Her body has not returned to its pre-pregnancy shape. Her breasts are sore and seem to belong to the baby. They are no longer there for her or her husband's sexual pleasure. Also, she has a totally dependent infant to care for.

If this is the first child, both may be anxious about being good parents, using up any extra energy with anxiety. They may be getting up every few hours during the night. Household tasks have to be handled, meals prepared, the house cleaned, and other children tended to. Fatigue is an almost inevitable part of those first months after a newborn comes home. This combination of exhaustion and anxiety may mean that the woman never becomes aroused. If she ever does have enough energy to feel sexually interested and get things started sexually, about the time she relaxes enough to enjoy herself, she's likely to fall asleep or hear the baby stir. Thus, many women report diminished sexual desire after their first child. Even though sex is still as enjoyable for many, the frequency of sexual activity is less during that first postpartum year than it was before pregnancy.

In addition to the tiredness, there is a change in focus after the first child arrives. Instead of the primary focus being between the husband and wife, now the two of them are focused on the child. Sometimes the husband feels that the only connection is between the mother and infant. There is no place for him. Couples need to work together to get father and infant bonded. If father is home during the baby's fussy times, he can take his shirt off and carry the baby on his shoulder. Infants attach as they smell our bodies and feel our skin. This will also give the new mom a break. Fathers should be active in sharing the responsibility for the baby.

The new mother may be feeling not only tired, but also depressed. Depression causes sexual apathy. Postnatal depression may be the reason for infrequent sexual intercourse up to three months after delivery. The weepy postnatal blues often begin within a few days of the child's birth. In addition to being overwhelmed by the new responsibilities of motherhood and being exhausted, some women are affected by sudden hormonal changes—and in different ways. Depression is the result for some. Even though the lack of interest in sex is temporary, women worry about it and feel guilty, while husbands feel frustrated and unsure of how to bring relief.

For women who feel sexual desire after childbirth, the fear of pain from the episiotomy (cut in the perineum for the baby to be born) may cause them to wait to be sexually active. Intercourse after childbirth can sometimes be distinctly uncomfortable. Forty percent of women report soreness or pain during intercourse after childbirth. Pain needs to be taken seriously and remedied with the physician's help. When something normally pleasurable causes us pain, it is likely that we will pull away from the activity. Pain causes more havoc in sexual relationships than most people realize. It must be relieved!

Breast-feeding, too, can stir up feelings both in the woman and in the man. Initially, there may be anxiety for the woman about whether the whole process will work. Will she be able to produce enough milk? Once they are working, the breasts seem like they belong to the baby. A woman may feel an incredible sense of heaviness from the infant's total dependence on her body for survival.

Joyce breast-fed all three of our children. She began teaching nursing at the local university when Julene was just six weeks old, yet Julene never took a bottle. Joyce would often drive home with that sense of urgency for Julene—the sense that Julene could not survive without her. There were many intense prayers for safety on those trips home. The joy of arriving and being there for her baby was all encompassing. Cliff was often thrilled, too, as his Ph.D. studies may have been side-tracked by walking Julene for the past hour waiting for "mom" to come home with the "goodies."

Some women who breast-feed find they are less sexually interested, while others get turned on by breast-feeding which increases their desire for their husbands.

The sexual feelings that stir in women in response to the baby sucking their nipples may come as a real surprise, even shock and embarrassment. These feelings are a pure, natural physical response to that part of the body being stimulated. The feelings in no way impart the message that the mother is using the child as a sexual object. The increased sensitivity of the breasts may be very intense. Yet, they may get so used to the baby's sucking the mother is not able to switch gears to her husband's touch or lips and tongue. Besides, when her breasts fill up, they may ache and leak.

Two helpful suggestions: first, breast-feed immediately before a sex playtime so the breast will feel more comfortable and available; second, take time to discover the type of breast and nipple play that feels arousing, but different than the baby's sucking. It is important that the man not take these adjustments as a rejection of him, but rather as a time of rediscovery.

The man may have his own sexual inhibitions after bringing a baby home. He may have difficulty responding to the mother of his baby. In his eyes she may have become almost sacred—the Madonna syndrome—not a sexual person to be enjoyed for his pleasure. He may feel more like worshiping her than making love to her! Her being the "food factory" may enhance this nonsexual image to her husband. These barriers to sexuality need to be discussed.

Enhancing Sex after Bringing a Baby Home

The ongoing sexual relationship of the couple with a new baby requires nurturing. Life's responsibilities will need to be balanced so there is time for each spouse to get rest and have time for each other.

Write out a plan for each day. List the essentials for that day. Decide what can be skipped. Get as much help as you can afford. Allow friends to help by bringing a meal, taking an older child while the baby sleeps, or coming for a night or a few hours each day. Plan for the new mother to rest every time the baby sleeps. Divide responsibilities between the two of you, so that the stress is equally distributed. How much each of you assumes depends so much on the rest of your lifestyle. If the husband works 6 A.M. to 8 P.M., he is not going to be able to take on much more. If there are three children at home under the age of four, and no outside help, the mother will be able to handle only the minimal essentials.

Once the duties have been sorted out, decide what kind of time you each would enjoy with the other. Take turns being responsible for the times of your choice. For example, if the wife wants a time of relaxation for talking and low-key touching, she may schedule a babysitter to come in for an hour or two right after the baby has been fed. She may prepare the master bedroom to be cozy with candlelight, slice some cheese and apples, leave a message with her husband that he is to be hers from 8:00 to 9:30 that evening, and invite him to the bedroom with a clear message of her desires for that time.

If the husband would like to get away from the responsibilities of home, he might invite his wife to a short, light dinner out for an hour and a half. Getting away will be difficult during the first year after the child is born. If time away is important for your relationship, you will have to be deliberate in making it happen. Once breast-feeding has been well-established, pumping milk for the baby to be fed by bottle is a possibility. Start this in the first month or so to get the baby used to both breast and bottle. Doing a trial run before the real event is important. As we mentioned before, Julene would never suck from a bottle even if it was Joyce's milk.

An important element of sexual enhancement is the woman's physical condition. Pelvic exercises for the woman will increase her sexual awareness. She can speed the healing of the episiotomy and the return of her genitals to good tone by faithfully exercising her P.C. (pubococcygeus) muscle. This is the muscle that forms a figure 8 around the openings of the urinary bladder and vagina in the front, and the anus in the back. It controls the opening and closing of these orifices. When you tighten these muscles, you can stop the passage of urine or feces. You can also tighten and relax them in love-making to enhance sensation. These muscles contain many nerve-endings which record pleasurable stimuli. Their activity and liveliness are vital for every woman's sexual satisfaction. A man enjoys the firmness of his wife's muscles when she contracts them rhythmically during sexual intercourse. They play an important part in mutual pleasure.

To increase the tone and vitality, start exercising the P.C. muscle 100–200 times daily. Slowly tighten the muscles that you use to stop urination. Tighten until you cannot tighten anymore, hold to the count of four, and then gently let go. Practice this while urinating. Stop the flow of urine several times while you are emptying your bladder. You can do the same thing with the anal muscle.

When you're focusing specifically on the vagina, think of starting to tighten the vagina by bringing your labia (lips) closer together. Imagine that your vagina is an elevator and you are starting at the ground floor. Bring the muscles up from floor to floor, tightening and holding at each floor. Do not hold your breath while you tighten. Go to the fifth floor. Then go down one floor at a time. These more thorough exercises can be done 25 times a day.

Exercise some pelvic muscle every time you change a diaper, while you wash the dishes, cook dinner, breast-feed, read stories to your older children, and so on. The exercise will make a difference both in feeling and in keeping your internal organs in place! To keep the sexual relationship alive will take a conscious effort. Recognize that special times for the two of you are a priority.

Conclusion

Sex during and after pregnancy need not change. Except for the pain Joyce experienced after Julene, our sex life was not that different from before conception. We never thought that much about it. Our lifestyle, Joyce's quick labors, and a mutually satisfying sex life for five years before bearing children may have contributed to the lack of change. With Cliff as a full-time student and Joyce as the full-time financial provider, roles had to be shared. We did not fit the traditional husband-wife, father-mother stereotypes. Mutuality became a must!

Each couple is different, each pregnancy is different, and every childbirth is different. Finding what is mutually satisfying for you as a couple is vital. Do not be forced into a pattern of behavior just because the books or experts say that is how it should be. Learn the principles, then apply them to your lives. Enjoy a happy family life together. Learn to laugh and cry together when stress is more than you can handle.

For Further Study

Carrera, Michael. *Sex: The Facts, the Acts, and Your Feelings.* New York: Crown Publishers, 1981. "Pregnancy."

Close, Sylvia. *Sex During Pregnancy and After Childbirth.* Wellingborough: Thorson's Publishers Limited, 1984.

Coleman, A. and L. Coleman. *Pregnancy: The Psychological Experience.* New York: Bantam, 1971.

Davis, M. Edward, M.D. and Reva Ruben, R.N., M.N., *Obstetrics for Nurses.* Philadelphia: W. B. Saunders Co., 1962.

Jessner, L., "Pregnancy as a Stress in Marriage." *Marital and Sexual Counseling in Medical Practice.* D. F. Abse, E. M. Nash, and L. M. R. Louden, editors. Hagerstown, Maryland: Harper and Row, 1974.

_____II

Children Impact the Sexual Life

Mommy, What Are You and Daddy Doing in There?

It's Saturday morning. Your seven-year-old son had a friend over for the night and they love to watch Saturday morning cartoons. Even though you are not sure about all the learning that is taking place from those cartoons, you brush it aside with the thought that somehow this one time isn't going to make any difference. The TV does function as a good babysitter.

You go to the bathroom and brush your teeth. Then you wake up your spouse in anticipation of a relaxed, enjoyable sexual time together. You're refreshed, and feeling that specialness of making love right when you wake up. The bodies are warm and relaxed, and the minds are sleepy.

You get into the sexual experience and are just beginning to get aroused. You're laughing and giggling together. All of a sudden there's that knock on the door. "Why do you have the door locked? What are you guys doing in there? Can I come in? Tommy just spilled his milk all over the carpet."

Suddenly, the morning that had great promise has been jolted by reality. The fact is that you live in a home where you aren't completely in control of your time, nor can you choose exactly when you're going to make love.

Children are both an interruption and an intrusion in a couple's sexual relationship. Yet the stability and solidarity of a home is enhanced by the mutually satisfying, ongoing sexual life of the parents. Therefore, the marriage must take priority. There will still be many times when the needs of the family are attended to first. But the long-range priority has to be the marriage. The solidarity of the marriage is very much like a good foundation for a building. If the foundation is set on solid ground, with good reinforcement-steel in the concrete, then the building will withstand all the buffeting of the above-ground activity. The same is true for a marriage. One of the best gifts we can give to our children is the gift of a marital relationship that is solidly based on love—and a fulfilling sex life. This is a major source of security for a child.

A Solid Marriage

A solid marriage has a number of ingredients. We would recommend the following:

Keep open. Openness between husband and wife, and then the family, is basic. As you maintain openness with one another, the children will model that style. When we talk about openness, we are not recommending inappropriate exposure of private feelings and behaviors which would be confusing and emotionally upsetting to children, but rather, an openness about feelings, reactions, impressions, expectations, and dreams that help members of a family share together.

Keep the decks clear between you as a couple. This can be accomplished by following the Marriage Encounter format of writing to each other. Another way is to provide a time to share specific events on a regular basis. Or perhaps this sharing happens spontaneously in the course of life by not letting anger, resentments, and frustration build between you. By always keeping the feeling channels open and clear, you will be a positive example for your children.

Keep together. This is not a united front against the kids, mom and dad on one side and the kids on the other, but rather a joint front with and for the kids. This also does not mean that the two of you can't disagree even in front of the children. But it does mean that in the middle of your disagreement you send a message of respect, care, and concern for each other. You do *not* undermine the other parent as a way of furthering your own purposes or gaining some advantages with the kids.

Keep committed. Every marriage is very much like driving along a mountain road. The ground underneath may be as solid as granite, but you are always only a few feet from going over the precipice. For a relationship to function at a high level there must be a diligent focus to keep it soundly on the road. Getting close to the edge may lead to havoc and destruction. Those edges usually involve overcommitment in other areas such as work, church, volunteering, or community action. Extensive involvement in other relationships, with either the opposite or the same sex, test those edges. Overcommitment to the children, so that the marriage is always in second place, can also be a danger. If we are going to show our children that the marriage is a priority, it must be evident in our actions.

Keep balanced. While each of us has different needs, we all require variety. We need private times, social times, times for exercise, work, reflection, even time for paying the bills. When we become overfocused in one area, we take away from the balance that allows us to be whole individuals, able to share the intimacy of a marriage, and give to a family. Check out that balance with each other on a regular basis to help keep on track.

Keep scheduled. For most of us, with the busy lives we lead, it will be necessary to do some planning for our times together. For most couples the demands of the immediate family, the extended family, and the community—church, school, sports events, and other social involvements—usurp all available time. Occasionally, there is time left over that is given to the marriage.

If we are going to maintain a solid marriage, we must make time together a priority. How often have those of us who would claim that our marriage is our top human relationship been invited to go out to dinner, looked at the calendar, and discovered that the time was set aside for us? Did we then say, "No, we're not doing anything that night, we'd be delighted to go"? This sends the message that we, as a couple, are a low priority rather than one that must be taken seriously.

Finally, *keep "turned on."* A young couple in a class that we were teaching recently asked, "Could you speak on keeping your sexual love relationship exciting for both partners throughout the marriage years? What would be some obstacles that might occur after the honeymoon is over? What are ways to continually be pleasing to each other?"

This couple is already taking care of keeping their love relationship alive by thinking about it and asking questions. They accurately imply that it takes a conscious effort to keep the sexual relationship alive. The reason it takes a conscious effort is that the intense passion and craving for each other which is present before marriage changes once we can have each other day after day, and week after week, for the rest of our lives. In fact, now sex is not only readily available, but rather it has become an expected part of the relationship, sometimes a demand.

Even though the marriage is the most secure and trusting relationship in which the sexual joys can grow, there is also much about married life and family that we associate with being asexual. We didn't see our parents as sexual, so when we become parents we may turn ourselves off sexually. Here are some guidelines that can help you keep "turned-on" in your marriage:

First, make certain that your sexual experiences are satisfying for both of you. The experiences need to be free of demand and anxiety, and full of care, warmth, pleasure, and fun.

Second, both of you must be able to allow intimacy, to be willing to lose yourselves with each other, and be open with your sexuality.

Third, take care of your body. Staying in good physical condition will help keep you in tune sexually. This includes everything: eating the kind of food that is best for your body, getting the right amount of rest, doing physical exercise that stimulates your cardiovascular system, and grooming your body.

Fourth, keep in touch with your own sexual feelings and responses in your body. You may need to discover those for the first time. Until *you* know your body, it may be difficult to share yourself with another person.

For the woman, it is important to learn to do the pubococcygeus (PC) muscle exercises (Kegel). Let yourself be aware of your sexual thoughts; affirm your body's sexual feelings as you experience them. Let yourself be aware of all your sexual dimensions physically, emotionally, and mentally.

If sexual feelings get triggered in response to others of the opposite sex, manage and control those feelings by channeling them into your marriage. Bring the spark home to bed!

Fifth, the sexual relationship must be made a priority. Scheduling quality time to be together physically is most difficult for many couples. From what most of us experienced before marriage, what we've read, and what we've seen in movies and on television, we believe that a truly romantic sexual experience will automatically and spontaneously burst forth from within us. We believe we will make mad, passionate love throughout our marriage, and if we don't, something is wrong with us.

The fact is that most of the time this is not how it works. After a few months we find that the newness becomes repetitive. Other claims upon our time are barging in on us. We find ourselves having to make more of an effort to be sexual.

This should not be surprising. Something we've been looking forward to for years, that was forbidden before marriage, is now completely open and available to us. As availability is gained, intrigue is lost. That initial sparkle has to be kindled through other means. For many couples, it is important to schedule blocks of time to be physical together.

These are times that are designed for physical pleasure and may or may not lead to sexual intercourse. There can be talking, touching, caressing, and loving without demand for response. If that should lead to sexual interest and arousal for both, then proceed with a total sexual experience. Some resist the idea of scheduling "sex." Many feel that scheduling takes away the aura of romance. Often those couples who fear "losing the mystery" are the ones who are experiencing conflict. We are all for spontaneity when your sexual life brings you total happiness without scheduling. But if you are in conflict about what you want, or are unhappy with what happens between you, or find that sex is a quickie at the tired end of the day after the eleven o'clock news, then you may be a couple who could ignite the flame by quality scheduled times.

Sixth, learn to give and receive bodily pleasure without demand for sexual response. Before marriage there is usually hugging, kissing, and caressing, making out or petting with intense "turn on." After legitimizing our sexual activity by being officially married, we tend to cut out all these preliminaries because now we can do the "real thing," sexual intercourse. What we fail to recognize is that all of the touching, caressing, and pleasuring is part of the sexual experience. When we neglect that part, we diminish the joy, pleasure, and satisfaction.

So it is crucial that we learn to touch one another totally, bodily, without demand for arousal or release. Arousal is likely to grow out of this touch when we are relaxed, but it doesn't always, and that's

OK. Chapter 13 in *The Gift of Sex* explains the process of learning to receive pleasure through touch. The whole body is a receptor of pleasure. Allowing the tingling sensations of skin-to-skin contact can help us keep the sexual spark alive as the years go by. Many women, especially, report that they would rather touch and cuddle than have intercourse.

Seventh, take responsibility for your own sexual pleasure. Go after what feels good to you. Don't demand that your spouse produce a positive response in you. Many of us have the idea that we are in the sexual experience for the other person and will get the most out of it when we are focused on bringing the other one happiness. But our finding is that when we take responsibility for our own sexual feelings and enjoy our spouse's body for our pleasure, we give the most. Of course, this means eliminating anything that violates, hurts, or offends the other person. We must each let the other know if something feels negative.

It is a vital thing, especially for the woman, to learn that being in a sexual experience for her own pleasure will ultimately bring the most pleasure to the man. The reason we emphasize this for the woman is that many men already tend to function that way, but women don't. If you ask your husband, he will affirm to you that he enjoys the sexual experience immensely when you get the most out of it—not just when he gets his satisfaction. So, it is vital that you go into the sexual experience taking responsibility for your needs, verbalizing them, so your spouse can relax and enjoy you. We do not see this as selfish, but rather as the way you can give the most in the sexual experience.

Eighth, plan special treats. Like every other part of life, sex can become boring and humdrum. You can add sexual excitement by bringing treats to the experience. These tell your spouse that you have thought ahead. Such actions send a little extra message that you care.

No major productions are necessary. It may be a rose on the bedside stand or the lighting of the candles while she is in taking her shower. It may be preparing a love nest in front of the fireplace that's ready when he gets home late from work, or buying a sexy nightgown, or having a bowl of fresh fruit in the bedroom that you're going to feed to each other. The special treats can be as elaborate as surprising the wife with a special weekend in a city or resort nearby, or can be as simple as a message to him under the dinner plate that says, "I'm going to attack your body tonight."

Ninth, be free to experiment! Plan experimentation in your sexual experience. This is especially important if the two of you find that experimenting does not come naturally. For some couples, creativity and experimentation is as natural as getting up in the morning and brushing one's teeth. But for others, it is much more difficult.

Whenever we do something exactly the same way, on a repetitive basis, it is likely to get boring. If you started eating your favorite meal every day for the next six months, or if you got together with a social group and planned exactly the same event over and over again, or if you went to church on Sunday morning and sang exactly the same songs and heard the same sermon, you would become bored. Our sexual lives are no different.

There is no way to discover the five perfect steps to sexual happiness and then follow them for the rest of our life. We can practice principles, but the actual behavior must vary. Each sexual experience is a new event waiting to be discovered. As we are willing to stretch ourselves and experiment, to play, tease, and explore, we will discover that we have an endless capacity for new experiences and feelings. Continually uncovering the unknown keeps sex alive.

Tenth, include specific times for teaching. These are times when you focus on teaching each other what brings you pleasure, showing how you like to be genitally stimulated, how you like to kiss, how you like your body touched. This is like a periodic review, not only in words but also in action. These can be fun times which may even turn into sexual arousal, but that isn't the goal.

Eleventh, schedule sex-talk times when you are not fatigued and not in the middle of a sexual experience. Keeping yourselves turned on over the years of marriage will mean learning to talk about sex. From time to time you need to touch base by talking about how you are feeling in the sexual experience. What is it that you would like to change? What would you like more of, and how would you like to experiment? Some couples go through their whole married life never talking about sex and report that they are happy. But most of us need to talk about our sexual feelings and experiences regularly.

Twelfth, go for help when necessary. You may find that problems are persisting. There may be a lack of sexual desire, difficulties with arousal for the woman, impotence for the man, orgasmic problems for the woman, premature ejaculation for the man, or persistent pain during intercourse. Get help in dealing with the problems early. Start by self-help methods. Read, attend classes, or consult with your physician.

If self-help doesn't make a difference, get a referral to a sexual therapist. Ask your doctor or minister for a recommendation. Give us a call. You should find our number in the back of the book.

Just today as we were writing this, we got a call from the wife of a sixty-year-old man. The husband has been struggling with impotence, difficulty in achieving and maintaining an erection, for fifteen years. He doesn't believe he can be helped. Sexual problems can be reversed. Our strong encouragement would be to get help early. Early treatment diminishes the distress and the length and cost of treatment.

Being Parents and Lovers

When we have focused on keeping all dimensions of the marriage relationship solid, then we will be able to be parental and sexual. Children need not usurp us as lovers.

We believe it is great for our children to know that we delight in loving each other. If we teach them to wait until marriage to have sex and then we behave as if sex doesn't exist in our marriage, what are they waiting for?

We can communicate to our children the importance of our times to be alone. There is nothing wrong with the children knowing that we have sexual times and that we have fun. One couple struggled because their only love-making time was after all six kids were in bed. They finally decided to designate one night a week as their evening to focus on each other. Whatever room they were in that evening—whether it was the TV room, the bedroom, or the guestroom—was not to be disturbed. The older children were responsible to keep the younger children out. It soon became an established part of this family's life that Thursday night was Mom and Dad's time. The children eventually felt a sense of pride at cooperating with these evenings.

This approach ultimately builds a deep-down security. These children are hearing of families that are falling apart—and here their parents are so enjoying each other that they have special times just for each other.

Research has shown that when parents share positive, open attitudes about sexuality in the family setting, those attitudes are passed on to the children. This does not mean that we expose children to our sexual play, nor does it mean that we give a debriefing the next morning at breakfast! It does mean that we openly communicate that sex is still an enjoyable part of our life and we expect it to be for the rest of our lives.

As we mentioned earlier, most of us as children grew up not viewing our parents as sexual, so we struggle to allow ourselves to be lovers once we are parents. We have separated the sexual part of ourselves from the parenting part. The idea of being a mother and being intensely sexual is as dissonant as a striptease at the Sunday school class.

As parents, we have to start by giving ourselves permission to be lovers. In 1 Corinthians 7:5 the apostle Paul tells us not to forsake coming together sexually, except for brief seasons of prayer, and then come back together again to avoid being tempted. Paul's assumption is that the sexual life will go on for the purpose of enjoyment. Children are not a reason for limiting our sexual relationship. The Song of Solomon, which is purely an erotic, sexual love-poem, gives us an example of the breadth and intensity of loveplay that is expected of a couple. All of that is available to us even when we are parents!

Yes, children bring changes. Since sexual intercourse is a private act, we can no longer freely romp around the house.

Children demand our time and energy, so we have less available for each other. This is the reason for a significant decrease in sexual activity for most couples during the first year after a baby is born. (See Chapter 5, Sex during and after Pregnancy.) Fatigue, pain, and change in body image all lower the wife's desire and, thus, decrease the frequency of sexual activity.

Once the child reaches toddlerhood and is mobile, there is a new concern. We have to be cautious about being interrupted while we are engaging in sex. When we are on guard, because of fear of an intruder, we will not freely enjoy each other sexually. This is the time to get a lock on the bedroom or love-room door. A first priority when moving into a new home is to get that lock put on your bedroom door—and to use it. Many couples find that when there is going to be a love-making time, a special kind of security is felt when the door is locked. We know that nobody is going to walk in on us. This can be important even if a love-making time occurs in the middle of the night (particularly when the children are younger). There is something about a locked door that enhances freedom.

Should it occur that at some point your child walks in on you while you are making love, it is completely appropriate to ask him or her to leave. You may need to explain, especially to younger children, that "What Daddy and Mommy were doing was a loving thing, not a hurtful thing." To a young child the vigorous thrusting and the noises of release could seem hurtful.

The concern with noise becomes more pronounced as children get older. Where the walls are thin or children's bedrooms are right next to the parents' bedroom, precautions need to be taken—both for the child and for you as a couple. One thing you can always do is put a musical barrier such as a speaker or a radio between your room and the child's. Your sounds will be behind it so that the music serves as a buffer for your noises and helps you relax.

One mother reported about her curious ten-year-old who used to come knocking on the door. When the parents didn't respond, she called them on their other telephone (they had two lines). "What's going on in there? It sounds either like dad is sick or there's a dog vomiting." This provided a great opportunity to give a little sex education, since these are not images that we want connected with the sexual experience. We must keep in mind that the sexual noises are a different set of noises than our children will ever hear us make. It does take some explanation if the children are inadvertently exposed to them. Privacy, both in terms of a closed door and the noise, is as important for the couple as it is for the children.

As the children grow older, they begin to understand adult sexual behavior. For some parents this is a serious dilemma. The awareness that their children know what's going on makes them feel self-conscious about being sexual. So they are only together after all the children are asleep or away. Then they feel they must be very quiet. This inhibiting attitude is based on the belief that it would be dramatically and negatively shocking to the child to be aware of adult sexuality. This issue needs to be dealt with. Healthy attitudes can be communicated to the children. This is the surest way for them to grow up with good sexual feelings about themselves and about marriage.

As our children reach adolescence, we may feel even more limited. The new dilemma we've discovered with a couple of adolescents in the house is that they are often studying or coming home from social events later than when we want to go to bed. We find ourselves needing to gear our special times together around their time schedules. Sometimes it can seem as though there is no time when we have our home to ourselves.

In every stage of the children's growth there are adjustments for the sexual life of the mother and father. But there can also be much joy and fulfillment when time and privacy are provided for the two of you. The more we can appropriately share ourselves, the more open our children will be able to be with us.

In this chapter we have emphasized the great importance to the whole family of keeping the marriage a priority. This means that within the marriage, nurturing the sexual life has just as important a priority as being parents.

Whatever your dilemmas and whatever the joys, if the two of you stay connected and share this with your children, you'll give them something that will become a basic part of who they are. It will stand them in good stead as they move into being lovers *and* parents.

For Further Study

Leman, Kevin. *Sex Begins in the Kitchen.* Ventura: Regal Books, 1981.

McGinnis, Alan Loy. *The Romance Factor.* San Francisco: Harper and Row, 1982.

O'Connor, Dagmar. *How to Make Love to the Same Person for the Rest of Your Life and Still Love It.* Garden City: Doubleday and Company, Inc., 1985.

Penner, Clifford L. and Joyce J. Penner. *The Gift of Sex.* Waco, Texas: Word, Inc., 1981.

III

Teaching Our Children about Sex

7

Modeling and Communicating Healthy Sexual Attitudes

We are frequently asked, "At what age do you recommend that parents begin the process of sex education for their children?"

The answer "At birth" often shocks parents. But we think about our sexuality as a vital dimension of who we are throughout life. Our sexuality is so much more than sexual intercourse. We are male or female from the moment of birth until the final event of death.

This is true both physically and emotionally. All the sexual anatomy is present at birth, and it is working! A little boy has his first erection within minutes of birth and a little girl lubricates vaginally within the first twenty-four hours. These are the first physical sexual responses, even in adulthood.

Parents relate differently to infant girls than they do to infant boys. So, emotionally we begin at birth to influence the sexuality of our children. Think of yourself. Remember or imagine yourself talking to a newborn baby boy, then a baby girl. How might we communicate differently?

Recently friends of ours had their first baby. We received a call from the husband shortly after the delivery. His announcement was, "We've got a 'Tiger.'" There was no doubt in our minds that they had a baby boy. There is a difference in how parents respond to babies of each sex. Little girls are referred to as sweet, delicate, and pretty. Little boys are referred to as "tough" and "big guy." Moms love to fuss with bows in girl's hair.

This difference in treatment is important to help our children establish accurate gender identity. During the first two years of life adults give the baby many cues about its gender. The way we dress the baby, the tone of voice we use, and the toys we choose are all important in developing the sexual identity of the child. All parents teach their children about sex whether they know it or not. The question is, "How can parents guard against transmitting negative messages?"

Children *will* learn about sex from birth throughout life. The home is the primary place where this learning takes place. This is true whether or not parents *decide* to teach them. They *will* learn about what it means to be male or female. They will get a sense of what roles are associated with each sex, how we interact with the same and opposite sex, and what value we place on being male or female. Sexual feelings and attitudes will be picked up from parents. Vitality may become associated with one sex or the other. And eventually attitudes about specific sexual behavior, all the way from touching to intercourse, will be learned. Our children will learn by our modeling, relating, and communicating about sexuality.

Modeling

When both parents are in the home, the children learn by the interaction they witness between Mom and Dad—the affection, the communication, and the exercise of power. If Mom pulls away when Dad reaches out to pinch or touch, they probably learn that sex is something the man pursues and the woman resists. Or the opposite message may be transmitted when the roles are reversed. It is important that children see their parents express affection. It's wonderful for them to know we love each other and enjoy touching, kissing, and hugging. It is even good for them to become aware that we have special times together when we are alone, and that those times are sexual. Our being sexual with each other as parents, models to our children that sex in marriage is fun!

The communication habits we model to our children also influence their development into men and women. Do we give each other verbal praise? How do we communicate needs? How do we share our needs? How do we respond to each other's communication of needs? Do we take time to share our worlds with each other? Are we regarded and listened to by each other? How do we handle disagreement? All of these are part of sexual interaction as men and women. What do our children learn about the husband-wife relationship by observing us?

John and Nancy, a couple we saw in sexual therapy, attributed their sexual tension to the modeling of John's parents. His parents fit the stereotypical husband-wife communication pattern. His father would come home from work, grumble a greeting, grab the newspaper, and sit in his recliner and read. His mother would be preparing dinner. She would chatter a mile a minute about nothing. His father would grunt every now and then, but there was no obvious connection between them.

Now John found he was unable to connect with his wife. Nancy was eager to hug and kiss when they got home from work. She was interested in sharing their day with each other and expressing their love. John was too, but he felt awkward, so he often avoided her and hid behind the newspaper. Seeing himself emulate his father and wanting a more intimate relationship with Nancy, John decided that after work they would have a time just for the two of them. Sexual activity flowed more easily once they had time to bring their worlds together.

What about the exercise of power in our relationship? For a family communication exercise we had each of us, including our three children, answer a questionnaire about power distribution in the family. It was most helpful to get the children's view of us. They saw Cliff having control in some areas and Joyce in others. Some of their answers surprised us. We saw ourselves differently than they experienced us.

What kind of feedback do you get from your children? Who do they see as having the final word? Who makes the final decision about money, food, gifts, entertainment, church, devotions, and so on? When mutuality flows between Mom and Dad in most areas, children learn a sense of mutual sexual respect and responsibility.

What about the single parent? About 45 percent of the children in the U.S. spend some or all of their most formative years with only one parent. How can the male-female interaction be modeled to children when there is only one parent in the home? The children will learn by observing the parent in opposite-sex interactions. They might be present when Mom or Dad is leaving for a date, or talking on the telephone to a male or female special friend. The special friend may be included in family events.

When there has been a divorce and the parents are still in contact with each other, the children will learn from that interaction. There may be hurt and anger. These feelings need to be worked through, so that the children can learn positive respect. What needs to be modeled is that even when there is stress, we communicate respect and care for the other person. Never put down or belittle the children's other parent.

There is nothing wrong with our children observing our anger. But it is important that we are clear about the feelings behind the anger—the hurt, fear, frustration, helplessness—and use those emotions constructively. Dr. Neil Warren's book, *Make Anger Your Ally,* (New York: Doubleday, 1983) is most helpful in teaching effective ways to deal with emotions that are felt as anger. We recommend it highly.

Children from a single parent situation can also be provided with other couples as models. This can happen in extended family events, social situations, and church or Christian communities. This may take some effort and planning. You, as a single parent, may want to select a couple whom you admire. Then reach out to care for some of their needs in exchange for their spending time with you and your children. Swap services!

If you were in a healthy marriage the first eight years of the children's lives, most of the modeling will have been accomplished by that age. They will have learned a sense of mutual respect, affection, and positive male-female interaction. If the marriage was tense and shaky, the children may need to work through their insecurities and sexual identities in a therapeutic situation. Both you and your ex-spouse can take an active role in providing some healthy models for them. That model may even be a new marriage partner for one or both of you.

Relating

Not only do children learn male-female interaction from the parental or other couples' model, they also learn by the way the parents interact with *them.* From the same sex parent, they learn what it means to be male or female. If a mother feels good about her body, the daughter will too—even though she may go through the awkward, uncomfortable stages of puberty. If a father enjoys being a man with all that involves for him, his son will too.

Children learn to relate to the opposite sex by the relationship they have with the opposite sex parent. When a father shows his love and high regard for his daughter, she will grow up with positive expectations in relation to men. And we can say exactly the same thing for a mother and son. How a son is expected to treat his mother is probably how he will treat his wife.

Both parents and children may experience sexual feelings in relating to each other. These feelings are very normal. How they are handled is vitally important. It is natural for a mother to experience sexual arousal when breast-feeding her infant. Those feelings are a physical response to the sucking and are not harmful in any way. Likewise, children or parents might notice turned-on feelings at other times in the child's development. It is important to recognize that these feelings are normal. As parents, we must be responsible that those feelings never lead to sexual actions with our children. That is molestation and will hurt them. On the other hand, do not let the feelings keep you from being warm and affectionate at all ages. Remember the principle that we are to give love and affection to our children, but they are never to be the *objects* of our sexual gratification.

Communicating

Question: What guidelines would you give Christian parents for developing healthy sexual attitudes in their children?

We as parents are the key to our children's sexual education! Attitudes about sexuality are usually learned from us. We must begin by looking at ourselves. What are our attitudes about sex? What did we learn about sex in our homes? Did we get mixed signals? If the only time sexual language was used was to tell dirty jokes, then we learned that sex is something not valued highly. Was sex to be avoided, expected, matter-of-fact, anticipated? Was it something healthy and wholesome, or a bother? Was it the woman's burden and the man's delight? What specific sexual instructions did you receive? Maybe sex was nonexistent.

Picture the kind of messages you got from your home. What did you learn about your sexuality? What about masturbation or the male-female relationship? Then think of how you might be communicating these same attitudes. It is natural to communicate the same attitudes that were communicated to us. When those were positive, we have it easy. When we're not wanting to live out the attitudes we learned, we will have to make a conscious effort to be different.

Even we, as sex therapists, do not automatically respond in the manner we desire. We find we have had to learn not to fight or judgmentally react to our children's specific bodily discoveries or other more blatant sexual situations. Our spontaneous response is guarded rather than open. In contrast, it is natural for us to be generally warm and affirming. There is a real positiveness about being male and female, because our parental homes instilled that warm regard.

Joyce remembers proudly the first bra-buying experience with her mom. Starting her period was a positive sign of becoming a woman. Clear preparation had been made for this event. Similarly, beginning to shave, use a deodorant, and other indications of becoming a man were experienced as affirming events by Cliff. Our parents delighted in our growing up. Thus, it is inevitable that we exude a similar delight as we interact with our children as they become men and women.

What can we do to overcome the negative inhibitions so we don't pass them on to our children?

Sexual attitudes can be changed! We are not limited by our backgrounds. We can increase our positive feelings about sexuality by educating ourselves, affirming our bodies, and experiencing fulfilling sexual relationships in our marriages. Since we tend to communicate to our children what we believe about sex, we must look at ourselves before we worry about them!

How satisfying are your sexual experiences? Do you feel sexually inhibited? We chose to first write *The Gift of Sex,* a guide for enhancing the sexual relationship in marriage, to emphasize our belief that the parents' sexual relationship must be positive if they are going to communicate positive attitudes about sex to their children. So your individual sexuality and your sexual relationship in marriage must be addressed. For the married couple, we would recommend reading *The Gift of Sex* out loud to each other. For the single parent (who comes with a Christian perspective), we would also recommend *The Gift of Sex.* In addition, two secular books may be helpful: Loni Barbach's *For Yourself: the Fulfillment of Female Sexuality* (New York:

Anchor Books, 1979) and Bernie Zilbergeld's *Male Sexuality: A Guide to Sexual Fulfillment* (New York: Bantam, 1978).

Once we've taken a good look at how our backgrounds and our sexual relationships are affecting our communication about sex to our children, we need to ask ourselves, "What do we want to communicate?"

Parents should discuss sexual facts with their children. Children will develop pride in their bodies when parents can openly discuss physical processes with respect and dignity. When children sense that their parents view sex as healthy, they tend to adopt healthy attitudes themselves. Communication about sexuality is an important part of growing up. The following principles are basic to what we believe needs to be communicated to children.

1. *Sex is good and of God.* Our sexuality, bodily pleasure and sexual intercourse in marriage are part of God's perfect design and plan. They are good!

2. *Sexual curiosity is natural.* Children should never be punished or embarrassed for showing their curiosity. It is natural to ask questions about sex, to discover their own bodies, as well as observe others bodies' and have questions about them.

3. *Sexual responsiveness is natural* (when social and emotional barriers have not inhibited that). Our sexual response, whether aroused through self-stimulation, fantasy, mutual stimulation, or sexual intercourse, is a part of each person's body functioning. It is not a skill to be learned. It is an involuntary response that comes from within. It begins at birth and continues throughout life in healthy people.

4. *Sexual responsibility belongs to each person.* Sexual feelings need to be differentiated from sexual actions or behavior. Sexual feelings arise from our natural, involuntary sexual responses. What we decide to do with those feelings is our responsibility. Our sexual actions or decisions are in our control. Men are as responsible as women, and women as responsible as men for their sexual actions.

5. *Mutual respect is the guide for all sexual relationships.* Spouses must respect each other's rights and needs. Children must be taught and expected to respect their parents' sexuality and sexual relationship. Parents must respect their children's developing sexuality. When there is respect, no one will be violated! Abuse will not be present.

When we believe and practice these principles, our children will receive a healthy view of sexuality.

Sexual Identity

Question: What can we as parents do to insure that our child will grow up with a clear sense of being a man or a woman?

Since the "free speech" movement of the sixties and the civil rights movement of the last three decades, all of us have become aware that sexual identity is a vital issue in our society. Parental concern regarding the sexual identity of their children must be understood against the backdrop of the seemingly ever-increasing incidence of homosexuality. It is not our intention to give a definitive treatise on the subject of sexual identity but it cannot be addressed without attention to the issue of homosexuality.

Even as there is a whole range of heterosexual behavior, there is a wide range of homosexual behavior. In contrast to what is often taught, a homosexual orientation is no more of a choice than a heterosexual orientation. We can choose our behaviors, that is, whether we act homosexually or heterosexually, but usually the feelings of attraction to the same sex and lack of attraction to the opposite sex are not chosen. This is particularly true for men. Recent research has shed some light on why this is the case.

A research article by Dr. Frederick L. Whitman (*Journal of Sex Education and Therapy,* Vol. 6, No. 2, Fall/Winter 1980) of Arizona State University reports on the "Childhood Predictors of Adult Homosexuality." The research suggests that in studying the lives of homosexuals (especially men) there were clear indicators of the tendencies already present between the third and sixth years. The indications were that those who grew up to be homosexual frequently preferred the toys, clothes, and activities of the opposite sex during their preschool years. Let us hurriedly say, lest we alarm parents, that it is completely normal for all children to occasionally exhibit interest in and engage in behavior typical of the opposite sex. For the boy we are talking about a *clear preference* for dolls rather than trucks, for playing house rather than climbing trees, for skirts rather than jeans, and for the company of girls rather than boys. It should also be made clear that even in those instances where there was early cross-gender behavior, it did not necessarily mean that these children grew up to be homosexual. Rather, this tended to be in the background of those who did have a homosexual preference.

With the Bible's condemnation of homosexuality, society's deep hesitancy and discomfort with it, and the painful, never-satisfied quality so often present in the homosexual's life, it is important that we as parents do all we can to help our children make a positive connection with who they are as male and female.

How can we understand this dilemma? While no one knows for sure, we would like to present our theory about "critical periods" in the developmental process. This is theory, not fact! It grows out of our clinical experience, not research.

Since there is no convincing evidence to suggest a biological basis for homosexuality, we have to assume it is learned during three critical periods: birth to age two, age three to six, and early adolescence (age eleven to fourteen). In the first two years of life, the messages about being a boy or a girl are sent very indirectly but often clearly. Even those boys who might naturally be quite effeminate, not fitting the image of the masculine male, can grow up feeling strongly positive about themselves as boys or men if they are treated as such. That is, to develop strong feelings about himself as a man, a little boy must get positive messages about his masculinity, even during the first two years of life. His parents must delight in the fact that they have a boy. They must dress him so that the people in the world respond to him as a boy. For example, in our culture today it is not appropriate to dress baby boys in dresses as was done several generations ago or may still be customary in other cultures. All this begins the shaping process.

During the preschool years (three to six), the importance of a same-sex model is crucial. A boy needs to have a man around with whom he can identify, and a girl needs a woman. It seems obvious that one reason why there are more male homosexuals than female, is that boys have more opportunity to model women than girls have to model men. With the increasing divorce rate, we should continue to expect an increase in the occurrence of the homosexual preference.

Both boys and girls need reinforcement and affirmation for sexually appropriate behavior and identification. We are not talking about forcing all boys into enjoying baseball or all girls into always staying pretty and clean. Some very masculine boys will enjoy music, art, and other more delicate dimensions of life. Many very heterosexual women enjoy and are accomplished at what are normally considered male interests and activities. What is most important is that the identification occur with the same sex gender. Sometimes the identification is evidenced in the choices of the child's activities. This is why it is so important, during this critical period, to provide ongoing reinforcement to the boy or girl for being male or female.

If the parents have a low view of themselves as male or female, or are verbally derogatory of the opposite sex, either can have a severely negative impact on a child. In the past the research often described a pattern of a domineering mother and a cold, passive, uninvolved father. More recent research has suggested that the father became cold and uninvolved once he sensed his son was going to be a "sissy." Whichever was the cause or the effect, the lack of a strong, involved male model during the preschool age is detrimental to the development of male identity. Of the three critical periods, we would see this pre-school stage as the most important.

Finally, the third vital age is the time during early adolescence when the child is moving away from parents toward attachment to peers. This usually begins with attachment to peers of the same sex. In fact, in developmental terms, these years are sometimes referred to as the "homosexual stage." This is the time when boys are usually first learning to ejaculate and will sometimes compare experiences, watch each other, or even participate with one another in sexual encounters. In later years some then worry that they are "latently" homosexual. Just because a boy has engaged in homosexual play as a thirteen-year-old does not make him a homosexual. While less common, this kind of mutual play and discovery does occur among girls as well.

Also during these years a boy may be approached by an older homosexual male. If he already has weak male identification from the earlier critical periods in his life, he may respond to the invitation. Then the tendency toward the same sex gets sealed or confirmed. If it is not acted on, however, a positive connection with the opposite sex can still be made, even when there is an inclination toward the same sex. At the same time, there are some who don't act on their inclinations until their thirties, forties, or fifties, often having married and had a family. The strong homosexual preference has been present but not acted on for all those years.

During these junior high years, it is so important that the connection and attraction shift from the same sex to the opposite sex. Since this is the beginning of direct sexual behavior (even if it is just the poke or kiss-and-run variety), it is vital that boys and girls experience affirmation in these early heterosexual activities. This forms the basis for all later heterosexual involvement.

In summary, our critical period theory is this: In the first two years children learn about their sexual identity by how they are handled and talked to. During the preschool years, direct learning takes place from role models as well as gender-related activities. Finally, in the time of early adolescence, the behavior confirms or interrupts the tendency that is already established.

Once homosexuality is confirmed, either by feeling or activity, it is difficult to reverse. While the behavior can be controlled, the same-sex preference is stubborn. This is true even after extensive psychotherapy or spiritual conversion. Some approaches to dealing with the homosexual are now claiming greater success—especially in the charismatic wing of the church. Masters and Johnson are also claiming long-term success with those who want to change.

Because of the difficulty of changing sexual orientation later in life, we need to do all we can to prevent the development of homosexual tendencies. This prevention begins with a healthy acceptance of oneself as a man or woman. The outgrowth of that will be the vigorous endorsement of our children's maleness or femaleness. If you walk around with buried hostility toward the opposite sex, it will be communicated. Endorse who the child is and the natural ways of expressing that personhood—always in the context of the child's maleness or femaleness.

Spend time modeling what it means to be a man or a woman. Your child will learn from you. We have little evidence to suggest that left just to instinct, the child will develop normally. Mothers are the example to their daughters of what it looks like, sounds like, and feels like to be a woman. In work or play, spend time together so your child can learn both from your direct teaching and by osmosis.

It is rare to discover one's sexual preference by accident. But traumatic molestation experiences of a homosexual nature usually leave a child confused about sexual identity. The false guilt aroused by the molestation can be overwhelming. We must do all we can to teach our children the reality that they are in charge of their own bodies, and neither a stranger nor relative should touch or violate them in any way which leaves them uncomfortable.

One last word on this subject of homosexuality. People with a sexual preference for those of the same sex are human beings in need of our love, care, and respect. They may be doctors or lawyers, or they may be truck drivers, waitresses, or gardeners. They have feelings, they get lonely, and they experience pain just like any other person. They need our compassion and understanding as they struggle to make choices about their impulses and behavior.

For Further Study

Barbach, Loni. *For Yourself: The Fulfillment of Female Sexuality.* New York: Anchor Books, 1979.

Carrera, Michael. *Sex: The Facts, the Acts, and Your Feelings.* New York: Crown Publishers, 1981. "Gender and Sexual Orientation."

Ketterman, Grace H., M.D., *How to Teach Your Children about Sex.* Old Tappan: Fleming H. Revell Company, 1981. 7–76, 167–183.

Kolodny, Robert C., William H. Masters, Virginia F. Johnson, Mae A. Biggs. *Textbook of Human Sexuality for Nurses.* Boston: Little, Brown and Company, 1979. Chapter 3: "Development and Sexuality."

Stoop, David A., "Moral Development." *Theology News and Notes,* March 1978.

Warren, Neil C., *Make Anger Your Ally.* New York: Doubleday, 1983.

Whitman, Frederick L., "Childhood Predictors of Adult Homosexuality," *Journal of Sex Education and Therapy.* vol. 6, no. 2, Fall/Winter, 1980.

Zilbergeld, Bernie. *Male Sexuality.* New York: Bantam, 1978.

8

Affirming Sexuality in the Infant and Toddler

Children are born as sexual beings. They learn about themselves as sexual persons throughout life. Sex education does not begin with the father-son "birds and bees" talk.

From our understanding of human growth and development, from hearing hundreds of case histories, and from reading over a hundred sexual autobiographies, we are convinced that there are developmental stages for learning about ourselves sexually. These stages are common to most people. In other words, children will learn when they are ready, not when we are ready to teach them.

Touch: the Basis for Intimacy

During infancy (0–2 years old), children learn about sex from their primary caretaker, usually mother. However, the father may be an equal source of sexual affirmation for the child or he may even play a dominant role. There may be a primary child care substitute: the person or persons with whom they bond will be their lifeline to learning physical intimacy.

Hopefully this bonding can begin with mother immediately at the birthing event, and shortly thereafter with father. Skin-to-skin contact will help these babies grow happily and securely. It is this warmth and closeness to the bodies of those who love them that gives the tiny, helpless infants the emotional security to be able, as adults, to give their bodies to the spouses they marry.

It is sad that our western culture went through a twenty-year time span—the 1940s to the 1960s—in which hospital personnel control prevented this immediate bonding of mother and newborn. When both of us were born in 1941, home delivery with mother's arms being the first bed for that new little creature was common practice. When our younger brothers and sisters were born, our mothers were rushed off to the hospital and were frustrated by the hospital routine taking control of contact between parent and child.

This mode was predominant until about the time our oldest child, Julene, was born. Because we were graduate students receiving free medical care from a wonderful but elderly physician who felt uncomfortable with the modern trends, Julene was born with the hospital-in-control system of that time. Joyce's labor and Julene's birth was an easy three-hour process without medication.

The horror followed. At midnight, about an hour after the baby's birth, Joyce was wheeled into her darkened room (since her roommate was sleeping), Cliff was told he had to go home, and Julene was taken to the nursery. Joyce recalls, "I was wide awake and so eager to see and touch my new baby, to have her close to me, and to talk with Cliff about our experience."

Joyce tells the rest of the story: "Even though I requested many times during the next twenty hours to be able to have my baby, she was not brought to me until 8 P.M. the next day. Many fears overwhelmed me and many tears were shed waiting to be certain she was totally mine. I was never so happy as the day we were able to take her home from the hospital.

"Of our three children, she was the baby who sucked for hours when she breastfed. I believe that was her way of making up for the separation pain that occurred between us because of 'hospital policy.' "

What we learned, and what we would recommend to you, is to have the confidence to take charge of situations like the delivery and postbirth process. Inquire beforehand as to the hospital policy. Find ways to get your needs met. Remember, what happens during those first hours is an important part of becoming a family unit.

Infants begin to know about themselves as sexual persons by how they are touched, held, the tone of the parent's voice, and the comfort or discomfort they experience. Bodily pleasure is felt from the beginning. Babies who receive calm, warm stroking and close holding with unconditional love, will feel good about their body sensations and thus get affirmed.

If the mother or primary caretaker has difficulty with intimacy, or difficulty freely giving of herself, the child will feel anxious, distant, unsure, and tend to have difficulty forming intimate relationships later in life. Sometimes the child is held at a distance because the mother fears her own sexual warmth in relation to the child. Those feelings of warmth and closeness between parent and child are natural and good. *Never* is the infant's body to be used sexually for the adult's pleasure! But warmth, closeness, touching, and stroking in a general, loving, affirming way is necessary for positive personal and sexual development.

As sexual therapists, we are convinced that our toughest cases are those where bonding never happened between mother and infant. One most attractive couple came to us within the first year of their marriage with the wife complaining about her husband's lack of interest in sex. Even though he really wanted help, he resisted every attempt at working on the dilemma, in the same way he resisted his wife's sexual advances. It was as though he could not help himself.

After their first child was born, they talked with us about his mother's interaction with the baby. His mother wanted the baby to meet her needs, but was never able to give to the baby warmly. It became obvious to us that Jerry was suffering from a deep-seated difficulty. He was unable to give and receive bodily pleasure. There was an almost complete inability to form a physically intimate attachment to his wife. Mother had probably never really been able to *give* him warmth and closeness. She only knew how to enjoy a baby for *her* pleasure. She needed to get from the infant rather than having warmth to radiate outward.

If you see yourself as a person who is needy or unable to give that radiant warmth and unconditional love to your infant, get help! Find a mothering, giving person to give to you. We have recently taken on that role with a young couple in our community. It has been most rewarding to see them gain the confidence to give relentlessly to their little family. Parenting requires servant leadership that can seem like endless giving of oneself. Christ is the ideal model of that kind of giving.

As children grow from infancy to toddlerhood (two to four years old), they move from total dependence on their caretaker to self-discovery as they learn to master various dimensions of their world. Part of this process is learning the control of elimination and the naming of bodily parts. This is a most critical time for forming attitudes about sexuality.

Learning Control of Elimination

Since elimination and sexual functioning are connected with the same location in the body, what we teach about elimination will affect our children's view of their sexuality. If we are rather matter-of-fact, using praise and rewards for learning toileting, children will gain a healthy respect for their sexuality. If we are punitive and rigid, they may have difficulty freely sharing in genital discovery in marriage. If we are totally permissive, the children may not learn how to make decisions and feel in control of their sexuality, just as they may have felt out of control as it relates to elimination.

It is important that we teach good hand-washing practices after toileting. But we should not send the message that the genitals are "dirty" or "yucky," or that what they produce is repulsive to us. Children will naturally feel proud of their excretions. That pride can be enhanced and carried into their adult sexual functioning. This is not too young an age to let them know that bowel movements have germs, but urine, vaginas, and penises do not. In fact, our genitals are a very special part of us. Children will hear enough "shady" messages in their lifetime, so the more positive messages we can give them the better. The belief or teaching that sex is dirty often has its origin in what children are taught about their own genitals. If they get only the "unclean" message, they connect that to sexuality.

Genital Discovery

Genital self-discovery may begin during diapering, but, for certain, will be a part of this two- to four-year-old stage. We remember when our son was two and a half. We heard him giggling in the bathtub, only to find that he had discovered his penis. It is natural for both older infants and toddlers to reach down and touch their genitals, to play with them, and rub them in a soothing manner, almost like sucking their thumbs. They naturally poke their fingers in their noses, in their ears, and in their belly buttons, but somehow when they poke their genitals, we tend to react uncomfortably. We may say, "No," or move the hand away or give it a little slap, sending messages similar to when they go near a hot stove. The sexual part of us is very intense. It grabs us totally. These emotions complicate our dealing with our children's self-discovery as a very natural, healthy part of their development. By sending negative messages we may in this early impressionable stage of life teach our children that our genitals are "untouchable"— that they are *certainly* different than the rest of our bodies.

Question: Where do you draw the line in a toddler discovering his body yet not making him feel bad about curiosity?

The messages we want to transmit to toddlers are these: your genitals are special; they feel good to touch; they are private; we don't touch them in public. If these attitudes are taught with the same matter-of-fact style that we teach children not to put objects in their ears or their noses, then touching genitals will not become an emotionally loaded activity.

Along with our messages of acceptance of the genitals, we must make certain that we are providing our children with enough touch. Regular stimulation of the genitals by toddler-age children may be a signal to the parents to increase the amount of holding and hugging. In fact, that response is a good distraction, when your toddler's self-stimulation makes you uncomfortable. "Nancy, I haven't had time to hold you on my lap and read to you. Choose your favorite book so we can read for a while."

Children will discover that their genitals feel good. When they are receiving enough stroking affirmation from their parents (and are not given guilt-producing responses), the touching will not be an ongoing, controlling part of their lives, but it will be a natural response to how their bodies were made.

Naming the Genitals

Naming body parts properly is important as the two- to four-year-old learns to talk. We spend time teaching our children to say, "nose" and "eyes" and "ears." We're so proud when they can identify "elbow" and "wrist." Then we get to the genitals and we revert to "wa-wa" and "do-do." Call a penis a penis and a vagina a vagina, even if it shocks the grandparents. Knowing and naming genitals is an important gift we need to give to our children. Giving children correct anatomical names for genitals will help them develop the attitude that genitals are as valid and acceptable a part of their bodies as their toes, fingers, and nose.

By the time children are four years old, they may have picked up that sex is dirty and their genitals are both untouchable and unmentionable. Or they may have learned the difference between their sexual feelings and healthy toileting behavior. They may be comfortable naming their genitals without embarrassment or self-consciousness. They may well enjoy the natural touching of themselves sexually. It is to be hoped that we adults will have instilled positive attitudes of acceptance and respect of all the feelings and potential of those vital organs!

What if your children are all older than four and you've blown it? One parent confessed: "I have already mishandled my child's sex education; how can I undo the mistakes I have already made?"

Children are incredibly resilient. It is never too late to go to them and say, "Hey, we made some mistakes. We'd like to make some changes in what we taught you." We've had parents in their fifties have a talk like this with their young adult children, and it made an important difference! Take courage and go for it!

For Further Study

Carrera, Michael. *Sex: The Facts, the Acts, and Your Feelings.* New York: Crown Publishers, 1981. "Ages and Stages."

Ketterman, Grace H., M.D., *How to Teach Your Child about Sex.* Old Tappan: Fleming H. Revell Company, 1981, 79–97.

Kolodny, Robert C., William H. Masters, Virginia E. Johnson. *Textbook of Sexual Medicine.* Boston: Brown, Little and Company, 1979. Chapter 3: "Childhood Sexuality."

9

The Curious Years—
Preschool to Puberty

By the time children reach preschool age, their ability to give and receive touch and their view of their genitals has been well established. So what happens from preschool to puberty? Curiosity takes control.

Question-asking

Curiosity about sexuality begins around four or five years of age. We refer to this as the question-asking age. Parents are concerned about how to respond to these early questions—and rightly so! Many adults report that they never asked their parents another question about sex after age five. They got the message that sex isn't something you talk about with mom and dad. What happened?

Children's sexual questions often catch us off guard and trigger strong adult emotions. Sex is such a loaded topic for us that it is difficult for us to take the innocent questions from our young children for what they are. We tend to impose our adult feelings on what is being asked.

Question: What do you say when your preschooler asks, "Where do babies come from?" or, "How does the baby get out of (or into) Mommy's tummy?"

The five R system—reinforce, reflect, review, respond, and repeat—

is most helpful in dealing effectively with emotionally loaded questions, especially sexual ones. It serves two functions: stalls for time, giving us a chance to collect ourselves, and affirms the appropriateness of the child's curiosity. We both win!

First, *reinforce* children of any age for coming to you with such an important question. Emphasize that it is a family question and you're glad he or she came to you rather than a friend who might not have correct information. This positive response to the child's openness with you is particularly important when the question asked or experience shared elicits an alarmed response in you. That way children can feel good about sharing without being burdened with your reaction. Your child will probably come to you again, because children want your verbal reward. This is a good way to foster an open relationship with your children.

After reinforcing the question, we encourage *reflection:* getting a clear indication as to what children are really asking. Find out what is behind the question. For example, when we respond to the question, "Where do babies come from?" we are coming with vast information. We therefore tend to think that the child's question is more complicated than is usually the case. As we clarify, it becomes clear what specific bit of information children are really seeking. This way we avoid giving a twenty-minute lecture on sex education, when one short sentence may have been the most accurate response. It is important to query our children, "What are you meaning when you ask where do babies come from? Do you mean, were do they grow?"

Once we're fairly clear about what our children are really asking, we need to *review* what they already know. What is the context of the question? It is important to get into their world and find out where they are. They may have misunderstood previously shared information. They may have misinformation from peers or TV. If they share what they have heard and understand, we can respond to that content before we load on our views. It gives us a chance to correct and teach without adding confusion. This becomes even more important as children get older and gain more of their information from outside the home.

The time does come when we need to *respond.* We can stall only so long! If you know the answer and feel comfortable in giving it, then do so. If you are unsure, go to another resource. Be sure you get the child an answer somehow. It is best to give simple, factual, short answers. We can be as specific and explicit as the question warrants. For example, if we have determined that the child is wondering where the baby grows, then an appropriate response would be: "The baby grows in a special, thick, soft pocket in the mother's abdomen." It gets more difficult when they want to know how the baby gets started there. A factual response is, "A seed from the daddy joins with an egg from the mommy."

The next question usually is, "How does Daddy get the seed in there?" Now, we really get uncomfortable! But again, once we're pretty clear that we've heard the question accurately and we've reviewed what they already know or have heard, then the answer can be simple and honest. A natural answer is, "The daddy's penis puts the seed into the mother's vagina." As children get older they will ask for more of the emotional components. "When do moms and dads do this? Isn't it yucky? Did you do that?" Eventually they'll need to get the picture that sexual intercourse is a pleasurable expression of love between a husband and wife and not just for producing babies. That you still "do it."

Parents might question, "But I don't think they're ready for the facts." Our response is that when children ask, they are ready for the answers to their questions. If they have been set up by someone older to ask the question, you will have discovered that by the time you have reinforced, reflected, and reviewed. When you determine that the question is not theirs, find out what *they* would like to know and start the process again.

Once we've responded, there's a temptation to wipe our brow with a, "Whew, that's taken care of!" But, it isn't. We will need to *repeat.* The basic facts of reproduction, intercourse, and sexual pleasure may have to be explained a dozen times or so. From preschool to puberty (four to ten years old), children's ability to picture the sexual process change greatly. At each level of understanding, the questions will mature. The information will need to be repeated, but with greater depth.

What if your children don't ask questions about sex? You feel as if you're continually looking for an opportunity to teach about sexuality, but it doesn't occur naturally. First, look and see if subtly you are stifling communication. Or, some children tend to be shy and easily embarrassed. Whatever the cause, become active in providing opportunities for sex education. Associate with pregnant women. Talk about the pregnancy with the children: "Did you know Aunt Beth is going to have a baby? She looks fatter, but that's not fat, it's the baby growing inside her." Take the children to visit farms, zoos, or pet stores when the animals are having babies. Watch sex education series together on T.V. Plan a talk time after. Have the children write down thoughts or questions while they're watching. Do the same with sex education programs at school. Talk to them afterward concerning your beliefs about what was taught. Read books on sexuality out loud with them. Read books that are age appropriate. Create every opportunity to open the topic of sexuality.

Self Discovery (Masturbation)

Just as the curiosity of this age leads to question-asking, it also stimulates children's interest in their own bodies. When our daughter was four years old, Joyce walked into Julene's room after her bath. She found Julene sitting on the floor with her legs spread apart and her head down as she tried to examine her genitals. When she heard Joyce enter the room, she remained in the same position and casually asked, "Mom, what is that hole in my bottom?"

Joyce's first tendency was to respond with shock, but Julene's ease with the situation made her stop and think. She remembered that just the day before Julene had spent a long time in front of the bathroom mirror looking down her throat, trying to examine and watch her uvula at the back of her throat. There was no difference in Julene's intent in discovering another part of her body. She did not think that looking at her throat was fine, but looking at her genitals was "sinful."

Repressing her own tendency to react with alarm and discomfort, Joyce took advantage of the curiosity for a teaching experience. She got a hand mirror so that Julene could better see her own genitals. She sat down with Julene and pointed to the various openings, the lips, and the clitoris, and indicated their technical names. Julene's curiosity seemed satisfied. She responded rather factually, got dressed, and ran off to play.

Kristine, our younger daughter, went through a similar curiosity-teaching experience with Joyce. Greg, our son, never pursued information about the anatomy of his genitals. This is less likely to happen with boys, because their genitals are accessible and easily observable. There are no hidden parts to discover.

Boys and girls of this age will continue to touch their genitals. The good sensations will be discovered. That is the way God made them. This genital pleasure does not cause guilt unless we send negative messages about the activity. If the child is getting enough other physical affection, genital stimulation will not become a habit or preoccupation. The genital touching is likely to increase for children at this age especially when they are tired, sick, lonely, or sad. It is self-comforting.

In responding to children regarding genital exploration or stimulation, it is vital that we as parents not make too big a deal of it. It is usually not that important to the child. The basic principles to follow are: think of the genitals as a part of the body, rather than a unique separate entity; recognize that adult erotic emotions are not a part of children's genital touching; remember that physical affirmation needs to continue throughout life—our children need our hugs; teach children socially appropriate behavior in relation to the genitals just as we do in any other area of life (we keep them covered, don't play with them in public, use the toilet to urinate and defecate, and so on); and think of inappropriate or excessive sexual exploration and stimulation as a *symptom* of a problem, not the problem itself.

Exploratory Play

Question: Let's say you discover your young son and your friend's little daughter playing "doctor." How will you deal with the incident so they will not feel they are "bad"?

Similar to the self-discovery of the four- to ten-year-old, exploratory play is a natural manifestation of the sexual curiosity of this age. Not only are children interested in how they are put together, they're also interested to see their cousin or neighbor. "Playing doctor" is almost inevitable between the ages of five and seven. It is reported to us over and over again. When it occurs between children of the same age and is handled as a normal part of growing up, it causes no harm. When it is met with a traumatic reaction from parents, it leaves children with incredible confusion about their sexuality.

Exploratory play is innocent curiosity. It needs to be responded to as just that. Use it as an opportunity to teach. Get out the anatomy book. Explain safety precautions. Just as objects shouldn't be put in ears and nose, it is important that we don't stick things in vaginas. We can talk about the purpose of the genitals, for excretion, for reproduction, and for sexual pleasure. This is a good time for parents to share their values and teach about the specialness of sexual pleasure in marriage.

Set some limits. Recognize the naturalness of their curiosity and the good feelings of the genitals, but that panties need to be left on. Teach them about making decisions about sharing their bodies. Let them know that their bodies are their personal property. They are special and they must choose carefully when and with whom they will share themselves. Basically, the helpful response includes a balance of acceptance of what is happening with some teaching and limit-setting. But keep it low-key. Provide controls and safety without trauma.

Nudity in the Home

Before age four or five, children usually don't notice whether parents or older brothers and sisters have clothes on or not. But at this age of sexual curiosity, children begin to differentiate their bodies from those of others. They are aware of male-female differences. Feelings that are difficult to handle can be aroused in young children by nude adult bodies. Therefore, it is recommended that while nudity should not be studiously avoided, it also should not be flaunted. Take more precautions about being exposed to the children for extended periods of times, without communicating discomfort with nudity. If children walk into the bedroom and the parent is undressed, there is no need to quickly go for cover. However, cooking dinner in the nude is not recommended either.

From hearing adults tell us stories about childhood experiences, we find that both extreme modesty and totally free exposure have led to difficulty in sharing bodies openly in marriage. When nudity was not comfortable at all, the children learned a self-consciousness and negativity about the body that carried over into marriage. Sometimes there was an opposite reaction, especially for boys, that led to an extreme, obsessively curious, "peeping Tom" type of behavior. When nudity was experimented with as a lifestyle, the children tended to feel violated and exploited and became very protective as adults. They easily feel violated and exploited by their spouses.

One woman who could enjoy her husband's body totally but would panic if he approached her, reported that her father required that they have dinner in the nude. Another woman with a similar reaction to her husband shared that her father always wanted to be in the bathroom while she was bathing. There are many other such stories.

Nudity in the home needs to be a comfortable openness of accepting our bodies with respect for privacy and without demand, exploitation, violation, or teasing. Never should the children's bodies be exposed to us or ours to them for our emotional or sexual pleasure. That is child abuse!

Question: At what age do you feel it is best to discontinue mixed bathing with siblings?

There is no age that this is right for all children. Your observation of the behavior is a key to when separate baths would be recommended. It would be necessary sometime between the four- to ten-year-old age span. When it changes from being a functional, fun event to a specifically sexual event in terms of attention or play, it's time to change to separate bathing. It is best if the announcement of that change can be done as a positive sign of growth, rather than treated as a withdrawal of a privilege. For example, the older one can now use the shower or bath at another time like Mom and Dad. There are many possible invitations to a new system of bathing enjoyment. Again, the principle is to see bodies and sexuality as natural without exposure to erotic stimulation that is not age-appropriate. Children need to feel safe while they learn acceptance.

Stranger Danger

The teaching that occurs in the home regarding exploratory play and nudity can help prevent child molestation. There is additional teaching specific to prevention of child molestation that needs to be regularly reviewed with preschool and school-age children.

Children need to be told that there are some very sick people in this world. No, they don't have the flu. Their sickness is that they get a thrill out of hurting children. Those people must be avoided— *stay away from them!* Since these people look like us, how are our children going to know one when they meet one? Two things can help them. One has to do with strangers. But not all of these sick people are strangers. Sometimes they are friends, neighbors, or even relatives. So first, to avoid being hurt by a stranger, have your children follow these rules:

1. Always go to school or other places on the route planned with a parent—a route that is in plain view of others, never through alleys or out-of-the-way places.

2. Never use a public restroom by yourself. Have someone you know go with you.

3. If someone stops his car and tries to get your attention for any reason, turn and run the other way. If they say they are sick or hurt, still run, but ask an adult to go back and help them.

4. Never accept anything from a stranger.

Here are some other suggested answers to share with your children to help them avoid being hurt by someone who is not a stranger:

1. If anyone talks to you in a way you know is not right or tries to touch you or wants you to touch them in a way that feels uncomfortable, say, *NO!* If you can, leave that person. If you can't leave, keep saying *No* until your parents come.

2. Remember, you can be in control. Your body is yours and you don't need to share it with anyone, even if they are bigger than you or say nice things to you, or try to scare you.

3. It is *not* your fault when a person behaves this way to you.

4. It *is* important that you tell us, so that we can protect you and get help for the sick person. We will listen to you and believe you, even if it may seem unbelievable.

This is basically the kind of talk children need to have about once a year from age four through ten and maybe even older.

Conclusion

Sometimes preschool to puberty has been thought of as the nonsexual age. As is evident from the length of this chapter, this is a critically formative age from a sexual perspective. Attitudes and a sexual view of the self are developed. It is the age most important to us as parents with our children. They are most influenced by us. We should take advantage of it. This is our special time with our children!

For Further Study

Andry, Andrew G., and Steve Schepp. *How Babies Are Made.* Alexandria, Va: Time-Life Books, 1974.

Edens, David. *The Changing Me.* Nashville: Broadman Press, 1973.

Ketterman, Grace H., M.D., *How to Teach Your Child about Sex.* Old Tappan: Fleming H. Revell Company, 1981, 99–117.

Levine, Milton and Jean Seligman. *A Baby Is Born.* New York: Golden Press, 1978.

Rayber, Claire. *The Body Book.* New York: Barron's Educational Services, 1980.

Sheffield, Margaret. *Where Do Babies Come From? "He Told Me Not To Tell."* King County Rape Relief, 305 So. 43rd, Renton Wa., 98055.

10

The Squirrelly Years—Junior High

Preadolescence (10–13 years old) is a great age, yet it is a tough one.

The "great" part is that preadolescents are full of energy. Hormones are being released into the bloodstream. Hormones are chemicals which cause body growth and change, as well as affect feelings and provide the energy for the sexual drive. This energy can be used to get things done in life. Thus, junior-highers are loaded with the potential to develop all of who they are. Physical activity is vital for the ten- to thirteen-year-old. Investing long hours in academics and developing talents will make use of that energy in a productive and self-fulfilling manner. When that energy is constructively directed, preadolescents will be happier with themselves and will get more affirmation from family and friends. Their self-confidence will be stronger.

The "tough" part is the awkwardness of being neither child nor adolescent. In fact, when we speak to junior high groups, we usually refer to them as students. Calling them children would be a putdown; referring to them as adolescents doesn't quite fit; yet referring to them as preadolescents is somewhat cumbersome.

With all the changes going on around them, preadolescents' self-worth is in a constant state of flux. Their rapid body growth tends to cause clumsiness. They seem to knock things over at the table, drop things, and generally feel out of control of their bodies. In addition, their emotions are changing. Their feelings fluctuate. They sometimes seem as if they are on a roller coaster ride—up one minute and down the next. A critical comment or a disappointment devastates them, while success or a positive look from us elevates them. There doesn't seem to be an inner sense of self. Value is contingent on external input. It is difficult for us as parents to keep up. We're still concerned about the last low when they're on their next high. Unpredictable behavior is part of this syndrome also. Responsibilities that were handled competently at age eight or nine are suddenly neglected. At times, the internal confusion of all the change seems to keep them unsure of themselves, self-conscious, and mentally preoccupied.

A Time of Transition

Moving from dependence to independence contributes to the awkwardness. The transition from childhood (with parents responsible and in control) to adulthood (in charge of one's own life and decisions) begins during preadolescence. Peers become the transitional authorities. Because of their need to feel separate from parents while still feeling unsure of themselves, they have a strong tendency to conform—to do and be like the other kids their age. The more self-confidence junior highers feel, the less peer pressure will control their lives. Peers do become more and more the source of sexual information (many times misinformation).

The primary question that haunts the preadolescent is, "Am I normal?" Many feel they are the only ones thinking and feeling the way they do. It is important for them to know that everyone at this age has times of isolation and loneliness—of feeling different. Physical changes are inconsistent from one child to another. Some children start developing at nine, others not until fifteen. Those who develop early, feel self-conscious because they're ahead of their peers, and those who start late worry that they will never become adults.

Sexuality

Sexually, the juices of these young saplings are beginning to flow. Erotic feelings stir, leaving them restless and "squirrelly." They don't know why they're feeling the way they do. An explanation is often helpful. This can be followed by reminders like, "It might be helpful to go jogging to wear off some of that energy."

The actual sexual behavior that is age-appropriate is what we call the kiss-and-run games. It is primarily *group experimentation.* A group of guys and a group of girls meet behind the ice cream parlor. One guy in the group likes one girl from the other group. So, sort of like a pep squad, the groups are giving the guy and girl courage to kiss each other. They run and kiss and return to their group to giggle or act cool. This type of experimentation with male-female sexual interaction is very necessary to developing self-confidence in later serious relationships. That is why it is important that we don't set absolute rules like: no kissing until you're eighteen. The kissing that will be done at eighteen is *certainly* not the kissing the ten- to thirteen-year-olds will be doing if they are behaving age-appropriately.

Obviously, according to the statistics, some thirteen-year-olds are having sexual intercourse. They are engaging in sexual behavior that is adult in nature, not just junior high experimentation. These prematurely exposed children usually are extremely confused about what they are experiencing. But the ten- to thirteen-year-olds who are functioning at their age level *will* have boyfriends and girlfriends.

However, these relationships are much different than adolescent or young adult relationships. They are usually negotiated through others. Jennifer asks Tim if he likes Jody. Then Jennifer tells Jody that Tim wants to "go steady." Jody gives her response to Jennifer and Jennifer tells Tim. Now, before we react, it's important to find out what "going steady" means. When Julene was in third grade, she announced she was "going steady." Joyce's first image was of our personal experience of "going steady"—a step toward engagement. But Cliff calmly asked, "What does it mean to be going steady?" Julene replied, "It means we don't talk to each other any more because we wouldn't want anyone to know." When Kristine, our fourth grader, announced she was "going steady," and was asked what it meant, she shrugged her shoulders and said, "I don't know!" As junior highers, "going steady" for both Julene and Greg was a contractual arrangement without typical dating behavior. It meant they couldn't "go steady" with anyone else.

It is OK to be awkward and experiment as a junior-higher. It is less OK as a high-schooler and usually quite uncomfortable for a college-aged young adult. That is why severe restrictions of age-appropriate boy-girl interaction is not recommended. It is also what makes this time painful for the shy or socially unaccepted child. Many times the child will not have the opportunity or feel comfortable with boy-girl interactions. If their sociability doesn't progress by high school, they will continue to lack confidence in relating to the opposite sex. They don't have a chance to experiment while it is still innocent play.

The shy or socially unaccepted children need to be encouraged to get involved in as many social settings as possible. Junior high activities at church and school are great. Have mixed groups in your home. Give them a serving function so that they have a structured way to interact with the group. Let them know it's OK to feel awkward. Everyone feels awkward at this age, even though some may hide their discomfort better than others.

In addition to boy-girl experimentation, dirty jokes are another element common to preadolescent sexuality. What has been shocking to us is to discover that our ten- to thirteen-year-olds, raised in suburban Los Angeles, California, heard the same sexual jokes that we heard thirty years earlier in our small, rural Mennonite communities. This tells us that these stories are developmental. They are a part of the process of growing up—of trying to make sense out of the whole concept of sexual intercourse, while it sounds rather strange to them.

This doesn't mean we encourage our children to tell dirty jokes. What it does mean is that we recognize it as a reality of what is probably happening. In fact, a great way to open up communication between parent and preadolescent is to ask, "What are the dirty jokes being told at school these days?" or, "What are the sexual slang words used at school these days?" Then it is helpful to explain the accurate, clinical meaning of the words being used and jokes being told. The kids are often shocked to hear what these words really mean. It is an opportunity for education and a way of limiting that kind of language. It teaches internal rather than external control. Rather than parents forbidding children from ever using that word again, the youngsters no longer feel comfortable using it nor do they really need to, since the primary purpose of that spread of information is curiosity about sexuality.

Masturbation

Masturbation becomes an emotionally loaded issue during puberty. Touching one's genitals changes from a soothing, self-affirming act to erotic self-stimulation, probably leading to orgasm. This may not happen until adolescence, but for many boys it will begin around age twelve. Girls tend to discover their erotic responsiveness later in life. And some boys and girls never do masturbate. About 95 percent of boys do, and about 50–80 percent of girls.

It is now known that there are no physically harmful effects from masturbation and there is no psychological damage, except when self-stimulation is associated with guilt and sin. Although masturbation has been and is still condemned by some church groups, the facts are that the condemnation tends not to limit the behavior, but only makes it more secretive and guilt-ridden. This can sometimes lead to obsessive, uncontrolled masturbatory activity, very destructive to the self-image of the young person who feels so ashamed of the horrible thing he is doing.

Since the Bible has no direct teaching about masturbation, our encouragement is to teach developing children about their bodies and how they function. In the process, it is natural to let them know that God designed the clitoris in the female and the penis in the male as sexually pleasurable to touch. They need to know that the primary place to experience sexual pleasure is within marriage, but that their hormones will be giving them feelings that are sexual now. They will need to decide how to handle those feelings between now and when they are ready for marriage, which will not be for a long time. In the meantime, they will probably discover that the genitals are pleasurable to touch and this is natural and normal.

For a sensitive discussion of this issue listen to Dr. James Dobson's tapes on "Preparing for Adolescence." Masturbation during adolescence is certainly a tough issue.

Just this week we received a letter from an older adolescent who attempted suicide because of her guilt about masturbation. After several years of trying to stop masturbating and feeling condemned by what she was hearing from Christian leaders, she was in despair. She believed that God had put a drive in her and then rejected her because she couldn't help responding to it. We need to be careful not to make proclamations about issues that are not addressed in God's Word.

The Parents' Role

What specifically do preadolescents need from us as parents? They need our stability. When their emotions are up and down, they need us to be understanding and caring, but not ride the roller coaster with them. They need our steady perspective.

Our acceptance and praise can make such a difference. There is a tendency to want to correct, to shape them up. The more we correct and criticize, the worse our children will feel about themselves—and the more negative their behavior will become. We can have definite expectations and stick to those. But then we need to let our children know how much we love and enjoy them. Or if we're not enjoying them right now, we need to take extra and special time alone with them.

Find small attributes that you can genuinely praise. Look for the positive. Assume they still need you even if they behave as if they don't. Make special dates with them. Keep up the affection—back rubs, wrestling, and hugs are all comfortable ways of being physically affirming as our children's bodies are changing to adult bodies. Be warmly strong!

Our children need limits. It is best if our limits are clear and consistent, but allow growing freedom. Preadolescents will be making more and more of their own decisions as they move into adolescence and young adulthood. It is important that they learn to make decisions while we are involved. When our seventh grader asks if he can meet a girl at the pizza parlor down the street, the tendency may be to give an immediate answer. It helps him more if we guide him through the process of deciding. What does he think? How does he feel about it? How does this fit in with what he has sensed are our values? What are the plans? Help him examine whether it is a natural, harmless event or something that might lead to more pressure than is comfortable at his age. Assisted decision-making within boundaries is what we recommend at this age.

The limits we do set should be based on the values we teach, and how important it is to keep teaching and living our most cherished values! Don't harp on everything. Reserve your messages for the important things. You may want to write down what is absolutely most important to you for your kids. Then look at how those values are being instilled. Is your life consistent with the values you have listed? In other words, do your children observe you living what you believe or want for them?

Specific sexual instruction is most important for children from ten to thirteen. These are the years of greatest openness to being taught about sexuality. They need to be prepared for bodily and emotional changes. Both girls and boys need to know their body parts and their names. They need to know that boys grow hair under their arms, on their legs, chest, face, and around the penis and testicles. They need to know the penis and testicles grow larger and the voice becomes deeper. Erections, ejaculations, and wet dreams need to be explained as normal functions. For the girl, hair grows under arms and around the vulva and vagina, breasts enlarge and develop, and the vagina may discharge a white, sticky substance. Menstruation, ovulation, and the process of fertilization all need to be clearly understood (refer to Chapter 12 on sex education for more detail).

Above all, open communication with mutual regard for one another will be the most helpful in guiding our children out of childhood into adolescence.

For Further Study

Betancourt, Jeannie. *Am I Normal?* New York: Avon/Flare, 1983.

Betancourt, Jeannie. *Dear Diary.* New York: Avon/Flare, 1983.

Gardner-Loulan, Jo Ann, Bonnie Lopez and Marcia Quackenbush. *Period.* San Francisco: Volcano Press, 1979.

Ketterman, Grace H., M.D., *How to Teach Your Child about Sex.* Old Tappan: Fleming H. Revell Company, 1981, 119–166.

Kolodny, Robert C., William H. Masters, Virginia E. Johnson. *Textbook of Sexual Medicine.* Boston: Little, Brown, and Company, 1979. Chapter 4: "Puberty and Adolescent Sexuality."

Mayle, Peter. *What's Happening to Me?* Secaucus, NJ: Lyle Stuart, 1979.

The Decision-Making Years— Senior High

Adolescence and sexuality—we as parents would like to believe there isn't such a thing! It would be most convenient for us if we could strip all thirteen- to eighteen-year-olds of their sexuality—sort of put "it" on hold for five years. Then we could send them off to college and hope for the best. Their sexuality scares us, and rightly so. All of that dynamic drive for intimacy, closeness, and connection with the opposite sex is racing within them. Yet, they're still struggling with who they are, pulling away from their parents, and so influenced by their peers that we're not confident of their inner strength. Besides most of us are somewhat aware of the statistics:

- 50 percent of the nation's young women, fifteen to nineteen years of age, have had premarital sex.
- Seven million boys and five million girls are sexually active. This is a 66 percent increase in the last decade.
- Nationally, four out of ten teenage girls get pregnant every year. Two in ten give birth.
- The average age for teenage pregnancy is 16.4 years old.
- By age twenty, 40 percent of the women of this nation have been pregnant at least once.

- 70–80 percent of the country's twelve million sexually active teenagers *fail* to use birth control.
- 85 percent of first sexual experiences are unplanned, spontaneous.

What contributes to these statistics? The emotional fluctuation, uncertainty about "who I am," and the incredible internal need to be accepted by peers continues from preadolescence into adolescence. At this time while ego strength is still shaky, internal drives and sexual impulses are on fire! So at a time when adolescents are needing to "play" at learning adult behavior, as they played house at age five, their bodies and peers are pushing them to do more than just play at being couples. They are physically ready for the real thing!

Sexuality Is on Fire

The *sexual hormones* are the basis for these bodily urges. These hormones begin spurting about three years before any of the actual physical changes of puberty are evident. Now they are being secreted in full force. It is the hormones that trigger the *sexual drive*.

Fortunately, *sexual drive* gives us energy for much more than just bodily pleasure and sexual intercourse. It is the energy for life. Activity, productivity, developing talents and skills, all burn up sexual drive energy. Emotional intensity expresses sexual drive energy. The increased need for touch and physical closeness is a manifestation of sexual drive energy. Nevertheless, this drive *does* stimulate the desire for sexual arousal and release.

All of this outgrowth of sexual drive is new to adolescents. They do not know what to do with it. They tend not to recognize the potency of their drive, so they get themselves into situations where the passion of the moment controls. They engage in sexual behavior inconsistent with their values or emotional readiness. Alternative expressions are often not utilized fully.

Masturbation may not be acceptable. It has either been condemned as wrong or may be seen as the "chicken way out." "If you're a real guy, you'll have a woman!" Young women may have disconnected from their genitals in growing up, and may not even think of self-stimulation as a way of releasing some of the intensity they feel in their bodies.

Because of feelings of low self-worth, adolescents may not be burning up their drives by working diligently on academics, talents, or skills. Physical touching in the home is likely to decrease, at the very time when the need for touching is increased. Parents of thirteen- to eighteen-year-olds would do best to increase the amount of contact time. That is difficult, just by virtue of the fact that adolescents spend less time at home. Expect of them a certain amount of time at home and available (not on the telephone). Know that they need this time even though they're not likely to make it happen. You will need to make it happen. Be available when they are there. Tousle their hair as you pass by when they're studying. Rub their shoulders. Give them a peck on the cheek, a pat on the back, or a hug. Offer a back rub at bedtime. That's how Joyce keeps up the physical affirmation with our teenage son who is five inches taller than she, and rather difficult to hug comfortably. In fact, when he refuses his back rub at night, we tease him that he must be getting too much from his girlfriend, that he best get those touch needs met at home. Virginia Satir says that we all need four hugs a day to survive, eight hugs to maintain, and twelve hugs to grow. Start a hug chart! It can be a fun way to get past the awkwardness of hugging our adult-bodied children.

Dealing with Sexuality

What are the ways that adolescents deal with their sexuality? Some respond with *denial*. They shut down their sexual feelings totally. As soon as they sense any physical urges or thoughts, they become uncomfortable. They may become socially and relationally isolated. The feelings are so scary. Their way of handling their fears is to withdraw. If they don't date, this lack of experience leaves them feeling naive, anxious, and uncomfortable with the opposite sex.

There are two risks for the socially and sexually withdrawn. First, when they do choose a guy or gal, they tend to hang on and stick with a relationship that is not necessarily right for them. The other hazard is that these adolescents are most prone to sexual accidents. Their sexual feelings take them by surprise, since they've been denied so long. In addition, they need affirmation from the opposite sex since they have not been a part of the dating population. So they are especially vulnerable!

One constructive way that adolescents can handle their sexual drive is with *replacement*. We've mentioned this already. Adolescents need to keep aware of their needs and drives, feel good about those tingling sensations, but decide to use them in ways other than sexual play. They may be active in mixed social groups, but not in one-on-one relationships. They may become active in giving to others. Our daughter is a leader for a group of junior highers at a local church. They might work for a charitable organization. Developing themselves is a vital way to use that energy. Our son swims or works out for the water polo and swim teams. Our daughter dances and plays the harp. They both study hard. It's OK for adolescents to keep busy. In marriage, we want to save that energy for each other. Adolescence is the time to really go after all there is in life, to burn up that sexual drive energy.

Self-stimulation is a choice that most adolescents find comforting. It helps them be in a boy-girl relationship and to be responsible. Yet, this can be a source of conflict and pain for many Christian adolescents. Dr. Dobson's tape series, "Preparing for Adolescence," has been helpful to many in understanding the facts of self-stimulation and making decisions regarding it.

Others decide to get much of their need met by being active in a relationship with the opposite sex, but having clear *limits for sexual involvement*. When deciding to handle their sexuality in this way, adolescents need to have knowledge about their bodies and how they function sexually. They need to know that when you "get together," you are stimulating sexual arousal which is designed to lead to sexual release. So sexual play, even though it is limited, may leave feelings of frustration. Yet, this is probably the most common choice made by dating, responsible, sexually aware adolescents. And it is a very natural step in their growth and development. It requires a strong individual in a relationship that has *mutually accepted values*. Adolescents need to avoid relationships in which one is pushing for more and the other is always having to draw the line.

Finally, some adolescents do handle their sexual drive by *mutual stimulation to sexual orgasm and/or sexual intercourse*. A few may make the decision and proceed responsibly. Most fall into this activity in the passion of the moment. The force leading them may be their own drives, the feeling that they have to nurture the relationship, or not knowing how to say "no."

The Sexually Active Adolescent

When adolescents become involved in total sexual play, particularly sexual intercourse, what happens? They feel inept, afraid, guilty, and inappropriate. Their experience is that of being lost in a flood of their own emotion, rather than feeling close and warm with their partner. They are mainly focused on themselves. Because of their own discomfort and feeling of vulnerability, they tend to pull away and avoid each other afterward. Both are needing reassurance from the other. But neither is secure enough to reach out and give. So both end up feeling rejected and uncared for. The movie, "Little Darlings," did a great job of depicting these realistic reactions to sexual intercourse during teenage years. We'd recommend you see it. Then if you feel comfortable with it, watch the movie with your teenagers and discuss it. It can be a tool for opening communication.

Sexual intercourse is so much more than just releasing our physical drives and bringing two bodies together genitally. It is the union of two people totally. Two become one. We lose all of who we are with another person. That takes incredible security. Yet adolescents are still struggling with *who they are*. Their ego identity is unsure. So at a time when they are supposed to be finding themselves, they are losing themselves to another person. Most confusing!

When adolescents become sexually active, they bypass many steps of relating. They move quickly into physical intimacy without learning how to get along together. They don't know who to talk to about their feelings, how to let others know their likes and dislikes, how to share mutual interests, and how to resolve differences. In fact, many times young girls come into pregnancy detection centers crying. When they're asked how it happened, their response is, "It's easier than talking."

One authority wrote: "When you learn to fly, you don't get straight into any airplane and take off solo. When you learn to use your sexual powers, you don't start by trying to have sexual intercourse with somebody." Even the most liberal authorities on sexuality don't recommend sexual intercourse for teenagers. They see it as detrimental to psychological growth and development. The only reason they teach birth control is to encourage responsible sex, if adolescents are going to have it anyway. But the big push today is teaching adolescents that they have the power (and the right!) to say, "No." It is important for all adolescents to recognize that their bodies are theirs to share only when it is right.

Since 85 percent of the teenagers have unpremeditated sexual intercourse the first time, they are not protected. Therefore, teenage pregnancy is a high risk. There are no easy solutions to teenage pregnancy. A sixteen-year-old girl who finds herself pregnant is jarred out of the innocent bliss of adolescence. If sexual intercourse causes the adolescent to bypass important relational stages of growth and development, you can imagine how pregnancy interrupts. It is always sad and painful. As parents, our most important response is to stand alongside our child. Our rejection will help no one. Grieve the loss of her adolescence with her. Use the decision-making process we suggested earlier to help her decide how she is going to handle the pregnancy. Make certain she has accurate information regarding moral, religious, physical, and emotional issues. Be there for her!

Positive Parenting

Question: An example of negative messages might be the "thou shalt not" of sex before marriage. How can parents teach their children that a sexual relationship outside of marriage is wrong, yet God planned for sex to be a great joy within marriage?

That is a most difficult balance to present. The goal is to teach values that have limitations, yet promote a positive view of sex. It is best when the limitations are presented as part of the facts, rather than the overall slogan. For example, "This is what the Bible teaches about sex. The reason God gave us that rule was not to make us unhappy, but to take care of us. Sexual union is a deep, special act. It unites us with another person emotionally, spiritually, and physically. We are really married to a person once we have sex with that person." Then present the facts of what happens in our bodies during a sexual experience (see *The Gift of Sex,* Chapter 7). "It is a complex and beautiful response. We want to be very careful about sharing something so intense and special. But sex is to be enjoyed. Marriage is the place for it—and that is God's plan."

How can parents and adolescents maximize the positives of dealing with sexuality during this age?

1. *Be aware.* Be aware of the dilemma and pressure adolescents face. There is an increasing gap between physical maturity and readi-

ness for marriage. Education and financial demands are delaying marriage for most. That means the period from when their bodies are ready to function sexually until marriage is longer than ever before. At the same time, the media is flaunting sexual stimuli everywhere. The general behavior and attitude of society pushes children to be sexual before their time.

2. *Be educated.* Both parents and adolescents need to read accurate sexual information. Knowledge breeds responsibility, not sexual promiscuity. Premature sexual behavior is the result of the general influence of society, along with incomplete knowledge and lack of internal strength to resist pressures, external and internal. We are responsible to educate ourselves about how our bodies function sexually. We are responsible to understand the sexual drive and how it can be channeled. We are responsible to have a deep understanding of God's purpose and will for us as sexual persons. We are responsible to avoid unintended sexual activity. We are responsible for the prevention of venereal diseases. We need to be educated as to how they are transmitted, as well as aware of the signs and symptoms. We are responsible for the prevention of teenage pregnancy. Above all, we are responsible to be knowledgable decision-makers in all areas of sexuality.

3. *Be a decision-maker.* We believe strongly that the most important place to start in the effective management of adolescents' sexuality is with decision-making. Adolescents will be moving toward making many of their own decisions. They will need to decide what is right for them. They will need to start thinking about the kind of persons they want to be. How they want to be known or regarded will have to be considered. As they begin to wonder what life will be like for them when they're on their own, they will begin to question values. It is helpful if you have a clear sense of what your children value. What is really important? How is this the same as or different from that of friends and parents?

In making decisions about sexuality, begin by differentiating sexual feelings from sexual behavior. Sexual feelings include the *urge* to be touched, to be close, to be "turned on." Those feelings are part of who we are by creation. They are good! Our sexual behavior—our actions—is what we decide to do with those feelings. That is where decision-making is so necessary. These decisions need to be based on what we value and believe. As Christians, we are to use the Bible as our guide and strength for defining these beliefs.

Adolescents make choices. They are the ones who have to live with the consequences of their decisions. Ultimately, the decision about the extent of sexual activity is the adolescent's to make.

To help with the decision-making, we would recommend applying seven steps of a problem-solving process.

Define the problem: As an adolescent, how am I going to handle my sexuality? (or some specific version of that question)

What are the different alternatives? Refer to the "Dealing with Sexuality" section for ways adolescents can handle sexual feelings. (Refer to page 134 for a full range of sexual behaviors.)

What are the consequences for each alternative? The following two steps will help you determine these. The questions you need to ask: If I choose this alternative, what is likely to happen? How am I going to feel? How does it fit with what I believe to be right?

Gather data about the possible alternatives: Take time to know yourself. Write down your feelings. Clarify the physical, emotional, and spiritual consequences of the possible choice.

State your values: What is important to you in life? Brainstorm. List everything that comes to your mind, then prioritize your list. Where does God fit in? What about your family, friends, and Christian community? How do the various alternatives fit with what you value?

Make the decision: First, try it out in your mind. Then plan your activities and relationships around that decision. Don't get yourself into situations that make it virtually impossible for you to stick with your decision. Make your plan work for you. For example, date others with similar values and choices.

Evaluate the consequences of the decision: Is it working the way you thought it would? What changes need to be made? How can you continue with a decision that is effective for you?

Parents, use this problem-solving process with your adolescents. Teach them to use it for themselves. As much as possible, be an active consultant with them. See yourself as their ally—someone who is standing alongside them! Allow them to struggle with all sides of the issue. That is difficult to do. To have our children consider possibilities that we don't believe are right makes us as parents incredibly uneasy. But what we have to keep in mind is that we are not going to be with them when these decisions about sexual behavior are put into action. We don't go with them on their dates. We're not with them at school when they're making contacts. Unless they have thought through their options for themselves (and their consequences), they are not likely to be strong enough to stick with what they believe to be right for them.

We have to trust that what we have instilled in them since infancy is part of who they are. Ultimately, they do want to please us, and they want to do what is best for themselves. When they rebel against that and seem self-destructive, it is usually because they are not getting enough love, affirmation, and acceptance from us—not enough quality time. We can demand that! Or maybe they feel too smothered and controlled by us. The move from dependence to independence has not been allowed. They have not developed a sense of parental confidence in their decision-making.

One exception to these recommendations of encouraging decision-making for teenagers is the use of drugs or alcohol. Sometimes sugar can even influence certain people like a drug. When a person of any age is controlled by a chemical, he is incapable of confident decision-making. You are not relating to the person, you are relating to the chemical. You *do* have to take charge. Get help, immediately!

With the one exception of the chemically controlled adolescent, active decision-making by the adolescent produces behaviors most consistent with the values he has been taught. This is most true when parents have been reasonable, rather than rigid and controlling with rules. We have considered the child as a person. Talked with him. Listened to his situation. Expressed our concerns. Be clear about the important issues: alcohol, drugs, sexual intercourse—or whatever your important issues happen to be.

It works well to communicate something like this: "We want you to take charge of your life more and more. You know what we believe is important in life. A meaningful, ongoing relationship with God is number one. Developing your full potential is number two. Family times are number three. We'd like to be open in working with you on making decisions that are right for you. We'd like you to be thinking about the kind of person you want to be, about your goals in life, and how your choices fit with that.

"We hope we can be the kind of listeners who will allow you to work through your thoughts with us. When we're uncomfortable with the choices you're making, we'd like to express that, but then listen to the reasoning behind your choice. Our feelings may be unfounded, but sometimes they may be right and necessary to at least consider.

We'd like to practice a system of mutual respect. Above all, we'd like you to know that we are on your side. Even though we might get anxious when you start moving out more on your own, we want to trust you. We love you more than you can ever imagine."

In summary, we can help teenagers be wise decision-makers by: enhancing ego development (self-confidence) and reinforcing self-worth, allowing independence to grow, expressing trust in them, giving daily touching affection, allowing mistakes, and keeping communication open.

4. *Communicate openly.* Obviously, being involved in an active decision-making process requires open communication. How open we can be with our teenagers depends upon several factors:

- Our attitudes about sex.
- Our knowledge of the sexual facts—biblically, physiologically, and emotionally (*The Gift of Sex* is a great resource for parents).
- Our willingness to talk openly about ourselves—
    What did we struggle with as teenagers?
    What mistakes did we make?
    How do we wish our experiences had been different?
    What did we feel good about?
- Our being willing and able to listen without passing judgment. Not that we always agree, but we should reflect to them what they are sharing and feeling. We become a mirror to help them see themselves accurately. We are there to care, understand, and accept.

Question: Often teenagers say they have difficulty discussing sex with their parents. Some parents feel uncomfortable discussing sex with their children. Are there acceptable alternatives or teaching tools for those who cannot seem to communicate verbally about sexual matters?

When verbal communication is uncomfortable, we recommend reading something like this chapter out loud together, listening to tapes like Dr. Dobson's, attending sex education programs, watching and discussing sex education specials on T.V. together, and so on. The outside input gives you content, words, and a framework for talking.

5. *Keep involved.* Don't leave teenagers alone at home. Be home and present at their parties. This isn't necessary because you distrust

them. It is necessary because they need your support. Peer pressure can be so strong. Your presence is a message that you care. Go to their activities. You may need to take off work for that. Invite their friends into your home—and love them, too.

Plan special times alone with each child. We have developed special events with our children. With our teenagers, it may be a breakfast or lunch out. It may be a shopping day. Cliff takes Greg for a snow-skiing-talk-about-sex weekend each winter. Joyce takes Julene on a desert-spa weekend which may focus on sex, Christianity, or decision-making.

In addition, special family times are so vital. We attempt to reserve Sunday dinner and evening for that. When we allow life to infringe on that time, we notice the difference.

6. *Negotiate contracts.* With issues like dating, curfews, household and family responsibilities, it is best to negotiate a plan. Both the parent and teenager should write out a plan for what they think is acceptable. Then negotiate the differences. Both decide on the consequences that result when the contract is broken. Deal with issues factually, rather than emotionally. This will be a great preparation for your teenagers as they form life relationships.

7. *Be the parent.* This might seem contradictory to what we've suggested so far, but it isn't. Even though we're allies and consultants and on our kids' side, we *are* the parents. We're not to behave like fellow adolescents. We need to be strong and tender. We need to be firm with limits, when those are necessary. But we must reserve those limits for important times and when it is an issue within our control. Many times, however, parents have more power than they accept. We all need affirmation from our parents—and need breeds power. Use it wisely!

In conclusion, let us just encourage you by being very honest with you. If we could follow all of our guidelines at all times, we would be thrilled! Obviously, this is an ideal approach. And all of us are human. We bring our own backgrounds and limitations to our relationships. Fortunately, children are amazingly resilient and God's grace is bountiful.

Prof. Dr. med. C. van Emde Boas has published "Ten Commandments for Parents Providing Sex Education." We quote these with our additions and revisions in parentheses.

TEN COMMANDMENTS for Parents Providing Sex Education
Prof. Dr. med. C. van Emde Boas
Stadionweg 80
1077 SP Amsterdam

1. Thou shalt not separate sex education from any other education, but realize that sex education starts in the cradle.
2. Thou shalt realize that skin and hands are our most important sex organs.
3. Thou shalt neither curb spontaneous sex expressions of the child (when it is age-appropriate and not harmful), nor ever stimulate it artificially.
4. Thou shalt answer every question of the child according to truth, wherever possible immediately but always according to the emotional and spiritual level of the child; never answer more than was asked for.
5. Thou shalt realize that a living example carries more weight than words.
6. Thou shalt realize that sex information at school can never be anything but an addition to sex education in the family.
7. Thou shalt realize that overstressing of the biological aspects of sexuality must lead to underestimating of the emotional and relational aspects.
8. Thou shalt teach that sexual exploitation of another human being is equally as reprehensible as any other form of exploitation.
9. Thou shalt teach your children that the stem "co" in coitus means "together": being together, belonging together, becoming one and thus presupposes an intimate relationship (scripturally, marriage).
10. The Pill: rather a year too early than one night too late. (We would say: a clear decision about sexual behavior a year too early rather than one night too late.)

Decision-making
in Regard to
Sexual Behavior

Level of Sexual Activity:

Complete this form to define for yourself the level of sexual expression that fits with who you are and your values.

Individual Activity:

Masturbation: I do _____ I don't _____ It's OK _____
                Shouldn't _____ Causes me guilt _____
Sexual fantasies: Are a part of my masturbating activity _____
                    Pass through my mind occasionally _____
                    Preoccupy my mind frequently _____
                    Seem natural and normal _____
                    Aren't something I've been aware of _____
                    Are sinful _____

Relationship Activity: The following activities express the whole range of possible sexual involvement. With the knowledge that God designed sexual intercourse for marriage determine the limits of your sexual activity.

None _____
Handholding and hugging _____
Polite kissing _____
Total mouth kissing _____
Intense passionate hugging _____
Full body rubbing, with clothes on _____
Breast stimulation over clothes _____
Genital stimulation over clothes _____
Breast stimulation under clothes _____
Genital stimulation under clothes _____

Full body pleasuring no clothes _____
Oral-genital stimulation _____
Total sexual experience, except entry _____
Total sexual experience, including inter-
course _____
Ejaculation/orgasm by:
    Manual stimulation _____
    Oral stimulation _____
    Actual intercourse _____
Birth control or no birth control _____
If yes, what kind and what degree of
safety _____

I would like to get control of my sexual activity by _____

I would like to gain more comfort with my sexuality by _____

My goal for myself: _____
(Having decided to what degree you would see yourself being sexually active, how are you going to be responsible for that? What other types of intimacy might you develop? How might you use your sexual drive energy to be productive in other ways? What types of situations and activities encourage your goals and what gets in the way?)

PENNER & PENNER

For Further Study

Comfort, Alex, and Jane Comfort. *The Facts of Love: Living, Loving, and Growing Up.* New York: Crown Publishers, 1979. (Parents need to add their values.)

Colgrove, Melba, Harold Bloomfield, and Peter Williams. *How to Survive the Loss of a Love.* New York: Bantam Books, 1971.

Hass, Aaron. *Teenage Sexuality: A Survey of Teenage Behavior.* Los Angeles: Pinnacle Books, 1981.

Huggett, Joyce. *Just Good Friends? Growing on Relationships.* Chicago: Inter-Varsity Press, 1985.

Leman, Kevin. *Smart Girls Don't and Guys Don't Either.* Thousand Oaks: Regal, 1982.

Oraker, James R., Ph.D., *Almost Grown: A Christian Guide for Parents of Teenagers.* New York: Harper and Row, 1980.

Shearer, Lloyd, reporter. "Teenage Sexuality." *Parade Magazine, Star News.* January 16, 1983, 15.

Short, Ray E. *Sex, Love, or Infatuation: How Can I Really Know?* Minneapolis: Augsburg Publishing House, 1978.

Wood, Barry. *Questions Teenagers Ask about Dating and Sex.* Old Tappan: Fleming H. Revell Company, 1981.

"The Games Teenagers Play." *Newsweek,* September 1, 1980. 48–53.

Sex Education with Values

Why sex education? Those who severely oppose sex education say: "The major goal of nearly all sex education curricula being taught in the schools is to teach teenagers (sometimes children) how to enjoy fornication without having a baby and without feeling guilty" (*The Phyllis Schafly Report,* Feb. '81). Yet even the extreme liberals who promote sex education say, "We don't think it's a good idea for teenagers to have intercourse. Sex for teenagers is a health hazard. . . . Teenagers are too young, too vulnerable, too available for exploitation. They don't know that the first experiences of sex are usually grim. . . . We cannot teach sex education without values. Sex education without values is valueless. . . . We believe in morality, in values, and in the family. We need to re-emphasize that the family and parents *are* the sex educators of their children whether they do it well or badly" ("Sexuality Education in the 1980s—No More Retreats" by Sol Gordon, Ph.D., C.S.E., C.S.T. from *The Journal of Sex Education and Therapy*).

Controversy

Why the controversy? One dilemma is that sex education programs vary as much as the individuals responsible for them. Thus, conclusions are often made based on an inadequate, irresponsible program and then generalized for all programs. Another issue is fear without facts. What tends to happen is that a very small, loud minority will raise opposition to a sex education program without thoroughly evaluating that program. Conclusions are drawn because certain educators or groups are known as humanistic. So the assumption is made that the program promotes anti-Christian values. Many times that isn't true, but no one has bothered to check what *is* being taught. In addition, the average parent may fear that educating young people will cause them to experiment sexually, or to turn against the values of their family.

Should children be taught about sex? Doesn't it just give them ideas? In so doing, don't we destroy their innocence? What if the sex educator *does* communicate values that contradict ours?

We would like to address some of these concerns. As we've mentioned in previous chapters, children will be curious about sex and they will experiment. This happens without any formalized sexual program even in primitive societies. It is part of the developmental process. And children will learn about sex, whether or not we expose them to a planned sex education program. So refusing to provide sex education is not the answer to keeping them innocent.

Views in opposition to our Christian principles may be presented in a secular sex education program. We see that as a negative that can be turned into a positive. In fact, opposing thoughts can provide an excellent opportunity to implant our beliefs effectively. Throughout their lives young people will be confronted with values in opposition to those of their parents. Most times when our young people are exposed to contradictory values, we are not present to teach what we believe and why. So the outside information is added to what they've heard from us, leaving them confused and unsure of what to believe. Our presence and ability to clarify at the moment (or shortly thereafter) can have a positive effect similar to parents countering the effect of TV on their children. That is, research has shown that when parents watch TV with their children and react to what is being shown, the children do not absorb what is seen as true reality. They learn to discriminate. Expressing our views in contradiction to other views teaches children to critically examine the outside information. It teaches them to think for themselves and to realize that not everything they hear is the truth. So the important element to control the effect of opposing views is our presence or awareness of what has been presented and our willingness to interact with our young person about that input.

We would like to mention an additional attitude. It comes in response to the fear that our children are going to become sexually active if they attend sex education programs. The atmosphere in our homes will have a greater impact on how our children behave sexually than will any sex education program. We parents have a lifelong interaction with our children. We have the opportunity to instill enough positive input that the limited external teaching will not undo all our efforts (their own drives and peer pressure may, but not sex education per se).

Many times parents don't recognize the impact they have on their children's lives. Because some parents don't accept their position of power and influence, they fail to utilize it effectively. Parents react in two ways to their feeling of powerlessness in relation to their children. Either they assume a powerless, helpless role, leaving the children without any clear direction, or they tend to dominate and dictate, eliciting rebellion in their children. Accepting our position of power and influence with our children enhances mutual respect for one another in the family. It promotes a sense of wanting to make the very best use of these limited years with our children. It causes us to use every opportunity to listen to them, spend time with them, teach them, and share with them our thinking and feeling.

Formal Sex Education

Obviously, we are *for* responsible sex education. As sincere evangelical Christians, how can we take such a stand? Negative Christianity which takes a stand *against* issues rather than promoting the positive has too often been the dominant voice of our evangelical churches. We are active in teaching positive, responsible, biblically based sexuality to married couples, singles, and parents of children of all ages. We believe there is so much we can be *for,* that it is a shame to spend our energy only attacking and condemning. We'd like to see Christians everywhere become involved in the sex education programs of their communities. Think what a positive influence we could have! Even if all we do is present the biological facts with a clear call for responsible decision-making, we could encourage a positive trend.

What are the *benefits* of a formal sex education program outside the home?

First, the facts presented in a formal program will be more complete and graphic than what we as parents can share with our children in our homes. For example, there is no way that we can communicate all the detail of how the reproductive system works as do some of the films. Nor can we as vividly portray the varying growth patterns that are so typical during puberty. Many of the teaching films do an excellent job of capturing the attention of young people while describing both the physical and emotional dimensions of growing up.

Second, attending sex education programs with our preadolescents or having our adolescents share the content of their programs with us can be an excellent way to open discussion between parent and child.

Third, some parents need to utilize sex education programs outside the home because they are unable to share the necessary information at home. Either their discomfort with their own sexuality prevents them from communicating openly or they lack knowledge about the topic.

Fourth, some parents have not developed a rapport with their children that allows the children to feel comfortable discussing sexuality with their parents.

Fifth, it is very helpful for children of all ages to hear the questions their peers are asking and to hear what the sex educators are saying to everyone their age about certain issues in a group setting. It helps them realize that what they are thinking and feeling is normal. Sometimes a one-to-one discussion can make children feel that they are the only ones their age needing this talk. Or, at least, that this is how their parents view them.

Sixth, if adolescents are going to decide *not* to be sexually active, they are going to have to be informed. They are going to need to know about their bodies and how they work, to be aware of sexual feelings and drives and how to handle them. They are going to need to know how to separate feelings from behavior, so that they can say, "No, thank you."

Seventh, long-term comparison studies between adolescents who have had sex education and those who have not, show that either there was no difference in level of sexual activity between the two groups or that "those who did *not* receive sex education had a higher rate of sexual activity than those who did receive such education" ("Research Notes" by Elizabeth Rice Allgeier, Ph.D., Psych. Dept., Bowling Green State University, Bowling Green, Ohio). All studies report pregnancy and abortion rates to be significantly lower for those who have received sex education. Even though our ultimate goal as Christians would be to reduce adolescent sexual intercourse, we also are very concerned about eliminating out-of-wedlock pregnancy and, for sure, abortions.

It is not surprising to us that effective sex education would reduce rather than increase sexual activity. When we understand that most thirteen- to fifteen-year-olds are experiencing full hormone production and, thus, high sexual drives, we realize that they have to have tools to help them harness that energy. As one author wrote, they already have the keys to the car (their sexual drive). The tendency will be to go out and use those keys and have accidents (unintended sexual intercourse—pregnancy) unless we give them systematic driver's training (sex education).

Who Should Do the Teaching?

Where should formal sex education programs be offered? The church is our first place of choice. We would love to see the church assume responsibility for sex education so that sexuality and spirituality develop together. When sexuality becomes linked with spirituality, it will be enjoyed in marriage. Unfortunately, most children receive their sexual information through TV, movies, and friends. In those situations it is often linked with sin and guilt. Thus, sex becomes connected with something fun and exciting outside of marriage and outside of the church. When sin and sex go hand in hand, adults have difficulty enjoying sex without a feeling of guilt. We would love to have children grow up in the church with positive input regarding their sexuality—that it is a God-given force within them, that it has dynamite power which can be used positively or negatively, and that having information will help them make wise decisions regarding their sexuality.

Community organizations and schools are also important places for responsible sexual education to take place. Christian schools presenting a sex education program can have the same effect as the church teaching about sex. We have participated in such a program for the Christian school in our area. When sex education takes place in a secular setting, we recommend having clergy persons of all religious groups represented to interact with their people in regard to the content of the presentations. This is best handled by adjourning to small meeting rooms after the larger group presentation. The only way to influence this dynamic is to be involved. As Christian parents we must take an active role in influencing positive sex education for our children. Rather than trying to protect them because of our fear, let's turn that energy into presenting them with facts that lead to value-based decisions.

The person presenting the material or interacting with the audience must be comfortable with and well informed about the topic of sex. There has to be an ease in handling any question that might come from the audience. Being secure with regard to our own sexuality has been invaluable to us. We find it is important for us to have thought through our own values so that we communicate them when appropriate without imposing our beliefs on others. There will be some students in every crowd who will attempt to shock or stir up the presenter. It is important to be unshockable and nonjudgmental. In other words, keep cool! It helps for us to have a strong sense of ourselves, yet respect each other's feelings and views.

When parents and students are attending together, we recommend that questions be written and that students be allowed open discussion from the floor—but *not parents*. The reason for this is to prevent the insensitive parent from embarrassing his/her child. We have experienced some most unfortunate happenings when that limitation was not present. One mother openly and condemningly discussed the masturbatory habits of her daughter with the girl and her peers present. The chance of one child being hurt that severely is not worth allowing open discussion for parents from the floor. Always have pencils and cards or paper available for them to write their responses, questions, or concerns.

The Content

What should be taught and at what age level? Ideally sex education is a circular process for all ages. Because many adults have not been educated regarding their own sexuality and sexual relationships, we believe this adult education needs to occur first. That is why we wrote *The Gift of Sex: A Christian Guide to Sexual Fulfillment in Marriage,* before we wrote this book. How we experience the sexual dimension of our lives will have a significant effect on what we communicate to our children. A friend of ours once observed, "You know, it's interesting that most of us as adults spend a major share of our lives in a marriage relationship and as parents, yet our educational process did almost nothing to prepare us for those responsibilities."

Thus, we move from teaching couples how to handle their own

sexuality to teaching parents about children. Before about the fourth grade, age nine or ten, our primary focus is on teaching parents how to handle sexuality with their children. Parents need to know what and how children learn at various levels of sexual development. Chapters 8 and 9 will be most helpful. We will summarize that information in our Sex Education Model that follows at the end of this chapter.

Starting at age nine or ten, formal education is recommended as a supplement to the ongoing process of informal teaching that occurs in the home. Education for the ten- to thirteen-year-olds is best directed toward the children, but with the parents present and sitting with their children.

At adolescence, peers become the key to influencing positive decisions regarding sexuality. At this age, most children "turn off" to sex education from an adult authority, particularly in a large group setting— i.e., church or school. There is a self-consciousness about the topic, as well as a need to "know it all." It's as if the content is too close to what they are trying to sort out for themselves. It's too close to be comfortable, so there is a low receptivity to formal sex education during the high school years. Peer-power is dominant. Teenagers are listening to each other. Therefore, we recommend that a select group of desirable, emotionally and spiritually mature adolescents be trained and supervised by qualified counselors. These peer-counselors need to be visibly available to their peers through some formal or informal plan.

Then we complete the circle of sex education by teaching adult singles (refer to Chapter 13 for details on singles and sexuality) and couples preparing for marriage.

Sex education for the single adult is not much different than that for the adolescent. The same issue is alive: sexual drives are flaming while sex within marriage is not available. The gap between physical readiness for sexual involvement and the actual possibility of marriage is widening. Puberty is occurring at a younger age. Our economic and educational system is delaying marriage until later in life. Responsible decision-making based on knowledge and self-awareness is the only solution.

Premarital classes for couples can be an incredible boost to starting a happy sexual life in marriage. Much of the content will be the same as what adult married couples receive. There are some specific instructions to help couples with that first sexual intercourse. We were fortunate that Joyce received instruction from her gynecologist as well as a premarital class that was part of her school of nursing program.

This completes the process of sex education. We began with married couples and ended with those who are about to be married. We find the groups most receptive to education are the fifth and sixth graders and the married couples. They are eager and ready to learn, and they ask excellent questions. The *least* receptive are the high schoolers and the premarital couples. For both of these groups, there is an element of newness as it relates to sexuality in their lives; thus, they feel self-conscious and somewhat certain they don't need the information.

SEX EDUCATION MODEL

I. Educate married couples to enhance their sexual relationship, by teaching—
   A. Positive sexual attitudes—concept of mutuality.
   B. Biblical endorsement of sexual pleasure in marriage.
   C. Bodily openness and familiarity between the couple.
   D. Physical facts of how the male and female bodies function during a sexual response.
   E. The emotional and relational dimensions of a sexual encounter.
   F. Solutions for common sexual problems.
   G. Open communication about sex in marriage.
   H. Freedom without demand in the sexual relationship.
   I. Guidelines for resolving controversial sexual issues.

II. Educate parents of children to be able to model and teach healthy sexual attitudes to children 0–10 years old.
   A. For infants 0–2 years—how to affirm through touch.
   B. For toddlers 2–4 years—how to instill a positive acceptance of genitals (touching, naming, controlling).
   C. For preschoolers 4–5 years—how to handle sexual curiosity (questions and self-discovery).
   D. For the 3–6-year-olds—how to affirm gender identity.
   E. For school age 6–10 years—how to develop a regard for their sexuality in relation to others (exploratory play, nudity, molestation).
   F. For the physical developmental process (refer to chart at end of chapter).

III. Educate preadolescents with parents present

    A. 9–10 yr. old girls (fourth grade)—*Menstruation film* and display of menstrual supplies with teaching. *Question-answer time*—use cards for written questions and allow questions from the floor.

    B. 10–12-year-olds (fifth-sixth grades)—*Film* that describes biological and emotional changes of puberty, elementary biological facts of sexual reproduction, facts about masturbation, values of responsible utilization of sexual energy. (Suggested films: "Then One Year" or "Dear Diary" and "Am I Normal?") *Question-answer time*—have all students and parents write something on their 3×5 card and have volunteers collect cards and bring to speakers. Speakers respond to questions factually and sensitively. On moral issues, may present different views (including the speaker's view) and encourage parent and children to discuss after the program. If being conducted in the church, the position of the church may be taught. Recommend parent and child having discussion about content of the program immediately following.

    C. 12–13-year-olds (seventh grade)—Film that reviews biological, emotional, and responsibility changes of becoming an adolescent, biological details of sex and reproduction, a description of sexual intercourse as a special expression between a husband and wife that is for pleasure as well as reproduction, facts about conflicting views on masturbation, introduce decision-making—the concept of active choices. (Suggested film: *Human Growth III.*) Question-answer time conducted the same as for fifth and sixth grades. Small group discussions the next day would be great. (See Puberty Growth Time-table.)

    D. 13–14-year-olds (eighth grade)—Film depicting the peer pressures that students will be facing as they move into ninth grade with consequences of various choices shown, (*Running My Way* by Children's Home Society is excellent but will need updating in styles, etc.). Separate parents and students for discussion. Open discussion with decision-making form that follows on page 148. Summarize discussion time with call for clear decision-making that weighs the consequences of each alternative. Include reasons why both Christian and secular leaders are against teenage sexual intercourse. Bring parents and students together. Discussion leaders summarize the discussion content of both groups. Encourage parents and students to have a communication time after the meeting in which each share reactions.

IV. Educate adolescents (14–18-year-olds) informing parents of what is being taught.

    A. Teach classrooms of adolescents, separating gals and guys to promote freer discussion.

    B. Teach mixed groups of peer counselors.

    C. Content that needs to be taught:

        1. Sexual anatomy and physiology: what happens to the body during sexual arousal and release.

        2. Sexual feelings and drives as separate from sexual actions which require decisions.

        3. Various choices for responding to touching, relationship, and sexual needs; include statistics of adolescents and consequences of those choices.

        4. Values clarification *Choices* (1983) and *Challenges* (1984), books by Bingham, Edmondson & Stryker (Advocacy Press, Santa Barbara) may be used for this purpose with your moral input. If the course is taught within the church, the Bible is the best resource.

        5. Facts about venereal diseases.

        6. Facts about birth control, *not* as a recommendation but rather as the most responsible option if some choose to proceed to sexual intercourse even though that is not right for them, and for peer counselors to push for teenagers who are already sexually active.

        7. The choice of saying, "No," is the best option. For help with how to respond to the pressure of their own desires as well as the pressures of the opposite sex, refer to *Smart Girls Don't and Guys Don't Either* by Kevin Leman (Los Angeles: Regal, 1982).

        8. The positive expression of sexual intercourse in marriage.

V. Educate Single Adults:

    A. To know the facts,

     B. To know themselves,

     C. To struggle with the reality, and

     D. To find joy in the choices they make.

VI. Educate Premarital Couples regarding:

     A. Biblical affirmation of sexuality and sexual fulfillment in marriage.

     B. Making the emotional and relationship dimensions of sex work for them.

     C. Understanding their sexual response or lack of it.

     D. Learning how to give and receive pleasure for the sake of pleasure without demand.

     E. Communicating openly about themselves as sexual persons and their expectations for sex in marriage.

     F. Preparing for their first sexual intercourse.

     G. Preparing for sexual intercourse after marriage when there has been sex before.

     H. Keeping the "spark" alive.

Sex education is difficult for many. We bring to it the intensity of our own emotions and experience. We bring the attitudes that were developed in our own homes. Many times we are confused about what is appropriate to think, feel, and teach about sex.

May we continue to become more informed about our own beliefs, body functioning, sexual feelings, use of sexual drive energies, responsible decision-making, and sexual fulfillment as a gift from God.

TABLE I. PUBERTY TIMETABLE

7–10 y.o. = *Sex hormones* begin to spurt three years before physical changes are obvious. This will lead to enormously increased production of testosterone in males and estrogen in females.

8–13 y.o. = *Breast growth begins:* nipples swell a little. Usually occurs in one nipple before the other. Occurs three to four years before the girl's first menstruation. May occur in boys as well as girls. Boys' swelling goes away as their testicles begin to grow and produce more testosterone.

8–14 y.o. = *Pubic hair* begins in girls. Enlargement of the labia and clitoris follows.

9.5–14.5 y.o. = *Height spurt* in girls—may be more gradual than in boys (feet tend to grow before height).

9.5–13.5 y.o. = *Testicle growth* begins.

10–15 y.o. = *Height spurt* starts in boys (feet tend to grow before height).
= *Pubic hair* begins in boys.

10–16.5 y.o. = First *menstruation.* Ovulation may occur before or after.

10.5–14.5 y.o. = *Penis growth* starts.

11.5–15.5 y.o. (or later) = First *ejaculation* occurs about a year after penis growth starts, but this varies greatly. Orgasm can occur before ejaculation.

12–16 y.o. = *Voice change* for boys.

12.5–16.5 y.o. = *Penis Growth* stops.

13.5–17 y.o. = *Testicle growth* stops.

13.5–17 y.o. = *Height spurt* stops for boys.

13–18 y.o. = *Breast development* stops for girls.

Other changes that vary too greatly to list on timetable:

Growth of underarm hair for boys and girls.
Growth of facial hair for boys.
Acne for some boys and girls.
Body shape takes on adult characteristics.

TABLE II

Decision-making Process: To follow the film, "Running My Way."

I. *Define the Problem*
   A. What was the problem for Lisa?
   B. What was the problem for Sandy?

II. *What Are the Different Alternatives?*
   A. What were the alternatives for Lisa?
      1. She could not have sex.
      2. She could have had sex unprotected.
      3. She could have had sex protected.
      4. She could have a relationship with Tony on another level. (other forms of intimacy)

III. *What Are the Consequences of Each Alternative?*
   A. If she doesn't have sex, what is going to happen?
   B. If she does, what will happen?
   C. If she does, how will she feel?

IV. *Gather Data: To Predict Your Consequences Accurately*
   A. Have reliable information. (Biggest source of information is their peers—this is misinformation)
   B. Be informed—as parents and adolescents, know how your bodies work.
   C. What are kids' values?

V. *State the Values*
   A. What were Lisa's values?
      1. Telling the truth was important.
      2. Having a boyfriend.
      3. Running.
      4. Carefulness about sharing her body.
   B. What were Sandy's, Ray's, and Tony's values?

VI. *Make the Decision*
   A. Then try it in your mind. What will happen if I make this decision?
   B. Then actually act on the decision.

VII. *Evaluate the Decision*
   A. Need to think, feel and then act.
   B. What were the actual consequences?

For Further Study

Amstutz, H. Clair. *Growing Up to Love: A Guide to Sex Education for Parents.* Scottdale, PA: Herald Press, 1966.

Bath, Lenore. *Sexuality: God's Precious Gift to Parents and Children.* St. Louis: Concordia, 1982.

California Family Life Education. *Network Report.* Issues from Fall 1981 to Summer 1986.

Carrera, Michael. *Sex: The Facts, the Acts, and Your Feelings.* New York: Crown Publishers, 1981.

Nilsson, A. Lenart, Axel Ingelman-Sundberg, M.D., and Claes Wirsen, M.D., *A Child Is Born: The Drama of Life Before Birth.* New York: Delacorte Press, 1967.

Nixon, Joan Lowery. *Before You Were Born.* Huntington: *Our Sunday Visitor,* 1980.

Scanzoni, Letha. *Sex Is a Parent Affair.* New York: Bantam, 1972.

Schlafly, Phyllis. "What's Wrong with Sex Education?" *The Phyllis Schafly Report,* vol. 14, no. 7, Section 1, February 1981.

Sowby, Sherman K. "Problems of New Morality." A Home Study for Continuing Education for Registered Nurses.

The Study Group of New York. *Children and Sex, The Parents Speak.* New York: Facts on File, 1983.

—————————IV

SINGLE SEXUALITY

13

Single, Sexual and Sanctified

Life used to be uncomplicated. Sexuality for the single person was clearly defined. The old limerick put it this way:

> There was a young lady named Wilde
> Who kept herself quite undefiled,
> By thinking of Jesus and social diseases,
> And the fear of having a child.

It used to be so simple. After high school you went to college and by the time you were twenty or twenty-one you had picked out the man or woman of your dreams, and then you married and did what your parents had done: work, start a family, establish yourself in a job or location. Life was pretty clearly set.

It used to be so simple. Right was right, and wrong was wrong—and everyone knew the difference. There was no hazy morality. What was expected of the single Christian man or woman was clear.

We don't live in that simple a world any more. Whether we come from a rural part of the country or a metropolitan area, everyone has been bombarded by the cultural changes that are a result of the technological and medical advances of the past thirty years. Television has brought a variety of lifestyles right into our living room. Birth control has radically reduced the fear of having an illegitimate or unwanted child. Many Christian singles are actively, and often openly, sexually involved. Attitudes toward morality have changed. One thing that has gone full circle is the second point of the limerick—social diseases are again a major concern. Now with herpes and AIDS, disease is again a dreaded consequence.

Not only have there been moral and technological changes, but the social structure has changed radically. We are no longer oriented around family, church or community as we once were. Many times we exist in isolation from our neighbors. They provide no control. There has also been a significant increase in the number of women in the working world and the capability of the woman to function fully equal with a man (even though sometimes her salary still lags behind his). It is clearly possible for a woman to get along without a man. In addition, there are more single women than there are single men who are eligible for marriage. Single people choose to put off marriage. The stigma of singleness is diminishing. All of these factors force us to take a fresh look at the subject of being single in these closing years of the twentieth century.

Who Is This Single Person?

The answer to this question is no longer simple either. There are those who see themselves as temporarily single. This is the under twenty-five age group who graduated from high school, went off to work or college, and expect that they will be raising a family of their own. Many in the twenty-five- to thirty-five-year age range are focusing on professional goals without great thought or emphasis on marriage. Then there are those singles who intended to marry, but never did. These can range all the way from people in their late twenties to the seventy-five-year-old. The never-married group includes some who chose not to marry (even if they had the opportunity) or some who chose the celibate life to give their energy to the call of God.

Those who are single as the result of divorce make up a large portion of the single world. Relatively few people marry with the anticipation of divorce, so singleness comes as a shocking intrusion into their life plan. There are many variations within the divorced group. There may be the young woman of twenty-two whose marriage lasted only eight months because her husband was violent with her. She got out of the marriage and feels rather scarred. But she is young and has her whole life before her. On the other hand, the divorce group may include the thirty-eight-year-old husband whose wife left him with three kids. He is trying to be both mother and father—and breadwinner as well. Still others may have been divorced for fifteen or twenty years, and have no hope or desire ever to marry again. Some couples lived together until the kids were through college and married, and then got a divorce as a statement of how unfulfilling life had been for them during those family-raising years.

The single group also includes those who are single because of the death of a beloved spouse. The widows and the widowers face the shock (often violent) of the trauma of death at an unexpected time. They now find themselves floundering among the singles. The feelings they report are different from those of other singles.

Sexual experience, viewpoints, and needs vary greatly for singles. For the twenty-one-year-old virgin, whether male or female, the sexual drive is quite different than for the divorced person of thirty-three whose sexual life has suddenly been shut off because of the loss of a spouse. Thus, it is important as we look at singleness and sexuality that we consider all variations, recognizing that there is no one simple answer readily applicable to all circumstances.

It would be important for the authors to add a disclaimer. We are not single! We haven't been single for twenty-three years! We do not write about singleness out of our experience. Yes, we have talked with dozens if not hundreds of single people about their struggles, but that is different than writing from personal experience. We were married during our last years of college at age twenty-one, and have lived together now for almost a quarter of a century. We acknowledge that we write as outsiders, but trust that the insights gained from the open sharing of our single friends and clients will come close to defining your experience, and will be of some help in your life.

Painting the Singles Scene

Let's begin by attempting to get a realistic picture. There is an ever-increasing gap between the time when a young person's body is ready for sexual activity and the time when marriage is likely to occur.

If a young person is going to complete college or graduate school and begin working, it may well be that he or she will put off marriage until the late twenties or even early thirties. Many of us encourage couples to wait until their mid-twenties to marry. The statistics show that younger marriages have a higher incidence of divorce than do later marriages. This makes sense. We change a great deal after leaving the parental home. As we grow older we find ourselves to be more thoughtful in our choices. We know ourselves better.

This dilemma (of the body being ready for sexual activity and the educational and societal influences pushing marriage later and later) leaves many young adults with ten to fifteen years of sexual readiness before marriage. While the sexual urges are at their peak, there is no acceptable outlet. Granted, Charlie Shedd has called masturbation "God's gift to single people," but it is a gift with clearly limited potential for fulfillment. It takes care of the physical needs, but the emotional and spiritual dimension of sexual intimacy is absent.

Let us underscore the reality and vitality of every person's sexuality. We are sexual beings from even before birth. It is impossible for us not to be sexual. Our body functions sexually right from birth. A little boy has his first erection within minutes after birth, and a little girl has her first vaginal lubrication within hours after birth. We are sexual persons not only because of our physiology but also by the maleness and femaleness that is a part of who we are. As we move beyond puberty, we feel natural physical attraction to people of the opposite sex. That is how God designed us, so there is no way that we can be single and not be sexual. We are sexual and that sexuality is confirmed not only by our physiology but also by our emotions and by our spirits.

Obviously, the single person has to take responsibility for the expressions of that sexuality. As the limerick at the beginning of this chapter indicated, conception, infection, and detection used to be the controls on single, sexual activity. All three of these controls have changed radically. The easy availability of birth control methods, especially "the pill," have drastically altered the dating structure. The advent of the pill clearly is one of the benchmarks of modern social change. One can now safely engage in sexual activity without fear of impregnation, relatively speaking.

While the moral attitudes about premarital sex may still be endorsed in our homes, churches, or society, birth control provides the possibility of private involvement without the fear of pregnancy. It does require a conscious choice on the part of the single person to be sexually active. That is a difficult decision for singles who believe sex outside of marriage is wrong. Thus, about 85 percent of first-time sexual experiences of single people are unplanned. Since they do not consciously decide that they are ready for sexual intercourse, the couple proceeds unprotected. Hence the many unwanted pregnancies. Thus conception is an unnecessary dilemma for the single person. Birth control is readily available, but the conflict between sexual drives, social standards, and moral convictions keeps the person from actively confronting the decision of sexual behavior.

As mentioned earlier, infection is back in the picture. The incidence of sexually transmitted diseases rises every year. Infections are usually contracted outside of marriage. There is no cure for herpes and AIDS. Thus, the thinking single person has to be much more cautious. Virginity is again "in" on the high school and college campuses, at least as an option.

With the mobility and fragmentation of our society, detection is seldom an issue. Young people, even of high school age, are often home by themselves for extended periods of time while both parents are working. There is the freedom to use the automobile, the pick-up camper, or the van. After high school most young people live apart from their families in unrestricted settings. Hence they are free to make their own choices without detection.

At the same time as detection and conception lose their control, society saturates the single person with sexuality. Magazines, movies, videos, television, conversations—all promote an easy acceptance of not only sexual enticement, but also sexual activity. This is available for all to see from an early age. Young people are talking in sexual terms in the elementary grades. Junior high kids are very free in their language and the high school age students behave as if they are beyond the need for any kind of sexual education. This apparent openness and freedom surrounding sexuality should imply greater knowledge, and bode well for healthy sexual adjustment in later years. But it doesn't. While sex may saturate our world, accurate sexual knowledge and healthy decisions do not necessarily accompany freedom to use sexual language or to observe sexual activity on the screen.

Since the Christian community is a part of the world in which we live, its sexual practices for singles have changed as radically as those in society. Our research among single adult groups has confirmed what others have reported: sexual intercourse is an activity that many single Christians choose. This is occurring significantly more frequently than was true in times past. The response or justification varies greatly from one person to the other.

One twenty-six-year-old woman told us that as a Christian she had always felt she shouldn't be sexually active before marriage. But, since she was not sure she was ever going to marry and since she was going to be responsible in her activity, she decided to make the choice to be involved totally—and was not going to feel guilty about it.

On the other hand, a thirty-four-year-old divorced woman reported being very distraught because of her sexual impulses and desires. These urges had been so regularly and satisfyingly fulfilled in her marriage that she continued to fulfill them after her divorce. She told of the guilt that she carried for not following what she accepted to be the biblical standard of sexual intercourse limited to marriage.

Both of these women claim to be committed Christians, both are involved sexually, but their response to that involvement is completely different. These two are typical examples of singles who are sexually involved.

There are also single people who choose not to be sexually involved before marriage. When this is a conscious choice with an alternative plan to keep sexual feelings alive and other intimacy needs fulfilled, contentment is possible. Both the sexually active and the sexually inactive single will experience times of frustration.

The Frustration of the Single

The lack of physical, sexual fulfillment without the marriage commitment is an ongoing frustration for the single person of whatever age. There is that natural urge in us to connect in a vital way with another person. When that is limited or totally absent there will be frustration. Finding ways to minimize this frustration is an ongoing struggle for many single people. Some will struggle with their sexual frustration on a daily or perhaps hourly basis, while others only wrestle with it on occasion.

If you feel continually frustrated physically, we encourage you to look at your life and see what you are doing that promotes this frustration. Do you spend time watching or reading sexually explicit material? That will certainly feed your frustration. Are you physically involved with a partner, getting highly aroused without orgasm or intercourse? This will create physical frustration. Is your life empty, so that you have time to become obsessed with your sexual drives? Is self-stimulation an option? Obviously, there is a limit to the degree of fulfillment possible with one's self. Yes, an orgasm may be possible, but it may still leave you hungry for the intimacy of a relationship.

The lack of emotional intimacy is another of the frustrations of the single person. Every person needs the experience of close, vital, and meaningful relationships, whether that is with parents, brothers, sisters, friends, persons of the same sex, or persons of the opposite sex. In adulthood, most of us need the bond of intimacy with one person of the opposite sex. This emotional attachment, although possible outside of marriage, is often missing for the single adult. Intimacy, closeness, and affection that meet those deeper intangible needs can happen with people who are "just friends," or relatives. It can even happen within groups. Yet as we talk with single people, especially those who have been single for a number of years, we hear them speak of the hunger they feel for that vital connection with a significant other.

Not only are there frustrations of sexual fulfillment and lack of emotional intimacy, but there is also the frustration of not having a place in society. Most of society, with the exception of those cosmopolitan collections of single people in our major cities, is designed for married people and for families. The church is no exception. If you look at the roster of church leaders in any major church, whether it be of a fundamentalist, evangelical, or more liberal persuasion, the great majority of the men or women on that roster will be married people. Single people are rarely leaders in the Christian community. Yet they make up a significant portion of society. Most social structures within the church community are not designed for the single person. Many single adults feel unaccepted by their community. We have experienced the difficulty in including our single friends and relatives in our lives. Most of our social events are designed for couples. So the single person often feels out of place.

Being sexually active does not eliminate that sense of aloneness in the social structure. In addition, you may live with the ongoing agony of guilt. The biblical expectation and guideline is rather clear: sexual intercourse is reserved for marriage. If you are someone who claims to be a believer and desire to live by the standards of the Scriptures, then it is inevitible that you struggle as you actively choose to go against what you believe.

You may have come to the place where you reconcile yourself to the fact that you are going to have sexual intercourse. Yet, that underlying feeling of guilt may be a bur under your emotional saddle keeping your emotions continually troubled. This does not mean you are not enjoying the sexual activity, it only means that you have not been able to find inner peace. You are not living by the standard to which you claim to be committed. There is tension or ambivalence within you. All of this frustration calls loudly for a *decision*.

Make a Decision: The Options

The choices available to the single adult are many. First, let's consider the choices. Then we will look at how you go about making your decision.

Choice #1: Deny your sexual feelings. This may be one of the easiest choices even though the long-term consequences are quite severe. All of us were created as sexual beings. Our Creator has ignited a sexual fire within us. To deny its power is to close down on a vital dimension of our person. Long-term, we risk the consequence of being unable to rekindle those feelings when it is time to do so in marriage.

It is not uncommon for the young person who has either been raised in an emotionally/sexually unexpressive home to be unaware of sexual feelings. The single person who is intensely sexual may shut off those feelings because their power is frightening. Such a person may behave and feel as if he or she had no sexual feelings. This choice is understandable, but its detrimental consequences far outweigh its benefits.

We have worked with these consequences. There are young married couples who have no desire for one another. They just don't have the feelings! Sometimes one or both report that they chose the route of denying their sexual feelings. They felt this was what God wanted them to do before they were married. They hadn't separated their actions from their feelings. To be able to remain virgins, they had chosen to be asexual—only to discover, as they moved into marriage, that they continued to be asexual. The pain and the sense of being shortchanged are very powerful for these people. They had operated on the belief that if they did not let themselves be sexual before marriage, God would bless them with a free and abundant sexual life after marriage.

Sexuality does not work this way. It is an innate appetite, just like hunger. We can control how much we eat, just like we can control our sexual behavior. But when we shut down our appetite for food we become anorexic; likewise, if we turn off our sexual feelings we become sexually apathetic. Sexual tightness continues beyond the point when they say "I do."

There is another consequence of the denial of sexual feelings. That happened to the young woman who had always been pushed sexually by men. Finally she met her spouse. "He was such a gentleman. He really respected me." It was such a relief not to be pushed. The dilemma occurred after marriage. He continued to respect her. Now, her husband's lack of sexual desire created great frustration rather than relief.

Be on the lookout for the denial of sexual feelings. Any couple moving toward marriage who has decided not to engage in sexual intercourse before marriage should experience that decision as a struggle. To maintain the boundaries you have chosen should be difficult. If it is not, you should take a long hard look at yourselves and the relationship. In a close, loving relationship, abstinence should be a battle. Our bodies, our hearts, our emotions, our spirits, every ounce of our beings urge us toward sexual union. If you are not aware of this urge, you may have denied your sexual feelings for so long that it will be difficult for you to revive them. This will cause stress in your marriage—sometimes marriage-breaking stress.

Choice #2: Innocent involvement. Innocent involvement may grow out of ineffective attempts at the denial of sexual feelings. If you are unable to accept your sexuality and yet continually find yourself going beyond your sexual limits, you set yourself up for involvement beyond your readiness. The sequence usually goes something like this: you meet a nice person and begin some casual and then more serious contact with him/her. You innocently send off many warm and inviting messages with no intention of acting upon them. You let yourself get into situations—whether in a car, your parents' home, your apartment or even a motel—all the time convincing yourself that this is just a friendly contact which has no sexual purpose or intent.

Some couples even go so far as to sleep together without consciously intending to be involved sexually. As time together progresses, there is more and more physical involvement. You find yourself carried along, either by the urges in your body or your partner's body, and you end up making love. When it is all over, the rush of guilt and remorse is overwhelming. You commit to yourself and together that you will never do this again. You ask each other's forgiveness and you ask God's forgiveness. Two weeks later you find yourself in identical circumstances.

The consequences of this pattern are very severe. First of all, since you can't get yourself to plan for it, no birth control measures are taken, so you risk the chance of pregnancy.

Second, since you are not "intending" to do this, you don't provide yourself with the privacy that you need to really relax and enjoy it. You learn to have sexual experiences under tense circumstances, developing poor habits.

Third, since involvement isn't your intention, you develop a pattern of always connecting sexual activity with high risk. Later on in married life, you may still need risk as a part of your sexual experience to help you get the desired response of excitement.

Fourth, you violate your own standards, and thus yourself. You experience guilt and the chronic internal ache that guilt brings. This sets you up for the future in which you may continue to need guilt as a part of your sexual arousal. As we do sexual therapy with couples, we hear stories about risk and guilt patterns that were established early in a relationship. These are difficult to break.

Fifth, you may experience guilt in relation to God. If you are a Christian with a commitment to reserve sexual intercourse for marriage, then each time you violate that standard you will not only feel guilt in relation to yourself but also guilt in relation to God. God and your sexuality become mutually exclusive. Innocent involvement is one of the most irresponsible and destructive patterns with negative consequences later in marriage. We are not suggesting that you should "sin boldly," but we can say that from the perspective of marital and sexual adjustment, the next choice is clearly preferable to innocent involvement.

Choice #3: Chosen involvement. The couple actively chooses to complete their relationship with sexual intercourse. They work to make peace with their standards and beliefs. They prepare for their sexual times together. They behave as if they were married. If you are struggling with this particular choice, we would encourage you to read Dr. Lewis B. Smedes' book, *Sex for Christians* (Wm. B. Eerdmans Publishing Co., Grand Rapids: 1976). He discusses sex outside of marriage from an ethical perspective.

The Bible is very clear that sex is for marriage. Those who choose to have sexual intercourse before marriage, yet accept the Bible as their standard for Christian living, live with dissonance between their beliefs and their behavior. Couples often by-pass many other stages of intimacy as they jump into a total sexual relationship. Something is missing without the trust-building commitment of marriage. There is no data to suggest that good sex before marriage is an indication of how sex will be after marriage. In fact, we have counseled a number of couples who claim to have had a very fulfilling sexual life before marriage, only to find it falling apart after marriage. Obedience, commitment, intimacy, and trust are all essential ingredients to a long-term happy sexual life.

Choice #4: Chosen abstinence. This is a healthy choice that fits the biblical directives on sexuality. It is least likely to lead to irresponsibility and guilt, but it is not easy! Choosing to be a sexual person—aware of your feelings, knowing your impulses, responsive to kissing, touching, and caressing—and then choosing not to take your sexual desires to their natural conclusion, is extremely difficult. It is as conflict-laden as having a beautiful meal before you and choosing only to nibble at it rather than to heartily partake. For high school or college-age young people who have chosen to limit their physical involvement to general hugging and kissing—it is a boundary that is difficult but possible because it is consistent with where they are emotionally and developmentally.

As we can attest by our own experience, and the experiences of many other couples, abstinence before marriage is possible and is not a barrier to a fulfilling sexual life in marriage (as is often propagated by those who don't hold the biblical standard). For the thirty-year-old couples who have been active sexually, either unmarried or in marriage, and are now choosing abstinence, the internal pressure can be almost impossible. Once the floodgates of our sexuality have been opened, incredible inner strength is required to dam them and hold them back. We want to be sympathetic and understanding. We have not been through that struggle. The abstinence we practiced at age nineteen or twenty is not the same. But we know couples who have been able to maintain postsexual involvement abstinence and have done so joyfully. Abstinence is not easy to live with day after day and sometimes year after year.

When abstinence is the chosen route, it is important to plan for that. Do not set yourselves up to test the limits. Focus on all dimensions of the relationship. Emphasize activities and settings that are not tempting. Learn to enjoy physical intimacy within clearly defined limits that both of you respect. Richard J. Foster, in his book, *Money, Sex and Power* (Harper & Row, Pub., San Francisco, 1985), deals very specifically with this whole subject. We recommend it!

Choice #5: Celibacy as a lifestyle. In 1 Corinthians 7:8–9 and 32–38 the apostle Paul talks about the calling of celibacy. There is an important distinction to make between chosen abstinence and celibacy as a lifestyle. Celibacy is for those who experience themselves being called of God to stay single in order to serve humankind. It is very different than abstaining from sexual intercourse until marriage is possible. The apostle is saying that if you have your sexual desires well under control (not that you do not have any), and feel the distinct calling of God to serve, and you have an outlet for that calling, then celibacy may be your choice. We have known few people who fit into this category. These are people choosing to subjugate their sexual drive energy, and channel it into outlets of service as a lifestyle. Very few manage this well, but it is clearly one of the options.

Those are the choices. There may be some variations but every single person will fit roughly into one of these categories. Some singles may find themselves in one of the situations defined, but not by choice. This is indeed a difficult and trying circumstance. Then you need to make a decision as to how you will make the most of who you are as a sexual person, given the reality of your situation.

Make a Decision: The Necessary Ingredients

Now that you know the options, how do you decide on the level of your sexual involvement as a Christian single person?

Know yourself. To be responsibly decisive about sexual activity requires self-awareness. Let's break that down into the various parts. First of all, you will need to know your own body. How you feel about your body will have been influenced by the kind of touch and affirmation you received growing up. It is vital that you understand how your body works, what your needs are, how frequently you feel sexual urges, what kind of touch you desire, and how all dimensions of your sexuality converge to express the sexual you.

It is terribly important also to know your *emotions*. You may have grown up in a home where you learned to keep your feelings very much to yourself. You don't find it comfortable to have others express their emotions, nor are you eager to share yours. Or you may have learned a style that is open and expressive. In fact, you need openness to feel trust.

A married couple came to us for sexual therapy. The man had grown up in a home in the Midwest with eight brothers and sisters, a very controlling, domineering mother, and a rather irresponsible father. He had learned that he wouldn't get hurt if he kept his feelings to himself. So that was the style he brought into marriage. His wife, on the other hand, had grown up in an expressive home. Feelings were the road to intimacy. She had great sexual passion while the man felt almost no need for sexual contact because he had learned to function independent from anyone else's response.

As you are making the choice about sexual behavior, you will need to understand your emotional needs in relation to that choice. How can you make your choice work for you, given who you are emotionally?

Know your value system. What do you believe? What is important to you? How do you feel about sharing your body with another person? You are responsible for your body. You are the only one who can decide when and to what degree you want to share it.

Whether you were raised in a home where you were taught that sex outside of marriage is sinful, whether that is a new belief for you, or whether you believe that rule doesn't apply to you today—it is essential that you come to peace with your beliefs. It may be helpful to test them with your Christian community and the Bible. The decision you make has to be congruent with what you believe. You can seek information, you can read books, you can hear sermons, you can listen to lectures and tapes, and you can receive letters from your mother, but ultimately the decision has to be based on your own convictions. Your mother won't be there when you feel those strong sexual urges as your body is next to the one who makes you pulsate.

You have to make the decision. You can't count on anyone else at that particular moment. God's spirit can be with you and give you strength, but you have to want that spirit there as you struggle with your powerful urge. Single Christians need to be clear about their values and date only people who have similar values. Otherwise, you will find yourself pulled to be different than who you are.

A split value system can be a real dilemma. It tends to cause havoc within the individuals (especially long-term), as one tries to live out two sets of beliefs that cannot fit together.

Know your limits. Whenever we speak to single adults, we are asked: "How far is it OK to go? Where do we draw the line?" There is a temptation to quickly jump in and give an answer, to set a standard so that the questioner has been satisfied. We refuse to set the standard, other than the biblical one of intercourse within marriage. Rather, we like to provide a list of levels of sexual involvement, knowledge about the body's sexual responses, help in defining values and emotional awareness, and then guidance in setting a standard for oneself.

The levels of sexual involvement are:

> Handholding and hugging
> Polite kissing
> Total mouth kissing
> Intense passionate hugging
> Full-body rubbing with clothes on
> Breast stimulation over clothes
> Genital stimulation over clothes
> Breast stimulation under clothes
> Genital stimulation under clothes
> Full-body pleasuring, no clothes
> Oral/Genital stimulation
> Sexual stimulation to orgasm
> Intercourse

Decide upon the level of involvement that is necessary for you to be able to live a sexual life consistent with your values. The limits needed will depend on who you are emotionally and physically. No one else can tell you where your limits are. Your limits must be based on what you know about yourself and how you have decided to behave.

Know your strengths and weaknesses. All of us gain strength from a variety of sources. If you are someone who needs eight or ten hours of sleep to make wise decisions, then you must be responsible for that. You may be someone who needs to exercise regularly. Know that drugs and alcohol reduce your capacity to say no. It may be that you find great strength in being together with other people who have commitments similar to yours—a Bible study group, a prayer group, a sharing and support group, a group with a mission, an athletic, artistic or political group. It is vital that you know where you get strength and what causes weakness. A source of strength for many individuals is a commitment to be accountable to one other person regarding one's sexual behavior. Again, you must know yourself as you seek to live consistently with what you believe.

Questions Singles Ask

Question: I find that I and many of my friends who are single live much of our lives in frustration. What can I do about this?

Frustration for the single person can come from many different sources. Perhaps your frustration grows out of living as if life will begin when you find a mate. Or your frustration may be that your only contacts are with people who have a different value system than yours, and want to set the limits at a different place than you. You may find yourself continually sexually aroused, but always sexually frustrated. In all these circumstances, it is important to recognize that you can do something about it. Begin to live life as if it is happening now, not something you are waiting for. You can actively choose to be involved with those who live by the same values as you do. You can choose not to set yourself up to be perpetually frustrated. You can also choose to bring yourself relief through self-stimulation.

Question: What about masturbation for the single, committed Christian?

Masturbation is at best providing physical relief to the sexual urges and needs in the body until we have opportunity to do that in a relationship with another person. If you have committed yourself to save sexual intercourse for marriage, then your only physical outlet prior to that will either be through wet dreams, orgasmic dreams, or masturbation. As we understand the body, once we have reached puberty, it is designed to have regular sexual release. While not every person will experience the need for that release, most do. Self-stimulation provides that release without violating what we understand to be the biblical standard. As long as it is not an obsession, we find that masturbation does not cause turmoil in the individual's life, but rather brings relief.

Question: Is it acceptable for a Christian to fantasize about sex?

From our perspective, whether you are a Christian or not, you have an imagination and that imagination is filled with a variety of images. That is how we were created different than the animal kingdom. Since you are a sexual being, some of those images will be sexual. There is no way around that. It is impossible for it not to happen, unless you are so repressed that you have shut down all sexual feelings. What we do with those images will determine whether that fantasy moves over into a preoccupation with a specific individual and an intent to act on that fantasy. The answer is yes, fantasies or imagination about sexual subjects are very normal and natural. They become lustful when we are obsessed or enslaved by them, or when we would act on them if we could.

Question: When should the boundaries in a relationship be set and who should set them?

Boundaries should be set at 10 o'clock in the morning over a cup of coffee rather than 11 o'clock at night in the heat of passion. And *you* should set them. Determine your limits, independently, before you discuss them with your boyfriend or girlfriend.

Question: Can a single person ever be fulfilled in the sense of intimacy?

It is important to recognize that there are many different expressions of intimacy. There can be interests and involvements that make us feel intimate with one another. We can be open in sharing our feelings which can bring close emotional intimacy. We can share extensively about our relationship with God, which will usually bring spiritual intimacy. We may focus on artistic expression—the enjoyment of a symphony or the appreciation of great art which encourages an aesthetic intimacy. We may be committed to tasks which bring us recreational or vocational intimacy. Yes, a single person can be fulfilled in many areas of intimacy. The reality is that if you are choosing not to be involved in sexual intercourse before marriage, it is unlikely your sexual intimacy needs will be met as a single person. But that can well be compensated for by many other forms of intimacy.

Question: If we hold very carefully to limiting our physical involvement before marriage, can we count on God's blessing after marriage?

God's commandments do not come as a bargain. In His Word, God does not say that if we follow certain guidelines then we will have a happy or fulfilled life. It is a fact that many couples who have not had sexual intercourse before marriage have ended very happy in their life together. On the other hand, many couples who did not even kiss before they were married have ended up very unhappy in their sexual life. We can also tell you about those who were totally involved sexually before marriage who ended up unhappy—and others who found great fulfillment. So the reason for following the guidelines is not so that married life will be happy and fulfilling, but rather we have to trust that it is God's command and it will ultimately be for our best.

Question: What do you think of two Christian singles of the opposite sex living together without being sexually involved if they are intending to be married?

Frankly, we think it is very destructive. To live together, "turned on to one another," and not be able to respond to those urges, forces you to shut down on your sexual feelings. When you marry, it may be almost impossible to get that sexual arousal and response turned back on. We have only known this to be a detrimental pattern and would not encourage it at all.

Question: What if I never marry? Will I be an unfulfilled person never having experienced sexual intercourse?

If you have never experienced sexual intercourse, you are not less of a person. There are many wonderful people who have gone through their whole lives unmarried, never having experienced a total sexual union. They are still great friends, servants, caregivers, and wonderful people of God.

For Further Study

Bird, Joseph and Lois. "Reasons You May Never Have Considered for Staying Single." *New Woman,* January/February, 1982, 102–103.

Clarkson, Margaret. "Singleness: His Share for Me." *Christianity Today.* February 16, 1979, 14–15.

Colgrove, Melba, Harold Bloomfield and Peter Williams. *How to Survive the Loss of a Love.* New York: Bantam Books, 1971.

Forbes, Cheryl. "Let's Not Shackle the Single Life." *Christianity Today,* February 16, 1979, 16–19.

Johnson, James R. "Toward a Biblical Approach to Masturbation," *Journal of Psychology and Theology.* Summer 1982, 10(2), 137–146.

Laury, G.V., M.D. "Myths about Masturbation throughout the Ages", *Journal of Sex Education and Therapy,* vol. II, no. 5, Summer 1979, 3–4.

Linton, Calvin D. "Dying to the God Who is Me." *Christianity Today,* February 16, 1979, 14–15.

Penner, Clifford L., Ph.D. "A Reaction to Johnson's Biblical Approach to Masturbation." *Journal of Psychology and Theology,* Summer 1982, 10(2), 146–149.

Smedes, Lewis B. *Sex for Christians.* Grand Rapids: William B. Eerdmans Publishing Co., 1976.

Smith, Harold Ivan. "Sex and Singleness the Second Time Around." *Christianity Today,* May 23, 1979, 16–22.

Swindoll, Luci. *Wide My World; Narrow My Bed.* Portland: Multnomah Press, 1982.

Handling Adult Sexuality in Special Situations

The Unconsummated Marriage

FOUR TRUE STORIES

Craig and Evelyn

Craig and Evelyn sat fidgeting as they began to unfold their story. They were a handsome couple in their late twenties. He was a college professor and she a nurse. Obviously both were college graduates, and he had two advanced degrees. Evelyn had been raised on a farm in the Midwest with six brothers and sisters while Craig was from a large city on the West Coast with just one sister. Both had grown up in loving and caring homes, but with little sexual information. As they tearfully told their story, we were gripped by the pain of three and a half years of marriage without consummation, without intercourse, without entry.

During their dating months, especially after engagement, they had difficulty controlling their sexual impulses. But being committed to wait for marriage, they held off until their wedding night and honeymoon. With high expectations they left the wedding celebration for two weeks vacation in the Carribean. The excitement of being able to fulfill their love with each other engulfed them. Then came the disappointment. The first evening Craig had a firm erection for a long time, but when he attempted entry, it seemed like he was pushing against a brick wall. They tried again and again for the two weeks of their honeymoon, becoming more and more discouraged yet convinced that they should be able to make it work.

Craig and Evelyn began married life together. The adjustment went smoothly. They worked well as a team, except sexually. The excitement and desire for each other's bodies waned as they would try to have intercourse, at first once or twice a week, then less and less frequently. By the time they saw us, they hadn't attempted anything sexual for several months. Originally, he was the initiator and they would both get aroused. Evelyn would experience nipple erection, vaginal lubrication, and even enjoy pleasurable stimulation, and yet somehow they could not manage to guide the penis into the vagina. After the years of trying he began to lose his erection as he would attempt to penetrate. So now there were dual problems: both an inability to penetrate and his inability to maintain an erection.

The natural question is: what would perpetuate a long-term dilemma like this when sex is supposed to be something so natural? Is it that difficult to get the penis into the vagina? Several circumstances converged to conspire against them.

Evelyn had been raised in a strict Christian home. Her parents strongly disapproved of an older man she was dating. As she became more and more involved with him, she innocently or half-consciously let the physical involvement progress to the point where one time, in the car, he had penetrated her vaginally. She had screamed, jerked away, and shut out the experience from her memory. She behaved as if it had never happened, broke up with the man, and never told Craig. Now, whenever she engaged in sexual activity similar to that traumatic experience, her vagina would automatically tighten. The vaginal muscle became so tense that Craig could not enter.

Craig had been raised in a very meticulous home where they were clearly taught to avoid all messiness. His mother had communicated the message that anything that had to do with the genital area was dirty or "yucky." It was very difficult for him to enjoy Evelyn's genitals because they were aversive to him. This was especially true as she would lubricate. Since he experienced her lubrication negatively, he stopped any genital touching once she began to respond. This interrupted any preparation which would have been necessary to relax her for entry. He was very responsive, however, and so initially had firm erections. As his efforts at entry failed, he began to experience impotence. By the time they sought help, this impotence occurred in virtually every attempt.

By now Evelyn was very down on herself, feeling miserable that she was not "normal." Craig was feeling less and less like a man. Men are supposed to know how to do this and he was not succeeding. Depression, hurt, and bitterness were permeating their relationship which was so great in every other area. They had communicated effectively and really enjoyed each other. The sexual area began to overshadow everything else, threatening their relationship.

Suzanne and Tom

Suzanne and Tom were also in their late twenties. Suzanne worked as a secretary for a local church. Tom worked as a grocery store checker. When they came to see us they had been married six months. Before they were married they had thoroughly enjoyed rubbing their bodies against each other (fully clothed), and found themselves getting highly aroused. On the honeymoon, at each attempt at entry, Tom would lose his erection and "couldn't do it." In subsequent attempts as he would get an erection, he would attempt entry. At the point of contact he would lose his erection. General love-play and kissing did not bring him much arousal. Only oral stimulation got him firm enough to attempt entry.

Suzanne had been raised in a very prim and proper home in which sexual subjects were never discussed. The implied message was: sex is dirty; it is a pleasure that shouldn't be enjoyed; it will be painful—and sure enough it was! The longer they went on trying, the more frustrated and discouraged they became. Their experiences became briefer with less and less preparation. At first they tried once or twice a week, but as failure followed failure, the number of attempts diminished. Now even when they enjoyed love play together, they did not attempt intercourse.

Suzanne came to the marriage with relatively little experience and with conflict about sexual pleasure experienced during dating. On the wedding night she was absolutely exhausted from all the family stress centered around disagreements with her mother about the wedding.

Tom had developed the habit of masturbating during adolescence, but with a great deal of guilt. His particular approach had been to stimulate himself to ejaculation, often without a full erection. After ten years of practice, this pattern of sexual release without an erection was deeply ingrained. Yet, Tom came to the wedding night without any anxiety about their performance. He knew how aroused she became when he would stimulate her breasts and when they would rub their bodies together. He had no fear or concern about how they would do together.

Fred and Carol

Fred and Carol were in their middle thirties. Fred was pastor of a growing suburban church. Carol, a social worker, counseled at a community mental health center. They came for help regarding their unconsummated marriage. They had been married four months without sexual "success."

Carol had been married before and had been sexually active between her divorce and her marriage to Fred. After her divorce she had been traumatically raped, but felt that this should not be impacting their sexual experience since she had had sexual intercourse with other men after the rape.

Fred came from the opposite end of the experience spectrum. He had been raised in a rural community, had always been a bright student, and was dominated by his mother who had pushed him into pursuing education. She discouraged emotional expression and depreciated involvement with girls. Thus, Fred was shy. He did not go through the kiss-and-run stage of junior high. He had almost no dating experience and virtually no sexual awareness. At age fourteen, he had been part of a group of boys at a church camp who sat around, talked about sex, and stimulated themselves. He still harbored the guilt from this sexual experimentation.

On the wedding night he had been both excited and apprehensive. He was eager to be with Carol but anxious because she had so much more sexual experience than he. He was naturally concerned that he wouldn't measure up. He was not able to keep an erection that night, and thereafter was impotent at the point of entry. Because of Carol's negative experiences with men, she brought a heavy load of anger into the marriage. After a few moments of stimulation, she would soon become bored and impatient.

Being an analytic type of person, Fred became a spectator. He began withdrawing from the pleasure of their experiences to watch what was happening. He became preoccupied with her needs. This only made him more and more anxious. By the time they came to us, his sexual desire was nonexistent and her frustration was at the breaking point. For her, his impotence was one more indication of men's incompetence. They both continued to function well in their chosen professions. Fred was very successful as a pastor, and was well respected, even admired by his parishioners. Carol carried a full counseling load.

Joe and Elizabeth

By the time Joe and Elizabeth sought us out for sexual therapy, they had consummated their marriage. But their story illustrates a pattern associated with pain for the woman and the unconsummated marriage.

Both Joe and Elizabeth had been active sexually after high school, but not to the point of intercourse. As their Christian commitment deepened, they made a decision that they would severely limit the degree of their sexual involvement before marriage. Both were eager on the wedding night because they anticipated that their sexual life would be wonderful. They had felt so much arousal during whatever physical play they had before marriage that they were totally shocked on their wedding night when they were unable to complete the sexual act. The reason for not being able to enter was Elizabeth's experience of pain. Penetration was possible, but it was so severely painful that she drew back from it immediately. As is always true with pain, her desire diminished very quickly. A year after their marriage, the stated problem was her lack of desire.

Sexuality was not discussed in Elizabeth's home. It was the "unmentionable" subject that brought a mixture of titters and frowns. Joe was a meticulous if not obsessive person. His career as an architect fit him nicely. He was very successful at his work. Since he was highly goal-oriented, it was difficult for him to back off from striving for intercourse, and this only elevated Elizabeth's resistance, pain, and eventual depression. By the time they saw us it had been eight months since they'd had intercourse.

What's the Problem?

When a couple is unable to consummate their marriage, one of four possible problems is present. There may be an awkwardness with much bumbling, impotence, pain, or vaginismus. Let's talk about each of these. If your lovemaking is a *bumbling experience* in which each of you feels like you don't know what you are doing, it would not be surprising if you grew up in homes where there was a clear lack of physical affection and attention. It may be that you were not stroked, held on your parent's lap, patted, or wrestled with. As a result you do not feel comfortable in physical contact with another person. Even if you enjoy it, it may be awkward because you don't know how to do it. It is likely that you avoided the usual kiss or poke-and-run behavior of the typical early adolescent, and then didn't do much dating in high school. In our society, those activities have the positive effect of getting us through our awkwardness and on to confidently relating to a person of the opposite sex.

There is a famous experiment in psychology, often referred to as "Harlowe's Monkey Experiment." The researchers isolated baby monkeys from their mothers, fed them from bottles, and kept them away from anything soft. When it came time for them to mate, they didn't know what to do. While we are certainly more complicated than monkeys, the same is true for us. The couple who cannot get things to fit and work together, usually needs education and practice making up for the lack of affection of childhood and the experimentation of junior and senior high school years.

Impotence is the inability to achieve or maintain an erection. We have written about this extensively in *The Gift of Sex.* Self-help is available in that book; however, usually sexual therapy is required to reverse an established pattern of impotence. When impotence is the reason for an unconsummated marriage, the impotence is due to anxiety about performance (like Fred), or is a response to the inability to penetrate the woman (as was true for Craig). In a case like Craig's it is considered secondary to the primary problem of vaginismus.

Pain is the underrated sexual troublemaker. There is no way that a woman will enjoy the sexual experience if it produces pain. If it hurts every time the fingers are in contact with the vaginal opening or every time there is an attempt at entry, the woman is going to have an automatic tightening response. This will make entry more difficult and radically interrupt the sexual responsiveness of the woman.

Both husbands and wives, as well as physicians, often play down the significant impact of pain on the sexual experience. First of all, there is the idea that the initial entry is supposed to hurt anyway; then there is the myth that women make a bigger deal out of pain than is actually true; and finally, there is the expectation that time and experience is the only cure for pain during intercourse.

There is usually a little pain at first entry. This will generally diminish after the first few times. This initial pain will be lessened by regular stretching of the vaginal opening before the first intercourse. Taking plenty of time to pleasure each others' bodies and using a lubricant will also minimize the discomfort of the first intercourse. Women can and do learn to tolerate intense pain as evidenced by their stamina in bearing children. There is no evidence to support the idea that women exaggerate pain. Time and repeated painful experiences do not cure the problem. In fact, as pain goes on, there is less and less likelihood that it will be resolved. Pain tends to perpetuate itself. The more pain—the more tightness; the more tightness—the more pain. Pain during intercourse requires systematic intervention. The physical cause must be ascertained while the ability to relax and receive pleasure is being taught.

Vaginismus is the involuntary muscular tightening of the vagina. It can tighten to such a degree that it is impossible to insert even a small finger, let alone the penis. This constriction of the muscles in the vaginal outlet (the lower or outer third of the vagina) is a conditioned response to past trauma (like Evelyn) or to ongoing pain or anxiety. Sexual arousal occurs causing blood and fluid to rush into the lower third of the vagina to form the orgasmic platform. Instead of being a pliable thickening, it becomes tense and rigid. The woman may continue to experience full sexual desire but without the possibility of entry.

A very clear symbol is suggested by vaginismus. The woman is unconsciously shutting out the man. She is protecting herself from painful past feelings. Sometimes the past cause is one specific traumatic event from the dating process (Evelyn) or from molestation or rape (Carol). Vaginismus is not what we would think of as a disease but rather is a response of tension that exhibits itself in the front or outer third of the vagina—the area of the pubococcygeus(PC) muscle. It is a very treatable response. We would encourage any woman who struggles with vaginismus to seek help now. You can learn to have control of that muscle and have enjoyable sexual intercourse.

Do What Comes Naturally!

No young couple goes into marriage with the expectation that they are going to have sexual problems. It always comes as a shock when sex doesn't work as it is supposed to. There may have been little instruction, and a few off-the-cuff remarks. A very common one is, "Oh, don't worry about anything, just go do what comes naturally!" If all of us had been raised out in the forest, running around naked as jaybirds and lived in completely natural settings, it might work for us to follow this instruction of doing what comes naturally. Healthy sexual intercourse is not modeled for us. We learn how to walk and talk naturally because we model what we see. And in those instances where there is a struggle with consummating the marriage, unnatural events in the past have created obstructions. The individuals cannot freely express themselves sexually. It is not natural.

Most couples also believe they should allow their problem to be resolved naturally, so they are hesitant to go for help. Hence the Evelyns and Craigs waste three years trying to let it happen naturally. Part of the investment in resolving the dilemma on their own is the embarassment of admitting their unconsummated marriage. We would encourage any physicians who read this to be alert to the new bride. Ask specific questions as you do routine gynecological exams. In *every* instance that we have dealt with, the woman had tried to talk with her physician about it. Both because of the woman's hesitancy and because of the physician's hurried schedule and perhaps insensitivity, the problem was never fully exposed or dealt with in the physician's office.

What to Do . . . Ten Steps to Consummation

1. *See your physician.* You need it confirmed by your physician that structurally everything in and around woman's vagina is OK. Have as much of a pelvic exam as is possible, given the tightness of the vaginal opening. Some women with vaginismus have no problem with the woman's examination in the physician's office, but tighten up once there is arousal and attempt at entry with the penis. The physician,

while examining the woman, should have her tighten the vaginal muscle over her/his gloved finger and have her hold that for several seconds and then release the muscle. That tensing and releasing will often have the effect of freeing the vagina to greater openness. In most instances, it will be discovered that there is nothing physiologically wrong.

2. *P.C. Muscle Exercises.* Four times each day, do twenty Kegel exercises. These are exercises which tighten and relax the vaginal muscles. For vaginismus, the relaxation is the most important. To learn to do the exercise, begin by sitting on the toilet and stopping and starting urination. To tighten, begin at the outer edge of the vagina. Squeeze the vagina tightly, hold to the count of three, and then relax—totally let go.

Then imagine your vagina is an elevator. Start at the outer edge of the vagina and move in (or up). Tighten, as if going up the elevator, stopping to hold at each floor until you are on the fifth floor. Come down by letting out the tension at each floor. When you're at the bottom, the vagina should be completely relaxed. This will take time to learn. Your vagina has been tight for a long time. Relaxation won't happen immediately.

3. *Use dilators.* The physician or sex therapist should give clear instruction in the use of graduated sizes of penis-shaped dilators. There are some manufactured specifically for this purpose. If those are unavailable or too costly, sterilized syringe covers of varying thicknesses from the physician can function just as adequately. Before the smallest dilator is inserted, the woman should again tighten her vagina and hold it for three to five seconds, and then relax. Tightening first will allow greater relaxation of the muscles. A lubricant such as KY jelly, Allercreme, or Albolene should be applied to the dilator. Guided by the woman, the man gently inserts the smallest dilator into the vagina, being very careful not to cause any pain or distress. The woman will feel most comfortable if she can watch the process in a mirror. The dilator should be kept in the vagina for at least fifteen minutes—preferably an hour.

4. *Pleasure.* While the dilator is in the vagina, the woman is comfortably relaxed while the man pleasures her total body as set forth in *The Gift of Sex* or other books that describe sensate focus. Do not focus on arousal but rather pleasure, the skin-to-skin contact. Arousal may occur for the woman but that is incidental. The goal is to help

her relax and enjoy pleasure while the dilator is in the vagina. This can be followed by the woman caressing and pleasuring her husband.

5. *Communicate.* It is vital that the couple keep talking to each other. During the pleasuring times it would be best to focus on the enjoyment of the touch and the bodily sensations. Away from the pleasuring time, talk about fears, anxieties, concerns, and past experiences that seem to be connected with this involuntary vaginal closure. If communication is difficult for the two of you, get professional help.

6. *Increase dilator size.* The dilators should be used for three or four fifteen-minute segments per day. When the husband is not around, the woman can insert them herself. It is always important to tighten the vaginal muscle and hold it for a few seconds and then relax before penetrating with the dilator. The size of the dilators can increase quite quickly as the woman learns to relax her vaginal muscles. If it is possible to sleep with the dilator in place, that is even more helpful.

The goal is to move to the largest size possible, as quickly as possible without causing pain. The ideal is for the couple to have a daily pleasuring time with the dilator inserted. When the woman inserts it on her own throughout the day, it would be best if she could just lie down and relax, listen to enjoyable music, read, or doze.

7. *Insert fingers.* After the woman is able to receive pleasure with a dilator in place, using the same procedure, the man can insert a finger or two into the vagina (after the woman has tensed and relaxed). Keep the fingers in the vagina for a few minutes without movement or thrusting. Once the woman has relaxed with a finger or two, attempt slight movement. Allow the woman to guide. She needs to feel in control. At no point in the process should pain be allowed. If pain occurs, back off immediately. If pain persists, with every attempt, wait until the woman has been able to tolerate larger dilators for longer periods of time.

8. *Paintbrush.* To paintbrush is to introduce the vagina to the penis without any demand for entry, so that the vagina can remain relaxed and receptive even when the penis comes near. Both husband and wife can use the penis as a paintbrush to pleasure the woman's genitals. The penis can be flaccid or erect. It really doesn't matter. The penis is stroked over the clitoris, between the labia (lips), and across the opening of the vagina. There has to be a clear contract that entry will not be attempted. This is a trust-building step for moving toward intercourse.

9. *Intercourse with woman in charge.* When the woman has graduated to a dilator the size of the erect penis, the couple is ready to attempt entry. Begin with a time of mutual pleasuring. Have some focus on the woman's pleasure, as well as the man's, until there is a full erection. Keep in mind that if the woman has been able to insert a stiff, plastic object that is the size of the penis, the penis will be much more comfortable since it is soft and pliable.

First, apply lubricant between the labia (lips) and on the penis. With the man lying on his back and the woman kneeling above him the woman very gently guides the penis into the vagina in the same way that she has guided the dilators. Be sure to spread the lips so that they will not be pulled into the vaginal opening as insertion takes place. Move at a slow and comfortable pace. You may want to insert only the tip of the penis this first time. With each attempt, the penis should be inserted a little further.

Once full entry has taken place, it would be best to experience a time of lying quietly together with the erect penis in the vagina—quiet vagina. This will help the man get used to being inside the vagina, and help the woman to relax the vaginal muscle. She may even want to tighten and hold the muscles for a few moments and then relax. When the woman is comfortable with the penis in the vagina and gentle thrusting, then more vigorous activity can be attempted. The woman needs to be in control so that pain is avoided and comfort and pleasure are found.

10. *Free intercourse experiences.* Once consummation has occurred, the process of pleasuring, tensing and relaxing the vaginal muscles, entry with the woman on top, quiet vagina, gentle thrusting, and then more vigorous experiences should be repeated. Do this until the two of you feel the barriers have clearly been overcome. Then you will be free to proceed to intercourse in any way the two of you desire.

There Is Hope!

It is always a high risk to suggest one hundred percent success. But with unconsummated marriages, we have never had a couple come to us (who were both willing to work with the problem) who were not able to achieve intercourse happily and successfully. When you work with an unconsummated marriage, success is easy to define. There either is entry of the penis into the vagina or there is not. Our message to you is that you can be successful. It may seem discouraging right now, but it is possible to get past the barriers. Our bodies were designed for sexual union. It is virtually always possible to consummate a marriage. Yours is no exception!

For Further Study

Kaplan, Helen Singer, M.D., Ph.D. *The New Sex Therapy.* New York: Brunner/Mazel, 1974. Chapter 20: "Vaginismus."
Masters, William H., and Virginia E. Johnson. *Human Sexual Inadequacy.* Boston: Little, Brown, and Company, 1970.

Sex and the In-Laws

What does sex have to do with the in-laws? An awful lot! As we have worked in sexual therapy for the past decade, we've been impressed with how frequently the parents' influence impacts what is happening sexually in a couple's life. Their influence may be affecting the son or daughter by their actual physical presence in the community or their presence in the home of the married couple.

To our knowledge, no one has previously addressed the issue of the in-laws' effect on the sexual relationship of a married couple. We believe it is an issue that needs attention.

First, we will explore the impact the in-laws have on a newly married couple. Then we'll look at how sexual adjustment throughout married life continues to be affected by parental influence. The effect of visiting the parents' home and long visits from parents will be addressed. Finally, we'll discuss the impact of a parent living in the home with the couple, especially when that parent has a long-term illness.

Newlyweds and the In-Laws

Marsha was in a real dilemma. Her husband wanted to leave for the honeymoon immediately after the wedding. Marsha's mother was insistent that they stay around for a few days since so many relatives had traveled such a great distance to come to the wedding. It wouldn't "be fair to them" not to give them a chance to visit with the newly married couple. Mother had planned several special events honoring the couple. As Greg and Marsha tried to resolve this dilemma, Mother's wishes continually dominated the discussion. It finally became clear that there was another motive influencing the decision. Mother wanted to protect her daughter, to keep her nearby, to be sure she was all right and was not being "used" by her new husband.

Newlyweds need a private opportunity to become adjusted to living with each other both relationally and sexually. Mother and father's influence that was predominant during childhood is over. Now the children need to be left on their own. If they are old enough and responsible enough to marry, they are old enough and responsible enough to find their way sexually. This will be true throughout the rest of their lives.

It is difficult for some parents to let go of their children, allowing them be responsible for themselves—making their own mistakes. Yet if they are going to bond and grow as a couple, they need the freedom to do that. So regardless of how tempting it is to become involved in their lives, parents need to move into the background. Let your adult children know you care and are available to them as they need you, and then stay out of their lives except to enjoy them. You are no longer responsible!

The one exception would be abuse, or any other harmful behavior. If you get the sense that your child or in-law is being abused, and is immobilized, you may need to take action. Offer your assistance to find protection or professional counsel.

Parental Influence Causes Sexual Turmoil

When a couple comes for sexual therapy and reports the main problem to be their parents, it is usually a case of a very close but not healthy attachment between parent and child that has continued beyond the marriage ceremony. This influence takes the form of collusion between parent and married child. When they carry on as special allies, the other spouse inevitably feels left out and depreciated. The stereotype is that this connection occurs between mother and daughter; we have also seen it between mother and son.

This is not a sexual problem. Rather, it is a dependency problem. It is necessary to help the individual recognize the importance of his/

her marriage separate from his/her parents. When the Bible talks about leaving mother and father and cleaving to one's wife, that is exactly what it means. In the last two decades there has been some teaching in the Christian community that fosters lifelong obedience to parents. This is both unscriptural and destructive.

Visiting Parents' Home

Many of us did not grow up with the possibility of sexual openness in the home. Therefore, we have difficulty allowing ourselves to be sexual when our parents are around. It is particularly difficult to let ourselves be sexual in our parents' home. The spouse must recognize that a genuine inhibition occurs because of restrictions that are unspoken but clearly felt. This isn't a fantasy but may be directly communicated by the parents. It can show up with behaviors like coming to talk with you in your room at bedtime, walking into your room without knocking, or parents continuing to behave as they might have when you were a child. There may be no recognition that you are now a married person and need to have your privacy respected. If the visit is a longer one, this will become somewhat frustrating for the couple. You may decide to go to a motel for a day so that you can bring joy to one another with freedom.

It can be terribly disruptive when parents are excessively interested in the newlyweds' sexual activity. The young couple can't be natural or spontaneous. In one situation, a husband of one month walked into the bathroom next door to the bedroom where he and his wife were sleeping to discover his mother-in-law bent over at the register there in the dark. She was attempting to hear what was going on in the newlyweds' bedroom!

There may be inhibitions that have nothing to do with the parents' attitudes or behaviors. Here again so much depends on the kind of openness that was present in the family growing up. The new bride may find that she is inhibited around her in-laws and her own parents because she is not used to being overtly sexual. Or that may be true for the husband.

It is most important that the two of you discuss the subject openly. Establish some guidelines of how you want to function. Be as clear as possible about those guidelines to your parents. Recognize that it is best if the two of you make *your* relationship a priority.

If it is possible to make sex an enjoyable game, you can add some extra excitement and titillation to your love-making experience by play-fully accenting the fact that you are doing something a little bit naughty under the nose of your parents. This can add a special spark. Some of the most intense times that a couple can experience are those when they feel very aroused and rambunctious and yet have to make love in complete silence. It can build an incredibly positive tension in us and bring extra fulfillment.

They're Coming for the Whole Winter

A couple has just established themselves in a marriage and are trying to work out their communication differences as well as their sexual life. Mom and Dad call to announce they're free for a couple of months, so would like to spend some time with them. Adapting to the reality that there are now two other people around who have to be taken into consideration may cause some serious stress. This is especially so when the two people happen to be parents who have a powerful impact on how we behave and feel. To minimize the inter-ruption, make sure that you keep your relationship a priority. Work together to keep those old child feelings from getting in the way of your togetherness. If you find that one or both of you is inhibited or has lost your sexual appetite when your parents are around, talk about it, plan dates for yourselves, or sneak away at lunch. Do anything to keep your relationship alive and well even as you also enjoy the visit from the parents.

Grandma Is Moving In

While this is occurring less and less in our society, it is still a reality for many couples. The need for adult children to care for their parents usually occurs about the time children leave the nest, just when they are finally free to be alone. Father has died, and Mother is not able to care for herself either physically or financially. You have an extra room, so it makes good sense for her to move in with you. It is the loving, responsible thing to do. But it may also work havoc with your sexual intimacy. It may well change your living patterns. Bedtime may be interrupted. Time alone at home may be almost impossible to find. The biggest effect may be the emotional impact on either or both of you.

One husband told us what happened when his mother-in-law moved in. His wife and mother-in-law had never gotten along since his wife was twelve. But the mother's inability to care for herself and their available space led to this move. The mother and daughter were in such continual stress that the husband and wife had almost no sexual life. In another situation, a wife told us that ever since her mother-in-law moved in, her husband hadn't had any interest in her sexually. He was always doting on the mother. These marriage-wrecking circumstances need to be taken very seriously! They are best anticipated before the move takes place, and must be dealt with openly and honestly between the couple. Professional help may be necessary.

Long-term Care of a Parent

When a parent is ill and has to be cared for, there is the added stress and drain of caring for someone who is ill. This can drain off sexual energy just as much as a newborn child or remodeling the house. It is often difficult for the child of the sick and elderly parent to actually perceive the effect. They may need the objective words of a friend or counselor.

In conclusion, let us say a word on behalf of the parents of the married couple. Most parents have no intention to meddle or disrupt. The influence on the married couple is a continuation of some habits that have been established long ago. We do want to be loving and caring to our elders, but it is important to recognize that our primary commitment has to be to our own wife or husband and family, then to our parents.

We are reminded of the couple who lived in the family home taking care of mother. They were unable to establish a successful sexual life until mother left for another city. They were on the verge of divorce before she left, and yet suddenly found new life and fulfillment with each other once they were without the inhibiting influence of a third party.

It is extremely difficult thing to have three or four adults sharing a home. The impact on a couple's sexual life can be very powerful and its influence should not be taken lightly. Openness, honesty, and flexibility are the only way to survive as you work this out together.

16

Sex When Illness Hits the Family

How we feel about ourselves as sexual persons and our sexual relationships will be affected by illness. That is true whether one of us or one of our children is ill, or we are responsible for the care of an ailing parent.

Any stress that demands our emotional and physical energy will use up sexual-drive energy. Illness is no exception.

The Stress of Parenting the Child Who Is Ill

It is not unusual for parents of a terminally or chronically ill child to find their marriage crumbling. At the time when they most need each other, the demands of the situation get in the way of being able to relax and enjoy each other. The "spark" gets smothered with the emotional pain and fatigue of medical tests, waiting for results, hospitalization, surgeries, and wakeful nights. It's no wonder they no longer desire one another sexually! Yet, many never connect their loss of feeling for each other with the illness of their child.

Cindy told us her story, tears coursing down her cheeks. Their first two and a half years of marriage had been happily normal with sexual satisfaction for both of them. After their first daughter was born the frequency of their love-making had decreased, and David complained occasionally. After Melissa (their second daughter) arrived, they never reestablished their sexual life.

When Melissa was two months old, doctors discovered that she had a severe kidney problem. Cindy never felt like making love any more. She was always tired, overworked, preoccupied with Melissa's condition. When she wasn't running to a doctor's office, or waiting outside the operating room, she was trying to catch up with her normal duties as wife and mother.

David tried to understand but grew increasingly frustrated and distant. It seemed that they shared almost no close moments now except times to talk about Melissa or argue. Both David and Cindy experienced their difficulty as a loss of love for each other, rather than the result of a distracting stress.

The Stress of Caring for a Parent Who Is Ill

A similar distracting effect happens when we find ourselves responsible to care for an aging or sick parent. This is especially draining when the parent is in our home. Our society and lifestyle do not equip us for caring for members of our extended family. We find ourselves torn between the guilt of not giving enough to Mom or Dad, yet not wanting our own family and marriage to suffer.

The struggle really is between Genesis 2:24 where the command is given to leave father and mother and cleave to one's wife in sexual union, and the wisdom offered by Paul that honoring our parents will bring us long life upon the earth (Ephesians 6:1–3). Given Scripture's high view of the marriage relationship, we believe that it would not be God's intention for us to sacrifice our marriage to care for our parents. But within the context of building our immediate family, we must make certain that aging or sick parents are cared for and loved. We need to find a balance between the priority of the marriage and the responsibility to parents.

When One of the Spouses Is Ill

The external stress of caring for a sick child or parent drains physical and emotional energy from our sexual relationship. However, maintaining the sense of ourselves as total, complete men and women is most tested when one of us as spouses is afflicted with illness.

Maintaining sexual wholeness during illness is particularly difficult in our society where satisfying sexual intimacy is connected with the act of intercourse with an emphasis on erection for the man and orgasm for the woman.

When one of us is experiencing physical impairment, finding sexual fulfillment is possible if we are able to broaden our view of what encompasses satisfying sexual expression. Our sexuality involves body, soul, spirit, and emotions. We can't limit our sexual expression to intercourse or orgasm.

Our sexuality is present at birth. This is evident emotionally, relationally, and physically. Mothers and fathers of newborn babies will hold and relate differently to children of each sex. Our maleness or femaleness interacts with the maleness or femaleness of that child. Physically, a little boy has his first erection within minutes of birth and a little girl lubricates vaginally within twenty-four hours of birth.

These natural body responses continue throughout adult life, *unless* interrupted by an illness that inhibits the physical, sexual response of the body. Adult men have erections and adult women lubricate vaginally every eighty to ninety minutes while they sleep. So our sexuality is within us.

Because our sexuality *is* so basic, it is not something that can be taken away. Frequently, we hear, "I just don't think I'm a sexual person. As far as I'm concerned, sex could go away forever." Or as Cindy ended up feeling, "God gave sexual capacity to every woman except me."

Even if we feel no desire for sexual intimacy; experience no sexual arousal; believe we don't have the capacity for release; or live in a body that has been invaded by disease, impaired functioning, weakness, or pain: *nothing* can take away the fact that we *are* sexual persons. You are and always will be a man or woman with sexual need and potential. That fact, and all the emotions that go along with it, continues to provide us with the full credentials to maintain sexual intimacy to the end of life.

We may be stripped of all the external elements of genital sexuality that we see promoted through the media. But we can never be stripped of our maleness and femaleness. Thus our ability for some form of satisfying sexual expression is necessary to maintain an intimate, warm, loving relationship. That is a God-given capacity in every person. Even Cindy, through the process of sexual therapy, discovered that to be true for her. She found that all the sexual enjoyment she could have with David had been smothered by the stress caused by Melissa's illness.

Factors That Interfere with Sexual Fulfillment When There Is Illness

If our sexuality and the capacity for satisfying, intimate sexual experience is *a given* for all of us, what gets in the way of this expression when illness invades the family?

1. *Physical Demands of the Illness*

It is normal for the physical, energy demands of illness to consume all of one's drive for sexual intercourse. That is true whether you are the patient or the caretaker. Since we tend to limit our view of the sexual drive to going to bed with someone, we don't pursue alternative methods of sexual intimacy.

It is important to know that our sexual drive provides us with energy for all of life: (a) getting things done, achieving, being productive; (b) emotional intensity; (c) the desire for touch and bodily pleasure; and (d) the energy for sexual arousal and release.

Since sexual drive is primary to *all* of life's energy, the need for physical intimacy and affirmation remains even when the drive for intercourse has been used up by the demands of adapting to the stresses of illness. Learning to be close, to touch, care, and soak in the pleasure of each other's bodies without demand to feel sexual, get turned on, or have a climax, can be a great strength to the relationship during this stressful time.

2. *Emotional Stress*

Unfortunately just as physical stress can keep a couple apart, an emotional stress reaction to the presence of illness frequently forms a wedge between two people. This comes at the time they most need to be affirmed by each other. The negative emotions can take the form of guilt, blame, anger, helplessness, feeling left out, uncared for, or unloved. David experienced most of these feelings both because of Cindy's lack of sexual interest, and his own difficulty accepting Melissa's poor health.

When we suffer the loss of health in ourselves, spouse, or child, we will grieve that loss just as we grieve when someone dies. The grief work will not require as much of us as when we lose a loved one, because the loss isn't as total. Nevertheless, loss of health *is* a loss and we *will* experience the whole set of emotions that go along with facing that loss. When we recognize that these are normal and necessary feelings, we can freely share them with each other.

It is not unusual, however, for even the most psychologically aware to find that their grief, their emotional pain, is creating a distance between the two of them.

When Kristine, our youngest child, was two months old, we started to supplement her breast-feeding with baby cereals. She reacted with intense abdominal stress which caused her to awaken anywhere from five to ten times a night. As we continued to work with various doctors and try her on new food, this pattern of awakening plus frequent illness continued until she was two years old. During this two-year process, we became more and more fatigued.

But in addition, we went through intense emotional reactions. There was the sadness of having produced a child with a physical problem. We felt that God was allowing us more stress than we could handle, that our lifestyle commitment to our two other children and our professional calling just didn't allow room to deal with a sick child. We felt the typical guilt-blame syndrome: "If only we wouldn't have started foods so early; if we had been calmer; if only. . . ." and on and on the thoughts would flow.

The most distancing came between us in handling the waking up at night. That kept us apart sexually. The waking up at night was not a child's short-lived crying out that one could decide to ignore. It could involve up to forty-five minutes of intense screaming with a distended (bloated) abdomen. There was no doubt that Kristine was in pain and needed a caring person with her. Even though we knew one of us needed to be with her and there was no way we could feel angry with her, there was anger at having to get up; we took that anger out on each other.

This anger surfaced in both active and passive forms. When we were most exhausted, we would argue about who had been up the most times, or we might pretend we were asleep, hoping the other would get up. Many times each of us would feel angry at the other for not taking enough of the responsibility. With the distancing effect of that wearing down process, our sexual times became fewer and farther between. Thus, the one area where we *could* have found renewal with each other wasn't even working for us. At that point we sought outside help.

When the physical drain and emotional strain of illness begins to interfere with the *strengths* of our relationship, a third party is usually needed. No matter how great the marriage is and how satisfying the sexual life has been, no marriage can survive the endless stress that comes with a long illness. We need outside support and objectivity. A psychotherapist can guide us in working through the emotional problems the situation has stirred up. A counselor can assist us in expressing our hurts and needs in a way that enlists the other's care and love, rather than creating distance.

An outside facilitator of any type, professional or friend, can help us sort out some way to find relief from the demands of the situation, and get some time for each other. Time is needed to communicate effectively and to touch and love each other physically.

When the emotional reaction to illness begins to pull us apart, there may be a snow-balling effect. The anger keeps us apart sexually; then not being together sexually causes us to be short-tempered with each other so more anger is felt and expressed—thus creating more distance. You can see the dilemma. This negative pattern must be interrupted.

3. *Bodily Disfigurement*

Bodily disfigurement or impairment may keep us from wanting to be sexual. How we feel about our bodies, i.e., our body image, has a critical effect on our ability to open ourselves to each other and be vulnerable, physically and emotionally.

When we are dissatisfied with our bodies, our feelings about ourselves may be uncertain, or even negative. We may feel undeserving or unworthy of receiving or giving sexual pleasure. If that is the case, the person who has been marred will need much affirmation in order to risk sexual intimacy. That requires both genuine acceptance of the physical change and security in the relationship. When the spouse is able to give, concerns about the body image may be broken through.

Many times, the spouse may also have difficulty with the disfigurement. For example, when a woman has had a mastectomy (removal of a breast), her husband may have a difficult time accepting her as a sexual person, even as she does. Each person and each couple are unique in their reaction. For some men and women, breasts have little to do with their view of sexuality; for others, they are the key.

For a wife, it may be particularly trying if the man's disfigurement or impairment means he has to be passive while she must become the sexually active one.

Other consequences of disfigurement which make it difficult for the spouse to respond sexually include major alterations in physical appearance that are visually difficult to face, or body odors and changes in the texture of the skin that are negative to touch.

When either or both spouses react to a bodily change with lack of acceptance, those negative feelings will interrupt sexual satisfaction. Outside help may be necessary. Someone may be available who has experienced the same body change, such as a person from an ostomy group. A professional therapist or counselor may be enlisted. Or the two of you may do some self-help body image work together (see page 52 in *The Gift of Sex*). There is always a way to maintain some level of comfortable sexual intimacy. This requires willingness to work toward that goal.

4. *Physical Pain*

Physical pain will cause a person to pull inward. This is a self-protective response to help us cope with the pain. In pulling away and allowing his/her body to survive or heal, the person will avoid sexual contact and emotional intimacy. Each of us has different needs at that point. Some of us simply need space to be left alone. Others find the security of having someone close by can help relieve the intensity of the pain. Some find the distraction and relaxation of touch can actually help relieve the pain, as well as provide a way of maintaining sexual closeness and gratification.

5. *Lack of Sexual Function*

In addition to the physical and emotional demands an illness brings to the sexual life, there are sometimes specific changes in the body's ability to respond sexually. These can result from the disease itself or a negative side-effect of the treatments used for the disease.

For example, when a spouse has multiple sclerosis, there is actual scarring and damage to the nervous system. A person with MS may experience loss of sensation or lack of sexual response in the genitals. That doesn't mean the person is no longer sexual or the couple's sexual relationship has to stop. It does mean adjustments will need to be made.

What are the sexual dysfunctions a person might experience as the result of the disease or its treatment?

For a woman, it may be the inability to get aroused. She doesn't get turned on or sexually excited. There is little or no vaginal lubrication or nipple erection when she is sexually stimulated. The normal vasocongestion of blood and fluid rushing into the sexual parts when they are stimulated is not happening.

The other complication the woman may experience is the inability to have an orgasm. The reflex action that automatically gets triggered when sexual arousal intensifies to a certain point does not occur. It feels like getting ready for a sneeze and never letting go.

For the man, difficulty or inability to get or keep an erection can be a serious loss for the couple, since sexual intercourse may not be possible. This definitely requires openness to learning new ways to find sexual satisfaction together.

Retarded ejaculations, difficulty or inability to ejaculate, is the same as when a woman is unable to be orgasmic. Even though the man desires release and receives more than sufficient stimulation, the orgasmic reflex does not get triggered. This can be frustrating, but is usually not as devastating as impotence, unless the couple wishes to get pregnant.

It is important to be aware that these difficulties with arousal or release for men and women that can be the result of a disease or its treatment, are also common dysfunctions of people *without* physical disease. Therefore, if you are experiencing interruption of your body's normal sexual response, seek out a medical doctor who is competent to treat both your particular disease and the sexual disorders that result from the disease. Or the physician may consult with a sexual therapist.

The best resource book available in this situation is the *Textbook of Sexual Medicine* by Robert C. Kolodny, William H. Masters, and Virginia E. Johnson (Boston: Little, Brown & Co., 1979). Your difficulty should be evaluated to determine if it is an interruption with the physiology that is reversible or if it is an emotional barrier that has surfaced which may require sexual therapy. The *Textbook of Sexual Medicine* deals in detail with physical disorders and their effect on sexual functioning.

For our purposes here, we would like to list various physical difficulties and treatments that are likely to interfere with sexual functioning.

We don't expect that this will tell you if your sexual dysfunction has a *physical* basis, but we hope it will help you determine if that might be true for you.

Disorders and Treatments That Interfere with Sexual Function

1. *Endocrine Disorders*

The endocrine system in our bodies is our regulatory system. It works through our hormones and neurotransmitters. Because hormones greatly affect our sexual drive and responsiveness, and the sexual response is triggered by messages transmitted through the nervous system, it is logical that the endocrine function is key to sexual response. Therefore, diseases of the endocrine system, such as diabetes, thyroid dysfunction, pituitary problems, and sex hormone disease, are frequent and typical causes of sexual dysfunction.

2. *Cardiovascular Disease*

The emotional reaction to a heart attack is usually the reason for sexual dysfunction, not the physical changes in the body. There are cardiovascular disorders that can *physically* affect sexual functioning. However, when the disease usurps all the energy the system can produce, there will not be enough cardiac capacity left for a full sexual response. When the disease limits the blood flow to the pelvis, the natural responses of erection and vaginal lubrication will be hindered. Generally, however, sexual activity is a good cardiovascular stimulant.

3. *Disease of the Reproductive Organs*

Any disease of the external genitals of the man (penis) and woman (vulva) are likely to cause pain or difficulty with sexual intercourse. This is true whether the disease is venereal in nature, a structural difficulty from birth, the result of childbirth for the woman, injury for the man, or surgical removal of a tumor. Internal disorders of the reproductive tract that cause problems are urinary tract infections or problems with the prostate gland in the man, and diseases of the vagina and uterus in the woman. The effects of these changes on sexual functioning may be either physically or emotionally based. Renal (kidney) failure causes a high incidence of inability to function sexually due to the physical changes in the body.

4. *Alcoholism*

The chronic abuse of alcohol causes sexual dysfunction by inhibiting the production of the sex hormones, as well as by diminishing the normal sexual response. The other medical complications of liver disease, anemia, and so forth add to the difficulty.

5. *Neurologic Disorders*

Like the endocrine system, the nervous system is an integral part of the sexual response. Disorders of this system are likely to interfere with the ability to respond sexually. This *can* be true for brain tumors or injury, multiple sclerosis, cerebral palsy, muscular dystrophy, myasthenia gravis, poliomyelitis, and spinal cord injuries. For detail about the effect of each of these disorders, please check the *Textbook of Sexual Medicine* referred to earlier. Also, Dr. Jo Ann Brockway from University of Washington Hospital and Harborview Medical Center conducts classes about sexuality for the spinal-cord injured patient. To get more information, contact the Northwest Regional Spinal Cord Injury Center at 206–543–8660. This is in the Seattle, Washington, area. There are other such resource agencies throughout the country.

6. *Malignancies*

The sexual needs of the cancer patient have often been overlooked. In addition to the emotional impact of cancer on the marriage relationship, the growth or tumor itself may physically interfere with sexual functioning. The debilitating effects of the disease may make response difficult or impossible. Drugs, surgery, and radiation can also cause sexual problems. Again, specific information is needed for each situation in order to assess the physical or emotional effects of such a disease process on a specific person's sexual functioning.

7. Treatments

A. Surgeries

An operation can physically interfere with the sexual response when nerves are severed that control sexual body responses, when genital pain is a result of the surgery, or there is loss of genital sensation. The emotional sexual interference caused by an operation is usually due to body image disturbance.

B. Drugs

Both prescribed medications and street drugs may be potent sexual inhibitors. But their effects vary greatly from one individual to another. Some prescription drugs which reportedly interfere with sexual functioning some of the time are listed below:

1. Diuretic and non-diuretic blood-pressure lowering agents
2. Hormones (enhance or hinder)
3. Steroids
4. Tranquilizers and sedatives, especially barbiturates
5. Anti-depressants
6. Anti-cholinergic drugs used for gastrointestinal disorders
7. Digitalis (for cardiac problems)
8. Antihistamines (for allergies)

C. Radiation Therapy

Radiation therapy has a high percentage of reported interruption of sexual feelings and responsiveness. This may be a temporary effect that reverses when the radiation treatments are discontinued.

D. Chemotherapy

Little is known about the side effects on sexual functioning of the chemotherapeutic agents currently used to control cancer. There are some reports of dysfunctioning caused by certain of these chemical agents.

Keeping Close during Turmoil

Where there is a physical interruption of the body's sexual response pattern due to a disease or its treatment, look for some form of sexual intimacy that brings satisfaction and a feeling of closeness to both.

What can be done to keep the sexual relationship alive when there is little time or energy for each other, or when functioning is not there? What helped David and Cindy reconnect?

Crises shake up our usual system. Patterns are changed. Feelings are different. What was once solid is now fluid yet moldable. That is why a period of crisis can be a time when we allow our relationship to deteriorate, or we can make it even better than it was before. We will not be as set in our ways, so new growth is more possible.

David and Cindy not only regained what the stress of their situation had taken away, they added new closeness. David was a high-powered businessman who had not participated in home life. He became part of the bedtime routine and outings with the children, assuming more of the burden for Melissa. Cindy and David had never fought seriously, but neither had they communicated feelings and needs. The therapy process opened up a new world of knowing each other deeply.

There were ten ingredients essential to our work with Cindy and David that we believe will make the difference for you also.

1. *Identify the Problem.* Recognize the havoc this illness is playing on your relationship. Don't blame yourselves or each other. Give the relationship a chance.

2. *Build Communication.* Above all, get help to be able to hear each other. Take time to communicate. Tell each other what you would like both relationally and sexually. Find out and share what feels good and is possible. Set aside a period to experiment with touch even though time will be hard to find. Tell each other what kind of touch turns you on. You might want to take turns sitting in each other's laps and guiding each other's hands as a way of communicating what is pleasurable (see Non-Demand Touching Experience, *The Gift of Sex*, p. 145). Both verbal and touch communication are essential to growing together.

3. *Schedule Time.* Take time for the two of you to be together *without* any demand or expectation of sexual intercourse, sexual arousal, or release. Togetherness allows the possibility for sexual interest to build. It also provides a forum for finding mutual enjoyment with each other. This might be a two- to three-hour block of time once or twice a week. This is an occasion that costs little or no money, but is free of your usual responsibilities.

4. *Learn about Yourselves Sexually.* Start by becoming familiar with the physical and emotional dimensions of the sexual experience. The

sexual response has been measured and described by Masters and Johnson. Others have added to that knowledge base from their experience as sexual therapists. We have written about all dimensions of the sexual relationship in *The Gift of Sex.* The two of you may find it helpful to read that book aloud to each other.

5. *Learn to Give and Receive Pleasure.* Learn to touch and to enjoy the warmth of each other's bodies. Communicate feelings of love without pressure to please or to respond. These can open new worlds of enjoyment. This is true for any couple, but especially important for the couple who is under stress. To learn this you might start by giving each other a foot and hand caress when you are both freshly bathed. Take turns being the giver and receiver. The primary focus should be soaking in pleasure for both the pleasurer and the receiver. For the one doing the touching, you might find it helpful to think of discovering your spouse's hands and feet through your fingertips. This same type of pleasuring can be learned with a facial caress and a total body caress. Sexual arousal is not the intention or purpose of such experiences, but may be enjoyed if it should occur (*The Gift of Sex,* pp. 143, 145, 274).

6. *Take Responsibility for Your Own Sexual Response.* Many of the tensions and demands of a sexual encounter are relieved when each person assumes the responsibility to know and to communicate his or her needs for touch, arousal, or release. Make a mutual decision that each of you will assume the responsibility to go after what feels good, counting on the other to let you know if what you are doing is violating or negative in any way. Then you will find an enjoyment of each other's bodies that is mutually satisfying and yet takes into account the illness factor.

Incorporated into this system can be the freedom to exaggerate natural desires and body responses to heighten the experience, and to direct your partner to provide the touch for which your body is hungering. When we are assuming the responsibility for our own sexual needs, this directing of each other need not be taken as a putdown. Rather, it is a message that communicates what the other wouldn't be expected to know. We are the best experts on our *own* sexual needs.

7. *Plan for Creativity and Fun.* If there is any time we need to be able to laugh together, it is when we are stressed or feel self-conscious about our bodies. Take turns planning your scheduled times together. Vary the setting and the activity. Include a little surprise and maybe

a favorite treat. Sometimes the stress of the situation will leave us feeling empty of ideas. There are many good sex books filled with fresh ideas available. Feel free to go to one of these to add some spark.

8. *Distract from Anxieties and Demands.* When we are physically drained or feeling unsure of our bodies or their responses, we may avoid physical closeness. We are afraid we will fail. However, if our only goal is to find mutual enjoyment together, then *there is no way to fail.*

Yet, fears and demands tend to surface. The most effective way for dealing with these anxieties is to talk about them at their onset. It's very helpful to be able to say, "I'm avoiding you. I just can't get into this. I'm so tired. I don't think I'll be good for anything." And then if the other can accept that and respond with something like, "That's OK. I'm not in much better shape. What *would* feel good?" Or, "That's OK. I'm feeling pretty good. Maybe I could just enjoy stroking and holding you, if that would feel good." Distracting from the demand to perform by saying it the way you feel it can provide incredible relief, especially when the message is received for what it is meant to be.

9. *Experiment with Alternative Methods of Sexual Enjoyment.* Other methods of finding sexual satisfaction may be necessary when sexual intercourse is not possible. It may be necessary to enjoy the intimacy of being together and having a full sexual release through kissing, breast stimulation, general body caressing, manual stimulation, or oral-genital stimulation, but only when that is an acceptable sexual activity for both. A vibrator may be incorporated as a substitute or addition to an erect penis when the man doesn't experience this as a threat. A lubricant can be used by the woman when vaginal lubrication is not occurring.

When sexual arousal isn't happening, the focus on mutual body pleasure for the enjoyment of the touch can maintain the sexual close-ness. When there is plenty of stimulation, with lots of arousal, but the orgasmic reflex isn't working, the best solution seems to be to take time to hold and affirm. Allow the sexual intensity to dissipate slowly as you enjoy the physical and emotional closeness.

An experimental approach to your individual situation will probably lead to new ideas you have never encountered. Take courage and have fun!

10. *Maximize General Health.* Our ability to maintain a satisfying

sexual relationship throughout a stressful illness is greatly enhanced when the rest of our health is at its best. Daily exercise has been shown to decrease stress reactions considerably. Adequate sleep always makes the world look a lot brighter.

Making certain we are eating smaller, more frequent meals can carry our energy level on a more consistent basis. A snack between meals or at bedtime may be the most effective way to put this into effect. Eliminate sugar, white flour, and added salt. Increase fresh fruits, vegetables, whole grains, and proteins of all sorts to enhance nutrition, unless your illness or its treatment would require something different. Eight to ten glasses of water a day is great for the system, too.

Details of your specific nutritional needs should be worked out with a professional in your area. That could be a physician, a biochemist, or a nutritionist. Avoid getting caught up in a fad diet. Good general health is a great asset in positively coping with illness in yourself or a family member.

In Summary

Sexuality is closely linked with physical appearance and performance. It is necessary to unlink these and find sexual satisfaction even when the illness affects our physical appearance and sexual performance. You can do it! It is the only way to maintain your sense of well-being as a whole sexual person who can enjoy all the intimacy of a marriage relationship.

Always bear in mind the guidelines for sexuality suggested by Anderson and Cole in an article for the physically handicapped:

> A stiff penis does not make a solid relationship,
>   nor does a wet vagina.
> Urinary incontinence does not mean genital
>   incompetence.
> Absence of sensation does not mean absence
>   of feelings.
> Inability to move does not mean inability
>   to please.
> The presence of deformities does not mean the
>   absence of sexual desire.
> Inability to perform does not mean the
>   inability to enjoy.

Loss of genitals does not mean the loss of
sexuality.
Anderson, T. P. and Cole, T. M. Sexual counseling of the physically disabled. *Postgraduate
Medicine* 58:117–123, 1975.

Take courage, have fun, and enjoy the gift of each other!

For Further Study

Anderson, T. P., and T. M. Cole. Sexual Counseling of the Physically Disabled.
Postgraduate Medicine. 1975, 58: 117–123.

Carrera, Michael. *Sex: the Facts, The Acts, and Your Feelings.* New York:
Crown Publishers, Inc., 1981. "Disability" and "Drugs."

Cornelius, Debra, Sophia Chipouras, Elaine Makas, Susan M. Daniels. *Who
Cares? A Handbook on Sex Education and Counseling Services for Disabled
People.* Baltimore: University Park Press, 1982.

Kaplan, Helen Singer, M.D., Ph.D. *The New Sex Therapy.* New York: Brun-
ner/Mazel, 1974. Chapters 4–5.

Kolodny, Robert C., William H. Masters, Virginia E. Johnson, Mae A. Biggs.
Textbook of Human Sexuality for Nurses. Boston: Little, Brown, and Company, 1979. Chapters 5–11.

Kolodny, Robert C., William H. Masters, Virginia E. Johnson. *Textbook of
Sexual Medicine.* Boston: Little, Brown, and Company. Chapters 7–14.

Stokes, Naomi Miller. *The Castrated Woman: What Your Doctor Won't Tell
You About Hysterectomy.* New York: Franklin Watts, 1986.

Sex and Aging

"The old can do anything the young can do—it just takes them longer." An eighty-four-year-old man sits before us seeking sexual therapy. He has been married to his seventy-nine-year-old wife for fifty-four years. Since he is no longer experiencing the joy and pleasure they once shared, he asks, "Am I just too old for sex? Should I give up on the possibility of enjoying my wife like I used to?" His wife had always enjoyed sex, too, but recently seemed to be less interested, reportedly because of the difficulty he was experiencing. He isn't concerned about intercourse and orgasm. It's the intimacy he misses. He reports that he feels rather ridiculous coming for sexual therapy at his age, but on the other hand he asks why not? We couldn't agree more!

A sixty-five-year-old woman calls us on a talk show and tearfully expresses her concern that the sex life she and her husband used to enjoy has disappeared. Her husband visited his physician two years ago, and when he complained about slower sexual responses, the physician laughed and said, "What do you expect, you're sixty-six years old, aren't you?" Ever since then her husband has been less and less interested in initiating sexual activity and has a very defeated attitude about their diminishing sex life.

An elderly couple from the east coast (who didn't give their ages) heard us on a nationwide radio broadcast. They wrote to ask us a typical "Ann Landers" question. They believed that their children expected or assumed that their parents were no longer sexual. When sexual contact between the couple was implied, a derogatory attitude surfaced suggesting that sex among old folks is weird and a little perverted. The couple was seeking our opinion on this matter.

In a society that worships youth, and either depreciates or disregards the elderly, it is not uncommon to encounter the attitude that sexual activity among the "older set" is suspect or strange. The older male interested in sex may be perceived as "a dirty old man," and the woman as someone to be pitied. She must be showing the first signs of senility and regressing to her youth. Since sex is so highly connected with the virility and beauty of youth, it is no wonder that as the skin wrinkles and sags, the brown spots increase, the hair lightens or falls out, and agility diminishes, we also assume that sexuality disappears. If youth and sexuality are highly correlated, it only makes sense that as we age, sexuality will decrease and when we are old it will have vanished. Fortunately for all of us, this is a myth.

As is true with myths, there is a slice of truth in this view. It is a fact that our sexual powers peak in young adulthood. It is also a fact that conception is most possible in young adulthood. There is usually greater frequency of sexual activity among the young. But it is not a fact that sexual interest disappears with the process of aging.

Another part of the myth was begun by the Greek philosophers. They taught that each of us is dealt a certain amount of sexual energy or virility. This must be conserved and parceled out carefully lest one's sexuality be spent before life is over. In 1919, H. W. Long authored a book entitled, *Sane Sex Life and Sane Sex Living* (New York: Eugenics Publishing Company). This was available to be sold only to the medical profession. In it the author writes very openly for his time, but reflects the attitude that sexuality must be carefully dealt out throughout life.

Here is a quote from his section on sex and aging.

The question is sometimes asked as to how late in life the sex organs can function pleasurably and wholesomely for the parties concerned. And here, as elsewhere, the reply can only be that it all depends on the individual. But this is true: that, as a rule, the status of the individual during the years of active life will persist, even to old age, if the sex functions are used and not abused. There is no function of the body, however, that will "go to pieces" quicker, and ever after be a wreck, as will the sex organs, if they are not treated rightly.

And this works both ways: If too rigorously held in check, if denied all functioning whatever, the parts atrophy, to the detriment of the whole nature, physical, mental, and spiritual. The body will become "dried up," the sex organs shriveled, and a corresponding shrinking of the whole man or woman, in all parts of the being, is very apt to follow.

On the other hand, an excess of sex-functioning will soon deprive the individual of all such power whatsoever. A man will, in his comparatively early life, lose the power of erection, or tumescence entirely, as a result of excess, either by masturbation or from too frequent coitus; and on the part of the woman, many unfortunate conditions are liable to arise. However, for reasons that have already been stated, a woman who is strongly sexed, and of a pronounced amorous nature, can maintain even great excess of sex exercise without suffering such ill results as would befall a man who should so indulge. That is, an excessively passionate wife can far sooner wear the life out of a husband who is only moderately amorous, than can an abnormally passionate husband wear out a moderately amorous wife.

But if the sex nature of the husband and wife are well cared for during years of active life, neither too much restrained or too profusely exercised, the functioning power of the sex organs will remain, even to old age, with all their pleasure-giving powers and sensations intact. This is a wonderful physiological fact, which leads to a conclusion, as follows:—

This fact of the staying qualities of the power of sex functioning, even to old age, is the supreme proof of the fact that sex, in the human family, serves the purpose other than reproduction!

. . . If a wife is a normal woman, sexually, and has neither abused her sex nature nor had it abused or neglected, and is a well woman, she will enjoy coitus as much after she has passed her three score and ten date in her life as she did before! She may not care to engage in the act as frequently as in her younger days; but if she is well courted by her old lover, all the joys of former days are still hers, to as great a degree as ever. And what is true of her is true of her husband, if he is well preserved, as she is, and has never abused himself or been abused.

This is a reward of virtue, for old lovers, that pays a big premium on righteous sex-action in early years! (pages 164–66)

This long quote depicts beautifully the old myth claims that if one "indulges" oneself too frequently, one will use up one's potential for sexual response. Husbands and wives were encouraged to experience frequent sexual activity but to limit the number of times that they actually came to orgasm lest they spend themselves in their youth.

This concept of having a limited number of sexual responses was the reason for the teaching that frequent self-stimulation was a form of self-abuse. In addition, sexual release for a man was thought to make him weaker. Hence, the rule was established that a man should not ejaculate before competing in a sport or going into battle. It seems to follow that if people had been excessively sexually active they would have used up their share of sexual responses. Since Masters' and Johnson's research, however, we now know that we all have an unlimited ability to respond sexually. There is some truth, however, in Dr. Long's 1919 teaching about too little use. When the sexual anatomy is not used atrophy does occur. It is obvious from Dr. Long's report that in the early part of this century, our knowledge about sexual functioning was at a most primitive level.

What effect does aging have on sexuality? There is an implicit stance in our culture against older-adult sexuality. We find it difficult to imagine our parents or older people being sexual. For some, the idea of the married senior citizen having intercourse is repulsive. We imagine that sexual urges lessen with age. Yet we know that romance and sexual experience are a very common part of the lives of the elderly in homes for the elderly. Let's look at what actually does happen to us as we age.

Menopausal Changes for Women

For the woman, the reproductive years are marked by the onset of menstrual periods in early adolescence and terminated by the cessation of menarche as a result of the menopause. Menopause usually occurs when women are in their fifties, but it can occur as early as the thirties or as late as the sixties. For the woman in menopause there is a decrease in the production of estrogen—the female hormone. It is estrogen that increased noticeably during puberty. It nudged, then catapulted, the little girl into womanhood, setting off her reproductive functioning. Estrogen has a major role in keeping up the monthly production and release of an egg and the repetition of regular menstruation. As is true with most physical patterns, women differ significantly in their menopausal experiences. Some hardly notice the changes, others have moderate symptoms, while still others experience severe reactions over a period of years. The differences can be either physical, emotional, or both.

Hot flashes are the most common reaction that causes women discomfort. These sweeping waves of heat can flood the woman's body in a moment, and may occur several times a day or night. Some experience them only occasionally. For others, stress or anxiety triggers the hot flashes.

When you begin to experience hot flashes, prepare for them. Choose clothes that can be loosened. Whenever possible, don't use panty hose. Loose fitting, natural, absorbent fiber clothing serves best. Usually a woman can lessen a hot flash by quickly removing as many blankets or as much clothing as is appropriate.

While estrogen replacement therapy has been linked with endometrial cancer, the research on this is still very unclear and inconclusive. The latest reports indicate that the risk of cancer is lowered significantly by taking a combination of estrogen and progesterone. In fact, there is some suggestion that women who take a combination hormone may have less risk of cancer than women who take nothing.

Other physical symptoms may include general aches and pains, numbness in the extremities, or irritating skin sensations. Some women notice that there is a small amount of urine leaked during intense body responses such as sneezing or laughing. There is a rather simple remedy for this. Practice tightening and relaxing the pubococcygeus (PC) muscle around the vagina and the urethra. These "Kegel" exercises have many benefits, so we would encourage their regular use.

For those who are not familiar with these exercises, they are really quite simple. While sitting on the toilet urinating, spread your legs and practice stopping and starting urination. Learn to hold those stops for two or three seconds, and then relax for two or three seconds. If you are out of condition, you may need to do several hundred of these exercises per day, but once your muscles are in good tone, fifty to a hundred will keep you in good shape. Find some natural cue in your environment that gives you the reminder to practice, such as doing dishes, when the telephone rings, or waiting for a traffic light to change. (For further information, refer to Sex after Pregnancy, Chapter 5.)

While some women gain weight during menopause, most find it is the distribution of their weight that changes. It is most common for the body shape to become fuller and rounder. These extra fat cells produce estrogen which is necessary to the body.

Emotional reactions such as depression, anxiety, nervousness, irritability, insomnia, and unpredictable and erratic mood swings can be a part of menopause. For some women, the small things in life that normally would have been taken in stride are suddenly elevated into an overwhelming crisis. Tears come easily. For others, there may be an increase in tension headaches. Extreme fatigue, shortness of breath, dizziness, lightheadedness, heart palpitations, nausea, bowel disturbances, constipation, or diarrhea can all be symptoms of menopause.

For many women, the first sign of approaching menopause may be a noticeable lessening of self-esteem. It is puberty in reverse. When hormones are fluctuating, her feelings about herself vary also. She feels less secure. There may be changes in the woman's view of herself and her femininity. With her child production potential coming to an end, she may feel an overwhelming sense of loss or uselessness. When life has had disappointments, the losses will be exaggerated. For example, a woman who was unable to bear children may relive the grief she has worked through earlier in life.

An acquaintance of ours in her mid-forties struggled through eight months of depression and a lack of zest for life, until someone finally asked her if she might be menopausal. She headed right to the doctor, got a shot of hormones and B 12, and felt like a new person in several hours.

This is somewhat comparable to a mid-life crisis for men. The hormonal changes in the woman are responsible for the emotional fluctuations.

To minimize the negative symptoms and to maximize coping positively with the changes of menopause, it is important to consult a physician. It is also vital to recognize that these are passing symptoms and won't last forever. Life will settle down. The physical and emotional fluctuations will not continue for the rest of your life.

There are many positive benefits to menopause. There is no more menstruation. There may be an increase in energy. Much of life is ahead. You still have a long time to be productive. This may be an ideal time to reevaluate your life and make plans for your future. Many women make a major contribution to society after menopause. Life is not over!

What If I Had a Hysterectomy?

If you have had a hysterectomy with the removal of two ovaries, then you will experience a surgical menopause. When the ovaries have been removed, the production of estrogen will have been suddenly lowered. You will probably already be on estrogen replacement, possibly a combination of estrogen and progesterone. If only the uterus has been removed, then menopause will be identical to what it is for all women. The possible physical and emotional affects of a hysterectomy have been written about in a new book, *The Castrated Woman* by Naomi Stokes. Many women report changes in sexual desire and response after the trauma of a hysterectomy. If you are facing the possibility of a hysterectomy, read Naomi Stokes' book first.

Changes of Aging for Men

In contrast to what happens to women, there is no cessation of fertility or reproductive capacity for men. Fertility continues to be a possibility throughout life even though the sperm count does decrease with age. The male hormone, testosterone, not only decreases significantly from age sixty on, but is also less available for the body's use as a man ages. Some men experience what would be similar to menopause in women—this is called male climacteric. It may produce similar symptoms such as depression, listlessness, decreased appetite, diminishing libido, erectile dysfunctions, loss of potency, physical weakness, fatigue, or irritability. While these symptoms may be due to other causes, it is generally assumed that when four of these are present, it is possible that the man is experiencing a male climacteric.

This condition is treatable by prescribing testosterone. A reversal of the symptoms should be evident in a period of two months or they are assumed to be caused by something other than the hormonal change. While menopause is inevitable for all women, the climacteric response is not noticeable for all men.

The prostate gland surrounds the junction of the vas deferens (the tube that brings the sperm and seminal fluid from the testes) and the outlet from the urinary bladder. It is relatively common for men to suffer from prostate swelling, infection, or tumors as they age. Any man living to eighty years of age has a one in ten chance or ten percent probability of requiring surgery for the removal of a prostatic tumor. While in the past prostatic surgery would damage the nerves and end sexual functioning, new surgical techniques offer the possibility for men to continue to function after the prostatectomy. Some will experience a retrograde ejaculation which means that the sperm and seminal fluid are forced back into the bladder. But the sensations of pleasure and arousal, and even some of the pleasures of ejaculation continue.

It should be emphasized that prostatectomies do not inevitably lead to impotence, although there is a high probability. Impotence has to do with the inability to achieve and maintain an erection, not ejaculation. If it is not possible for a man to experience an enjoyable erection after this surgery, determine with the physician if this is a permanent consequence of the surgery. If not, go for sexual therapy. If so, the loss of that ability will be felt deeply. A penile prosthesis (implant) is a viable option. Learning to enjoy sex without erection, careful discussions with the physician, and a loving, cooperative wife will help the transition after prostactic surgery to be most positive.

Sexual Changes for Men and Women

A man can continue to function sexually throughout his whole life. There are reports of men in their nineties who function sexually. But even as the rest of the body begins to slow down with age, so does the man's sexual response. As we saw in the old saying at the beginning of this chapter, "The old can do anything that the young can do, it just takes them longer." This is literally true for the man. There are five changes.

1. In his youth the man may have come to every sexual experience already aroused. Arousal triggered his initiation of sex. Now it takes stimulation to get an erection. This has been an issue of such concern to some men that they have sought sexual therapy to remedy the dilemma. A steelworker and his eager wife came to our clinic seeking help with what they described as "impotence." As we listened to their story, we discovered that the real dilemma was that the man, who thought of himself as a "real man," had always come to the sexual experience already aroused. In recent years he had been noticing that he was experiencing less arousal. Since, for him, an erection was a prerequisite to taking sexual initiative, he had radically reduced the frequency of his initiation. If his wife initiated when he wasn't aroused, he drew away lest he be shamed by coming to the marital bed without being fully responsive.

This is a myth that develops rather naturally. In their twenties, men respond at even the hint of a sexual possibility. As we age, this changes and becomes a most unrealistic demand. It can bring great pleasure to have the woman participate in bringing about the arousal by direct stimulation. So, yes it does require direct stimulation of the penis and it may take longer to get an erection as a man gets older. But for many couples, this change doubles their pleasure. Women and men are more similar in their response as they age. Wives are usually thrilled that husbands have slowed down their pace. So it doubles their fun.

2. After a man reaches sixty, he may find that his erections are not as firm as they once were. He will still become erect, be able to enter, and experience full sexual pleasure, but may not be as hard.

3. The ejaculations are likely to be less intense. This is probably related to the reduction in the volume of seminal fluid produced as well as diminishing muscle tone. While the eighteen-year-old "spurts" his ejaculation, the sixty-year-old "dribbles." That does not make it less enjoyable, unless the sixty-year-old demands an eighteen-year-old "spurt" of himself. Then he sets himself up for disappointment.

4. There may not be a need to ejaculate with each sexual experience. Beginning around age forty, some men find that they can be fully satisfied in their sexual experience without an ejaculation. Ejaculation is likely to be inhibited if alcohol has been consumed shortly before the sexual experience. But most men report that the lack of ejaculation is not frustrating for them. They end up fully satisfied.

5. A man will need a longer time of abstinence between sexual experiences as he ages. This period is referred to as the "refractory" period and is the length of time between one erection and ejaculation and the next. This may be experienced as a diminished desire level, but it is not to be seen as a lack of sexual desire.

If the man is aware of these changes and accepts that they need not interfere with sexual functioning, he can continue with a satisfying sex life as long as he desires. If, on the other hand, he becomes anxious about these changes, or is unaware of their normalcy, then they may seriously impair his desire or potency. The anxiety about the changes, not the changes themselves, affects sexual functioning. This small bit of knowledge can make a major difference in the later years of sexual experience. Once the anxious habit of impotence develops, it is difficult to reverse. Avoiding the development of that anxious habit can save a couple much stress as they age together.

Sexual changes for the woman are less noticeable than is true of the man. Small reductions in the responsiveness of the breasts, the sexual flush, the engorgement or the expansiveness of the vagina may be noticeable to the researcher, but not to the woman herself. Two physical sexual responses are noticeably affected by aging in the woman. These are decrease in vaginal lubrication and a thinning of the vaginal wall. The walls get thin because of the diminishing estrogen production. This can actually hasten the atrophy that our 1919 physician, Dr. Long, referred to. But atrophy (a marked decrease in muscle and muscle tone) will occur mainly because of lack of use. Your physician may prescribe estrogen creams to help restore the vaginal wall. Certainly other lubricants are readily available to help reduce the impact of the decreased lubrication. Exercise is the most effective method to keep good blood circulation going longer. Thus, the PC (Kegel) exercises described earlier in the chapter are vital.

While there are obvious physical changes that affect the sexual functioning of the aging couple, these need not interrupt the sexual life. Rather, they need to be recognized and adjusted for as they occur in each couple's life.

Desire and Frequency Changes with Aging

The data is just now beginning to be gathered regarding the sexual habits of the aging population. The Kinsey Reports, the research of Masters and Johnson, or the most recent Consumer Union Report (*Love, Sex, and Aging* edited by Edward M. Brecher. Boston: Little, Brown & Company, 1984) are the common resources. Since this data has been voluntarily collected, it is not regarded as scientific research. But the data does give us a sense of how some of the older population is thinking and behaving.

First of all, it is interesting to note that women report their sexual activity and interest decreases as they get older, but they usually attribute this to some change in the man. They blame his decreased desire, illness, or impotence. On the other hand, as men report their decrease of sexual interest, they usually blame themselves for the same reasons that the women blame them. Also, women who take estrogen report a higher sexual interest level and greater sexual enjoyment. Statistically, there may be a decrease in desire or frequency as the aging process goes on, but there is usually an increase in the positiveness with which the sexual activity is experienced. This should be a loud message of hope for couples. It is true throughout life—sexual enjoyment can never be measured by quantity but always by quality.

Why the decrease in frequency? Let us look carefully at some of the factors that cause decreasing sexual desire as men and women age.

1. Physical changes will lessen desire. For men, the main physical culprits are diabetes and high blood pressure. While diabetes can also affect the woman's sexual response, it mainly impairs the nerve endings which help bring about and maintain erections for the male. The medications used to reduce and control blood pressure can have a serious impact on the man's potency. Blood pressure medications are designed to function as vasal dilators, relaxers of the blood vessels. For a man to maintain an erection he needs just the opposite, that is, vasal constriction.

If you have noticed a shift in your sexual responsiveness since taking blood pressure medication, discuss this with your physician. There are adjustments that can be made in dosage or in the type of medication which may not affect your erectile response.

Heart problems and alcohol can affect both men and women. While there are no reasons to stop sexual activity because of a heart condition, the fear that sexual excitement will further exaggerate the difficulties inhibits sexual fulfillment for many. Alcohol is a depressant; it decreases sexual appetite. While one drink may reduce inhibitions and allow us to be freer sexually, more than that usually deadens our sexual awareness. This effect increases as we age. We are more likely to want to go to sleep than have sex. In general, our sexual energy will probably decrease slightly as we age, just as our energy for life lessens.

2. The social expectations are a second reason why couples function less frequently and experience less desire as they age. When old people get the message that they should not be sexual, they *feel* less sexual. It becomes a self-fulfilling prophecy. Their sexual urges may elicit feelings of strangeness, so they shut off the feelings and operate within the norms that they feel society sets up for them.

3. A previous low desire level throughout early and mid-adult years is likely to continue in older age. When desire has been lacking it is not usually reversed as a couple moves into their sixth, seventh, and eighth decades.

4. Boredom, routine, lack of creativity, or lack of experimentation will bring about a decrease in desire with age. Sex becomes disinteresting. If a couple is going to keep the sexual life alive for forty to sixty years, it will take much creativity and experimentation.

5. The most common reason for the decrease in sexual involvement has to do with the perceived inability to function due to impotence

for the man. This is not an inevitable consequence of aging and can be reversed, but the man may need sex therapy.

6. Lack of activity diminishes desire. The surest guarantee to keep the sexual life alive over the years is to keep active. This is one situation where the "use it or lose it" adage is accurate. Through lack of use there is atrophy in the vagina, it seems to shrivel; and through lack of use it becomes more and more difficult for the man to get an erection. This is particularly true in one special set of circumstances described by Masters and Johnson, the widower's syndrome.

The Widower's Syndrome

The situation is predictable. A couple enjoys a normal sexual life. Sometime during her fifties or early sixties the wife is stricken with cancer, severe heart problems, or a stroke. The husband dutifully and lovingly takes care of her for a few years and then she dies. He mourns for a year or two, and then becomes connected with another woman. At the point when he attempts a sexual relationship, whether before or after marriage, he is slow or unable to respond. At first this may not cause much anxiety, but as repeated efforts fail, fear that he has lost his sexual potential creeps in even though his libido, (sexual interest) is still high. While there are variations to this sequence, it is so common that widowers need to be alerted. Be aware that when there has been a full sexual life and then a cessation (even if masturbation continues during the interim), it may take some time to regain the normal sexual functioning that was there before the catastrophe struck. This could also apply to the man who experiences a long-term illness with lack of sexual activity or when a divorce occurs late in life.

Professional help may be necessary, although we have known several couples who understood this syndrome and resolved it on their own. They came together lovingly and without demand, and gradually experienced full sexual responsiveness. When a man who is experiencing the widower's syndrome has a wife who can totally enjoy him without demanding a response and without expecting intercourse, over time he will regain an erectile responsiveness. This is clearly one circumstance where change is possible.

Keeping Sex Alive over the Years

As you move toward the last third of your life, it is crucial that you be prepared for the changes that will take place. Certain physical, emotional, and sexual response changes are inevitable. You need to be prepared for them. Beyond that, there are many ways the older couple can bring an extra measure of joy and fulfillment into their sexual lives. You are past the childbearing years, free of the fear of pregnancy and for that matter, free of the fear that the kids are going to walk in or hear you.

Brecher in *Love, Sex, and Aging* (Boston: Little, Brown & Co. 1984) has listed ten factors which contribute to long-term sexual satisfaction and marital happiness:

1. Ongoing sexual intercourse.
2. Mutual sexual enjoyment.
3. Frequency of intercourse is not nearly as important as having and *enjoying* sex with a spouse.
4. Contentment with the frequency of intercourse.
5. Regular orgasmic responsiveness by both spouses.
6. Ability to discuss the sexual activity.
7. A high interest in sex.
8. Easy sexual arousal.
9. Mutual sexual initiation.
10. Enjoyment of a variety of sexual activities.

If you are reading this at a time when you still have some years until you call yourself elderly, now would be a good time to evaluate yourself on these ten issues. How are you doing? This research strongly suggests that if you want to live a long, full, and satisfying married life, it is important to work on the sexual aspect of your life together. It is a large and significant dimension that will keep your relationship vital for years.

If you are elderly and want to keep sex alive, begin by bringing something new to your sexual experiences. Whether this is a new setting, a new touch, a new activity, or a new openness, creativity will enliven your sex life. Perhaps nudity has been uncomfortable—this may be the time to break down that barrier. Older couples enjoy breast stimulation and find that this is a great source of pleasure for both the man and the woman. Some couples get into more scrotal and clitoral stimulation during their later years. All of these will add spark and break down barriers.

Experiment with activities that you have avoided in the past, such as oral-genital stimulation. Go at this gradually. When there is no disease present and when the sexual organs are freshly washed, this can be most satisfying for the older couple.

If the man responds more slowly, with occasional impotence, this would be a good time to practice the technique of stuffing a partially erect penis into the vagina rather than having to have a full, firm erection. Sometimes this is easier in the side-by-side position or in any position that works for the two of you. Similarly, the woman may want to use extra lubricants as she ages to compensate for the decrease in lubrication.

Finding better times for love-making may also add spark. Many older couples have discovered that sex in the morning, when they are well rested, gives them a very positive start to their day and finds them at their physical best with each other. This will usually also allow more time for touching and cuddling, which seems to become more important with age.

Keep the sexual responsiveness alive by yourself. Individually, both men and women can practice the tightening and relaxing of the PC muscle. Some self-stimulation, with or without orgasm, may be helpful. Older couples seem to incorporate the use of fantasy on a regular basis. Many times these fantasies are of the couple's own special circumstances or memorable experiences of earlier days. What a great way to let the past enhance the present, as events from days gone by are used to bring added life now. Some couples get creative with each other sharing fantasies of pleasure and joy that bring them closer together even as they heighten the turn-on.

Finally

The message is clear. Procreation may be for the young, but sex is for the young *and* the old. Our sexuality does not die until we die. There is something beautiful about two people enjoying the touching contact in their fading years even as they did in their blooming years. Perhaps this poem by a seventy-four-year-old wife says it best (*Love, Sex, and Aging,* page 379).

FINDING THE FOUNTAIN

The slim young man I married
Has slowly gone to pot;
With wrinkled face and graying pate,
Slender he is not!
And when I meet a mirror,

> I find a haggard crone;
> I can't believe the face I see
> Can really be my own!
>
> But when we seek our bed each night,
> The wrinkles melt away:
> Our flesh is firm, our kisses warm,
> Our ardent hearts are gay!
> The Fountain of Eternal Youth
> Is not so far to find:
> Two things you need—a double bed,
> A spouse who's true and kind!

May you too experience this joy as you find continued pleasure in your marital bed—though it be well advanced in years.

For Further Study

Brecher, Edward M., and the Editors of Consumer Reports Book. *Love, Sex, and Aging.* Boston: Little, Brown, and Company, 1984.

Kaplan, Helen Singer, M.D., Ph.D. *The New Sex Therapy.* New York: Brunner/Mazel, 1974. Chapter 6: "The Effects of Age on Sexuality."

Kolodny, Robert C., William H. Masters, Virginia E. Johnson, Mae A. Biggs. *The Textbook of Human Sexuality for Nurses.* Boston: Little, Brown, and Company, 1979. Chapter 4: "Geriatric Sexuality."

Kolodny, Robert C., William H. Masters, Virginia E. Johnson. *Textbook of Sexual Medicine.* Boston: Brown, Little, and Company, 1979. Chapter 5: "Geriatric Sexuality."

Long, H. W., M.D. *Sane Sex Life and Sane Sex Living.* New York: Eugenics Publishing Company, Inc., 1919.

McCarthy, Barry, and Emily McCarthy. *Sex and Satisfaction after 30.* New Jersey: Prentice-Hall, Inc., 1981.

Stokes, Naomi Miller. *The Castrated Woman: What Your Doctor Won't Tell You About Hysterectomy.* New York: Franklin Watts, 1986.

_____VI

Tough Sexual Issues

_____18

Sexual Abuse—Incest and Molestation

"I have absolutely no interest in sex! In fact, every time I get into a sexual experience, my head starts screaming, No! No! No! If sex could go away forever and I knew that he could be happy without it—I'd never do it again."

This was the opening comment from Lynette, a pleasant woman in her middle twenties, who was seeking our professional help. As her story unfolded, we discovered that she had been raised in a fine Christian home. Her father, an attorney, had always been a church leader: deacon, trustee, or elder. He was a close friend of the pastor. Lynette's mother was more the quiet, reclusive type. She seemed to brood a lot and hence was not that close to Lynette. Her father had ruled with a steady, firm hand. The children respected and feared him.

As each of the three daughters (including Lynette) reached puberty, father took on the task of providing them with sex education. This education went far beyond the usual lecture and discussion with some pictures from a textbook. He not only took liberties with their bodies, but also insisted on their involvement with his. This started a pattern that continued until Lynette put a stop to it when she had her first boyfriend at age sixteen. While intercourse had never been attempted, the regular genital stimulation over a period of three years left her confused and withdrawn. Beyond insisting on her cooperation, her father was never forceful. At first the touching was a little strange but felt good. It was so affirming to get that much touching attention from her father, who otherwise was austere and distant. As time went on the discomfort turned into guilt, the pleasure grew into distaste, and trust became revulsion.

Gathering accurate data about sexual abuse is very difficult. There is no way to be sure that the results of any survey represent the truth. It is usually assumed that the information we do gather is an underestimate of the actual extent of the problem. We assume this because many do not remember or do not want to recall the abusing events. Others choose not to risk responding factually because of the emotional trauma associated with revealing what is usually a secret. Many times the abused children have been threatened with severe consequences if they ever reveal the secret. Sharing the facts and details stirs up old feelings that most would rather leave buried. While boys are sometimes the victims of sexual abuse, the great majority of victims are girls. For this reason, we will refer mainly to girls as the abused ones.

Sexual abuse impacts the lives of a massive segment of the population. It is estimated that from five to twenty percent of the population have been affected by incest or molestation. About ninety percent of the time, girls are the victims, while men or boys are the offenders ninety-seven percent of the time. Around eighty percent of the violators are known to the victims, with forty percent being fathers or stepfathers. In forty-one percent of the cases there are repeated offenses.

What do we mean by sexual abuse, incest, or molestation? Sexual abuse refers to any form of sexual contact or conversation in which the child is sexually exploited for the purpose of bringing sexual gratification to the exploiter. This could take the form of exploratory or stimulating contact with the child or requesting and demanding manual or oral stimulation from the child. It could be much less direct. Suggestive or derogatory talk can be very harmful. Even when no physical contact has occurred, the impact can be powerful.

Janice serves as a good example of this. She and her husband came to us with the complaint that she lacked sexual drive. She was always resistant to his advances. When Janice was a young adolescent visiting her best girlfriend's home, this girlfriend's father found ways to isolate her and exhibit himself to her (while she was in the swimming pool or backyard). He would do it in such a way as to make it appear an innocent event, and yet she knew he was intentionally "coming on" to her. This happened on repeated occasions without any physical contact. The images of this still impact her sexual life thirty years later.

If the perpetrator is part of the family, especially a father or stepfather, this behavior is called incest. When it is not initiated by a relative, all forms of sexual abuse except intercourse are referred to as molestation. Sexual intercourse with a minor is considered rape.

The Violator

The sexual abuser may be the fourteen- or fifteen-year-old brother experimenting with the five- or ten-year-old sister. His hormones are encouraging his natural sexual curiosity and feelings, but his behavior is not appropriate. He is taking advantage of the younger child to fulfill his needs. While he clearly understands that this behavior is unacceptable, the excitement, newness, and intrigue of the experience urge him on. Usually it begins with mild genital exploration and then moves to more involved play as the incidents are repeated. This activity may begin very innocently but gradually become a pattern accompanied by threats, coercion, and sometimes physical force or violence. These boys do not necessarily grow up to be adult abusers, especially if the pattern is broken before it becomes a habit. The pattern can be broken by learning to handle their sexual feelings in acceptable ways (see Chapter 11).

Often these boys lack the normal heterosexual social skills that would allow them to do their sexual experimentation with girls of their own age. Frequently they are unsupervised in the home and often are left in charge of the younger children. The young sibling or cousin may be desirous of attention or affection from someone who usually pays no attention to her. So she is caught in the conflict between the need for attention and shame and guilt for the behavior involved.

The older the violator the greater the likelihood that a compulsive pattern has developed. It is also more likely that the individual himself is a troubled person and part of a troubled family. Abusers are usually unhappy people who do not find themselves fulfilled in any relationship. This is true both in terms of outside friendships and the marriage relationship. While this unhappiness often takes the form of depression, it can just as likely turn to hostility. This is why it is not uncommon to find that physical abuse occurs in the same family where there is sexual abuse. Those who do the abusing, whether it be of their own children or those of someone else, tend to be men who experience feelings with a great deal of intensity and have never learned emotional control. They have not developed acceptable channels for their emotional expression. In this way they tend to be emotionally immature.

As we grow up, we are expected to learn control of our inner impulses. The sexual offender usually lacks control of these urges. Thus, the forces inside him drive him to abusive behavior.

The abuser has often learned this behavior from both his mother and father. The violator has, in many instances, been abused by his father. He perhaps did not experience his mother as a supportive presence affirming him as a boy or protecting him from the inappropriate anger of his father. So he falls into the compulsive pattern that has been modeled for him, even as he doubts himself as a man. Most abusers will, at various moments, face their abusive behavior, and chastise themselves for it, determining never to repeat the activity—only to find themselves engaged in it again. This self-doubt is as repetitive as the abuse. In many circumstances, it is fueled by alcohol and this reduces the capacity to control behavior and exaggerates emotional reactions.

The abusive male is generally a part of a troubled marriage marked by difficulty with communication, minimal levels of intimacy, and lack of sexual fulfillment. In fact, this may be one of the rationalizations used as a justification for his behavior. He can claim that he is the way he is because his wife is not providing him with what he needs and deserves.

This brings us to another important point. Society, in the past and to some extent at the present, depicts children as the parents' possession. The abusive father will often justify his sexual activity as clearly within his rights. He will claim that he is not being unfaithful to his wife—he is not involved in an adulterous relationship—because he is not going outside the family. This distortion is all part of the rationalization that allows the man to justify his ongoing abusive behavior.

There are those sociopathic men who evidently have regard only for their own wishes and desires. They care little for the havoc and emotional destruction they wreak upon their victims. We are reminded of a situation from the Midwest in which an uncle repeatedly raped and threatened his eleven-year-old niece, radically impacting the next thirty-five years of her life. He did this with total disregard for her feelings. The following Sunday he could stand up and teach his Sunday school class as usual, with no apparent discomfort at the incongruity.

While it is easy and natural to feel only disgust and disdain for the violators, and while it is rare for them to come forward and actively seek healing, it is important for us to remember that they are persons too. Usually they are acting out of a very troubled world. This is by no means an excuse, but rather should be seen as impetus for us to be active in bringing an end to these destructive situations by finding both control and help. This is a call for understanding and compassion as we deal with the violators, even as we take swift action to bring an end to their destructive behavior.

The Victim

No one stereotype describes all the victims of sexual abuse. A question often arises as to why one child out of a family might be singled out for the abuse. In many instances it is the oldest daughter. It may also be the softer, more compliant, less verbal child. Whether she becomes that way as a result of the abuse or was that way to begin with is not clear. But we do know that once the abuse begins, it has a tendency to make that child quieter and more withdrawn. In retrospect, in looking at the disposition of these victims, it is difficult to determine whether these emotional characteristics are the cause or an effect.

The kind of person the sexually violated woman becomes depends not only on the violation but also on the traits with which she was born and other environmental factors. Some turn out tough and others turn out timid. This would seem to be contradictory, yet both possibilities grow out of the same experience. The woman who goes the tough route is usually saying, "I'm never going to let anyone get to me again. No one can hurt me, especially a man." She is a fighter who believes, "This is the only way to stay safe." Underneath the tough exterior we usually find a scared, hurt person who has learned to put up a brave front. It is a shallow presentation.

On the other hand, timidity is probably the more natural response. The timid one tries to be unobtrusive, to slip into the woodwork so that she will not draw attention to herself. One woman talked about how she always dressed with several layers of loose clothing so that her body would not be seen by anyone, thus never elicit a sexual response. Panic set in when the response came in spite of all this.

Some abused children become very promiscuous in their adolescent and early adult years. Having been used as a sexual object, that is how they view themselves. It becomes a compulsion for them to repeat that event in search of satisfying love. They are in search of the perfect experience and never find it. Sometimes this behavior even leads to prostitution.

It is not uncommon for the sexually abused woman to at least seriously consider, and perhaps even experiment with, homosexual activity. When the experience with men has always been hurtful and violating, and she has never felt a full sense of love and acceptance from her mother, it is not surprising for the young woman to search for fulfillment with other women. It seems to be the only place of hope.

Some sexually abused women become habitual, anxious people-pleasers. They feel it is their responsibility to make everyone in their world fulfilled and happy. This is a heavy burden. It is the only way they know to get love and attention. Having begun this behavior as children during sexual abuse, they accept it as a way of life. This ongoing pattern of living life for others is a great source of disappointment since they never get what they need.

Darlene saw no value in herself unless she could be fulfilling the needs of others, even her abusive father. As the eldest daughter, she was responsible for the younger children. Mother was emotionally immature and unable to cope with her husband. Now as an adult, Darlene finds herself continually on the giving side of every relationship. Inside she is crying out for someone to take care of and love her, but she always seems to choose friends who need her and are verbal about their needs. So she goes on starved for the love that never came her way as a child, and it eludes her now.

Some victims become "spaced-out." This can take them to a psychotic point, but most often is manifested by an emotional shutdown. Nothing affects them in a positive or a negative direction. They live life with little or no show of emotion. Responses such as this usually grow out of severe abuse that was violent in nature.

At what age does incest usually occur? It happens to children of every age, even infants. We have dealt with all ages from the two-year-old toddler to the seventeen-year-old adolescent. Different patterns occur with children at various ages. Whether the abuse goes to the point of intercourse and begins at age five or at age fifteen, it is a devastating event that alters the life of the victim. This is true whether the victim is a boy or a girl and whether the violator is an adult man or a woman.

Bear in mind that about one tenth of the victims are boys. In these instances the abusers could be men or women. We have heard too many stories from men about molestation by a trusted leader at a camp-out. So be sure to teach your boys as well as your girls about appropriate and unacceptable touch.

Consequences of Abuse

Denial: When the perpetrator is known to the victim, the most common response is denial. This denial is not only to others, but also to one's self. It is not uncommon for us to be dealing with a woman who displays all of the symptoms of abuse, but reports no recollection whatsoever. In one instance it took a full year of weekly psychotherapy before the woman was able to acknowledge that her memory block was related to the abuse she had experienced from her brother thirty years earlier. It was not that she was consciously hiding this from us or attempting to deceive us. It was just not a part of her memory.

Even when abuse is recalled, it may be only a vague recollection. The victim has put the event out of her mind as a possibility. Children have an incredible capacity to deny what they can't handle. Women will talk about a vague feeling that something happened. Still others will have clear memories but because they have made a commitment to the violator and to themselves, they will never share this with anyone. To come out in the open with the story of their abuse is a most traumatic event. Secret commitments such as these are amazingly powerful. There is something magical about them. They have convinced themselves that if they never tell about the incident(s), the negative consequences promised them by the violator will never occur. They see it as a form of magical protection.

Lucy had been threatened that if she ever told anyone about what had happened to her she would be put in an insane asylum for life, severe harm would befall her family, and no one would believe her story about the abuser. Years later as Lucy shared the pain of her devastation, she continued to feel (even though she didn't believe it) that somehow this man had the power to influence good or evil depending on whether she kept the contract she had made with him. So it becomes understandable why a victim would not want to share the secret no matter how painful, and keep it locked up for a whole lifetime.

The denial usually extends to the spouse as well. A married couple will share many secrets, believing they know everything about each other, yet the abusive event may go untold for years. The wife fears that if her husband knew what had happened to her, if he knew that she was "damaged goods," he wouldn't want anything to do with her. She fears the loss of his respect and love. Maybe he will even desert her. While this desertion rarely occurs, it is still a powerfully traumatic event to share past abuse with a spouse.

Why deny? For children, the sexual violation may have been the only source of affection in their world. The mother may not have been very affectionate; the father may have given them little attention. Suddenly, someone is interested. He gives gifts. He touches. He is not violent and so, in a desperate way, a need is met. This experience sets up an unresolvable conflict for children. On the one hand, they feel all of the negative consequences of the event, including the guilt and self-depreciation. On the other, they are being touched where it feels good. They are receiving attention and affection. The only way to handle this conflict is to engage in denial.

We have had some women report to us that as children they would pretend to be asleep, with a mixed hope that this might make the abuser go away and not do what he came to do. It also made them feel less responsible for whatever went on. The conflict of childhood sexual abuse often makes it almost impossible for victims to totally enjoy the sexual experience in adulthood.

Fear is another impetus to denial. The fears of a child are usually only vaguely defined. They fear what is happening to them. They fear what might happen, not only to themselves but also to their family, if someone found out. They fear that they would be placed in a foster home, that mother would be extremely angry or father would show his anger through violence. The experience is ridden with fear.

Denial protects the self-image, since any inappropriate sexual contact from an older person makes the abused child feel different, strange, and unusual. It invariably alters the person's self-image. The denial serves as a way of keeping this image intact so they can pretend that this segment of their life is not a part of them. They tried to behave like normal kids, only confronting the abuse when they were at home. Denial then protects their public self-image. It is very important for all children to believe that their parents are good, caring, loving, wonderful people. When parents do not behave in this manner, the child will deny the reality to protect the image of having good, normal parents like everyone else.

Denial is a basic form of defense against undesirable thoughts, feelings, and experiences. It should never be seen as lying or deception but rather as a coping mechanism which helps the child survive what she is unable to deal with overtly and directly.

Distortion: Distortion takes place in almost every circumstance of abuse by a familiar person. A four-year-old girl reported to her parents that the fifteen-year-old male babysitter from next door and she had a secret. They were doing something that mom and dad would really like. They would be proud of her because it was something that moms and dads did when they loved each other. As the story unfolded in bits and pieces (even though the child had been warned not to tell), the reality was that this fifteen-year-old neighbor had convinced the four-year-old that what they were doing was loving and good. In the movie, "The Color Purple," the main character talks about men having to "do their business." This was a way of changing something painful and devastating into an event that was normal and tolerable. Distortion of this nature is not at all uncommon, particularly in cases of repeated abuse.

A woman in her early forties, who was finally dealing with abuse, reported that her father had begun intercourse with her when she was five years old. She remembers thinking that this was a normal event which probably occurred in all families. This is what fathers do with little girls. This becomes part of the line used by violators to convince children that the "loving" activity is a natural expression of family affection. Early in the experience the violators encourage distortion by suggesting that what is going on is a normal occurrence. They tell the child she will learn to accept this activity and that it is happening to other children as well.

Not only do the victims make the activity normal in their minds, they also distort the extent of the involvement. This makes it less painful and dramatic. Victims will say things like: "Well, he didn't hurt me." "It wasn't that often." "It only occurred on weekends." They will do anything to diminish the extent and significance of the involvement. *I'm sure that there are lots of people who had it worse than I,* they think. The distortion helps minimize the event and, thus, the pain.

Justifying the violator's actions is another form of distortion. The violator will often participate in this by talking as if the behavior is justified. One stepfather continually referred to his nine-year-old daughter as having such a sexy body that she really needed what he was doing for her. Often the justification comes in terms of what mother is not providing. The violator will complain that mother doesn't "put out" for him. The child will go along with these distortions in an attempt to make sense out of the events.

If the violation includes pain or violence, then the justification is that the child made him angry and so it is really the child's fault. The child distorts this by bearing the responsibility for the abuser's action. Overwhelming, debilitating guilt plagues the child throughout life. Even though the adult is responsible for the action, the child experiences herself as responsible. Hence she feels guilty.

Even when victims do not overtly believe the activity is their fault, that huge sense of guilt says they have done something wrong. Often it is easier for the children to blame themselves than to put the responsibility where it belongs: on the older, abusive adult.

To cope with painful abuse, a more severe distortion takes place. The girl may learn a form of detachment from that pain by having it spread out over her whole body rather than just feeling it in the location of the pain. This coping style, while necessary at the moment, tends to establish a pattern of detachment from pain or even life. It then becomes an ongoing part of the child's personality. As the child grows up, it invariably causes emotional havoc in adulthood.

Difficulty: Virtually every adult who was sexually violated as a child will have difficulties in life. Lack of trust is usually the biggest of these. When trust has been so severely violated, it is extremely difficult to rebuild. No excuses, no talking, no explanation, no extenuating circumstances can take away the damage. An additional trauma occurs in some instances, making the distrust even more severe. A child may seek out someone whom she trusts for help to stop the abuse, only to find that the person doesn't believe her or doesn't do anything even if he/she does believe. This is hopelessly devastating. Sometimes the child is violated again by the adult she thought she could trust. A thirteen-year-old girl, Virginia, had been repeatedly molested sexually by her two older brothers. As these experiences overwhelmed her, she decided to talk to her very special male piano teacher. Within a period of about three months, he was initiating sexual activity between himself and her, thus smashing her trust one more time. It was fifteen years before she risked sharing herself and trusting again.

When the protector becomes the abuser, it leaves the child in a severe state of helplessness, powerlessness, and mistrust. It is as if her world has been turned upside down. The very one who was supposed to protect her from danger has become the feared one. Trust is broken and confusion sets in even when only one incident occurs. Adults sometimes diminish the significance of a single incident of incest or molestation, but one incident can so radically alter a child's view of the world that it will affect him or her for life. When these trusted ones become the source of pain and confusion, it is as difficult to rebuild trust as it is to rebuild a broken egg. Abuse leaves a permanent scar—so the individual will always have a struggle with trusting another person.

Abuse also destroys the victim's self-worth. A child's ego is not developed enough to be able to see the violator as a sick person. The more powerful impact is on how the child sees herself. In their book, *Betrayal of Innocence: Incest and Its Devastation* (New York: Penguin Books, 1978) Susan Forward and Craig Buck quote an incest victim describing how she feels about herself. This is a common self-concept of the victim of abuse. She says, "Think of the lowest thing in the world. Whatever it is, I'm lower." The victim of abuse has an incredibly low view of herself. Her self-worth can be so low that she does not want to live. Suicidal impulses are common, especially for the victim of incest. These impulses reflect how worthless the individual feels.

Drugs, alcohol, enemas, laxatives, overeating, undereating, dangerous or foolhardy activities may all be a part of the self-destructive pattern. This grows out of a two-sided feeling. On the one hand, there is the feeling, "I'm not worth anything anyway, so who cares?" On the other, they feel, "If I can put up with all this, I am invincible and can tolerate anything."

A lack of confidence in her capabilities will often accompany the victim's self-depreciating stance. She may be bright, talented, beautiful, or capable in many areas, but she will not have internal confidence about herself. She will feel flawed. No matter how she feels on the outside, inside she is putting herself down, depreciating who she is.

Victims of sexual abuse deeply feel that they are unworthy of love.

Obviously if someone misused them so callously, how can they be worthy of loving? In adult life, abuse victims may find themselves repeating their childhood patterns. They connect themselves with men who are cold, distant, physically or sexually abusive, and emotionally neglectful. It is not uncommon for the woman abused as a child to marry a man who abuses her children even as she was abused. While it is never intentional, this kind of lifestyle perpetuates the low self-image.

Feeling "different" than everyone else is another difficulty. This is especially true for victims during their early adolescent years, when it is so important for them to feel normal and part of their peer group. Once there has been abuse, the girl usually feels set apart from everyone. This feeling of separateness occurs even with the very young.

Denise came to us at age forty with some severe sexual barriers in her marriage. As we were gathering her history, she shared her story for the first time. She had grown up in up-state New York. When she turned three, her mother found it necessary to go to work and left Denise with a neighbor lady for child care. The eighteen-year-old son of the caretaker was around the home and was often left to care for Denise and her sister. Over time a pattern of molestation and exploration of both girls was established by the young man. From the age of three, Denise felt different. She felt she knew something that other kids didn't know. There was a small sense of pride, but also great self-disdain and sadness. Having had this experience set her apart from everyone else. Since that time it had always been difficult for her to feel normal.

Intimacy is another difficult area for the abused person. There is a natural tendency to keep a safe distance from everyone. Victims of abuse feel "dirty." A piece of themselves has to be kept a secret. So they close themselves off completely from others. They find it difficult to form deep, lasting relationships. This is true whether they are children, adolescents, or adults.

The sexual relationship in marriage is particularly difficult for the victim of abuse. One of the major causes of sexual dilemmas for women is a history of sexual abuse. Though abuse has a powerful impact on the sex life, it is frequently not thought of as the cause for the problems that are experienced. The abused girl may be very sexual during her courting years. But once the relationship moves into the intimacy of marriage where sex is expected, the interest falls off with relative rapidity. Yet there is a sense of the woman being very sexual. Needless to say, this leaves the husband extremely frustrated. This frustration becomes the impetus for seeking help.

An important word to the husband: Some men feel the wife is blowing this whole experience of abuse all out of proportion. On the contrary, the impact of abuse on the sexual freedom of a woman is devastating. She cannot just "decide" to put it in her past. It needs to be taken with extreme seriousness. Even if there has been only one incident, it may radically impact the sexual life. Being tough about it and telling her to shape up and get over this problem only makes it worse. She re-experiences the pain and rejection with each such response. The most helpful stance is to be supportive and caring, but strong in taking the lead to get help.

Physical symptoms: Victims of abuse live with chronic physical complaints. In *Betrayal of Innocence: Incest and Its Devastation* Susan Forward reports that migraine headaches were present in about half of the people she counseled. Of course, not everyone who has migraines is or was a victim of sexual abuse! However, frequently when there has been sexual abuse, one of the consequences may be regular migraine headaches. Various other kinds of skin, gastrointestinal, or gynecological ailments are physical manifestations of the distress that the violated person experiences.

Perhaps the best way to sum up the consequences is to emphasize that these are the resulting patterns of abuse which have not been resolved. As victims confront the incest or abuse, change takes place. Victims do not have to live with these consequences for the rest of their lives. It is important to emphasize this.

Where Was Mother?

Whenever abuse is an ongoing pattern, both the victim and the violator will be communicating signals that should alert the rest of the family to the problem. In about a fifth of the cases, the mother or the rest of the family is completely unaware that anything is going on. In only a few instances is there active and knowing participation on the part of other adults in the family. Often there is an unconscious participation either out of ignorance, fear, or anger.

When a mother senses that something is going on between her child and an adult family member, she may feel powerless. Confrontation frightens her. She fears she will be unable to stop the behavior even if she does confront it. Mainly, facing it is too painful. We found this to be true of the mother of the wife of a missionary couple. The mother had sexually abused her daughter over a period of years. Father was the passive one; mother was the stronger of the two. He mildly raised questions about the mother's activity but never confronted it directly. Eventually he had left her for other reasons.

The silent one is often the submissive one. Most frequently the wife is submissive. The daughter learns submission from the mother. She learns not to stand up to the patriarchal authority.

Sometimes the mother contributes passively by neglecting her husband, thus pushing father and daughter into circumstances where sexual behavior could easily develop. She may have serious difficulty being affectionate with her husband and the rest of the family. She may have emotional or physical difficulties that make it almost impossible for her to participate actively in the emotional or functional life of the family. In several instances we have seen that abuse occurred during a time of extensive illness on the part of the mother.

The victims of sexual abuse may be both enraged and disillusioned by mother's neglect of them. If she cared, they feel, she would have done something about it. Once the abuse is discovered, mothers experience extreme guilt and inadequacy. Yet they often direct their anger at the child rather than at the abuser, especially if he is her husband, father, brother, or son.

In those circumstances where mother is completely unaware and then discovers the abuse, she needs to be loving, caring, supportive, decisive, and strong. Quick action is necessary to check out the physical health of the child and provide for the child's safety. Having the mother help the child work through the emotional trauma can be a life-changing event for the victim. This is very difficult for most mothers to do. We want to encourage everyone of you who find yourselves in this circumstance to take a clear, strong stand. Seek supportive help, whether that be from your doctor, your minister, or a professional therapist.

Getting Over the Abuse

A one-time molestation by a stranger can be faced and over come with relative ease. Valerie came to us with a strong block toward anything sexual. While being very attractive and even sexual in appearance, she could not find it within herself to respond to her husband. As therapy progressed it surfaced that at the age of thirteen she had been violated by a physician. With blatant disregard for her person and her tender age, the physician had callously catheterized her for a kidney problem while making sordid comments about her virginity to her mother. This traumatic experience had been forgotten until it surfaced in discussions with her mother. Within two weeks of the new awareness, she had worked through the scars from the event and was responding vigorously and enthusiastically to her husband.

It would be wonderful to be able to claim that all incest and molestation barriers are dealt with that easily. Unfortunately this is an exception. Alice's story is in sharp contrast. Her father had molested her over a period of six years. For months after the memory had surfaced she struggled before she could talk about her sexual feelings at all. It was not until two years after the therapy process began that sexual responsiveness was possible for her.

Just recognizing that sexual abuse had occurred and facing the memories are usually not enough. It must be shared with someone the victim can trust, who will not be judgmental, and who will be able to care without giving advice. The sharing process seems to be absolutely essential as a way of freeing oneself from the bondage of the violation. It is necessary to share some of the details, and the extent of the abuse. But it is particularly important to share the feelings, the self-concept, and the pain. Many times we find that inviting a woman to write her memories and then share them is very helpful. As new memories come along, they can be added to her journal of writings and then put back on the shelf. It is one way of getting the pain out of one's system.

Whenever we have experienced a severe loss, like the loss of innocence in childhood, there is a grief process to go through. When that grieving is delayed from the childhood event to the adult process, all kinds of baggage gets attached. Thus, the process can be painful and laborious. As with most grieving, when we survive the disbelief and distortion and can get to the anger, there is an overwhelming sense of rage. Fearing this rage may be part of the reason why it takes so long to face. So much anger is stored up inside the violated person, she fears its release.

Fear is another powerful emotion experienced as the incest or molestation is being dealt with. The fear can be a gripping, terrifying, trembling apprehension that all those threats made long ago will still materialize now. The abuse, violence, or even death which was threatened overpowers the emotions of the victim now that she is revealing the secret. A major part of the grieving process is dealing with the anger, the rage, and the fear.

When shame and guilt have been a part of life for ten, twenty, or thirty years, they are not easily overcome. Getting over shame and guilt requires a recognition of the patterns of being a victim. Patterns of promiscuity, timidity, or self-debasement all are an outgrowth of the abuse and need to be faced in the process of going beyond the devastation.

While some work through all these feelings with a helpful spouse, pastor or friend, others need to seek a professional counselor as they begin to tip-toe and then run through this minefield of emotions. The therapist whom you seek would best be someone experienced in helping people through the grief and pain of sexual abuse. The therapy process is designed to help you face the truth and reality of what went on in your life. Part of facing the truth is letting go of the hopes and dreams that somehow you can still have "the daddy" whom you longed for all those years. Hopes and dreams die hard. Group therapy for women abused as children is most effective in helping them move past the abuse.

Forgiving and forgetting is such a difficult process. In his book, *Forgive and Forget* (New York: Harper and Row, 1984), Dr. Lewis B. Smedes talks about healing the hurts we don't deserve. He explains that while it may be our intention to forgive at a given moment, forgiving is a process that happens over a lifetime. While hate weighs us down and eats at our souls, we should never demand instant forgiveness of ourselves. Letting go of the pain and hate has to be a gradual process.

What about confronting the violator? This is an issue that needs to be addressed carefully. In many instances, confronting the violator only causes more turmoil because of the violator's denial or anger. In other cases healing is possible. We have worked in two specific instances where a very special healing took place within a family as the violator was confronted, the anger heard, the pain shared, forgiveness sought, and relief experienced. We would be most hesistant to cite this as the norm. To encourage the abused person to confront someone whom she has feared all her life may set her up for further trauma. We need to be very sure that both individuals are strong enough to handle the confrontation.

We do find that as the victim can recognize who is responsible, and stop blaming herself or himself deliverance is possible. She needs to share out loud, go through the grief process, experience the anger, fear, shame, and guilt. She needs to let go of the hopes and dreams, face the truth, and begin the process of forgiving and forgetting. Then relief can come. Healing does take place. Reversal of lifetime consequences is possible. Sexual happiness can become a part of life. This seldom happens in an instant. It usually doesn't occur as a result of a quoted Bible verse or a quick prayer. It is like dealing with a cancer that has spread throughout a victim's body and is now needing to be removed one small speck at a time. But relief is possible, and we would encourage you to seek that relief with all the determination, strength, and energy you can muster.

Interrupting Abuse

Clues to Abuse: While we as parents do not want to be paranoid in watching for abuse, we must be on the alert for any indications of it. Obvious physical symptoms, such as blood or excessive vaginal discharge in the panties, should be investigated. Marked increase in fearful and hesitant behavior should lead a parent to at least suspect incest or molestation. Sometimes a child will change and become very withdrawn.

One patient reported that she had been happily playing at a family gathering when she was accosted and molested in a bathroom off a back bedroom. From that point on she sat quietly beside her mother for the rest of the event. Mother, who was not very sensitive to emotional variations, thought her daughter was getting sick but did not notice that she had no fever, was not throwing up, or demonstrating any other symptoms of illness.

This kind of withdrawn behavior may take the form of pulling away from friends or activities with a loss of normal enthusiasm. Taken to the extreme, it may even mean going into hiding where the child shuts herself off from the rest of the world in her room, the basement, or up in a tree far away from everyone else.

Sudden sleep disturbance—crying out at night, bad dreams, renewed bed-wetting—can also be a sign that something is amiss. Sudden accumulation of money or candy that has no reasonable explanation is also a warning signal. There are many individual ways that a child might demonstrate emotional turmoil, so it is crucial that we as parents remain sensitive to any emotional or behavioral changes. Obviously there are many other reasons besides abuse for these behaviors. We should not expect the same symptoms to occur from one child to another. One may lose her appetite while another may start eating more than ever. We need to be sensitive to individual differences in reacting to stress.

What do you do? If you suspect abuse, begin by asking some indirect questions that give your child opportunity for response. Start spending extra time with her. Always listen with an ear toward feelings. Be listening when she is talking with her friends. Watch how she plays with her dolls. If she is older, even pay attention to what kind of doodling she does. If you keep suspecting and don't get anything from her by the indirect manner, then confront her directly. Ask, "Has anybody been touching you in a way that has made you feel uncomfortable?" The most likely response will be a denial, but even the way the denial is expressed can give a clue as to whether there is any factual basis for your suspicions. If your suspicion becomes confirmed, reassure your child that she is not the one responsible for what has happened. Be sure she knows that you are available to help. You definitely want to know about what happened. Encourage her to tell you about it in whatever way she can. If it's easier for her to write it rather than tell you directly, give her the permission to do so. Assure her that you will not be angry with her but that you care deeply and want to protect her from harm.

If you know that abuse has happened, deal with it directly. Give the child the chance to talk and work it through. Let her express her feelings. Give her time for this. Introduce the topic when there is opportunity to talk. So many parents disregard their child's hints and clues because they don't want to face the problem.

While teaching a seminar in the northwest, we heard a frightening story. The daughter of the leading women's Bible study teacher in the church had been molested in the stairway of the education building. The incident was dealt with as a spiritual issue. This mother believed God would take care of the pain. They prayed to forgive the man and decided it would not be talked about again. While this may sound like a wonderfully spiritual example, we would have great fear for the consequences. As this nine-year-old child grows into adulthood, the failure to face the trauma realistically will undoubtedly impact her powerfully. Abuse must be dealt with whether we are comfortable with it or not.

If you are in a helping profession and have opportunity to recognize sexual abuse, know what your responsibilities are to report these situations. Follow the law to protect the innocent. While the temporary effects may be very jarring to the family, the process is crucial to let the child know that there is somebody out there in the world who cares and will act to protect them. Follow through. Make certain that the action taken is helpful, rather than destructive. Stay involved!

The subject of sexual abuse is one that we would like to avoid. Yet we do everyone a disservice, (especially innocent children) by failing to confront these issues head on. We must deal with them realistically and become agents of intervention to the ones whose innocence has been violated. We must stand up with a message of healing and hope.

For Further Study

Abramson, Paul R., *Sarah: A Sexual Biography.* Albany: State University of New York Press, 1984.

Carrera, Michael. *Sex: The Facts, the Acts, and Your Feelings.* New York: Crown Publishers, 1981. "Incest" and "Rape."

Forward, Susan, M.S.W., and Craig Buck. *Betrayal of Innocence: Incest and Its Devastation.* Harmondsworth: Penguin Books, Inc., 1978.

Gil, Eliana, Ph.D. *Outgrowing the Pain: A Book for and about Adults Abused As Children.* San Francisco: Launch Press, 1983.

Herman, Judith Lewis. *Father-Daughter Incest.* Cambridge: Harvard University Press, 1981.

Kolodny, Robert C., William H. Masters, Virginia E. Johnson, Mae A. Biggs. *Textbook of Human Sexuality for Nurses.* Boston: Little, Brown, and Company, 1979. Chapter 13: "Rape."

Kolodny, Robert C., William H. Masters, Virginia E. Johnson. *Textbook of Sexual Medicine.* Boston: Little, Brown, and Company, 1979, Chapter 16: "Rape."

Smedes, Lewis B. *Forgive and Forget: Healing the Hurt We Don't Deserve.* San Francisco: Harper and Row, 1984.

_____19

Sexual Infections

Who wants to learn about sexual infections? Our focus in this book has been to present a wholesome view of sexuality, as God intended, especially in a handbook for the family. Yet, the reality is that we live in a world filled with fallible human beings. There are germs in this world. Some of those germs are spread through sexual intercourse and cause illness. The havoc of AIDS and the pain of herpes have alerted all of us to the seriousness of sexually transmitted diseases. Yet, even simple, annoying genital infections that sometimes occur between a husband and a wife, in a monogamous relationship, can cause incredible stress.

Being informed is essential! This is not just the doctor's area. It is your body and your life that are affected when infections invade. You need to be a partner in the medical process. Be aware of your own body and its reactions. Read everything available on the subject. Seek medical help to correct situations that might make you more susceptible to infections and to diagnose and treat symptoms already present. Be an active participant. Share any information that you have which might add to or disagree with the physician's suggestions. It is your body!

Urinary Infections

Bladder infections (frequently labeled honeymoon cystitis), and urethritis, infection of the tube that carries urine from the bladder to outside the body, are among the most common female diseases. About 85 percent of women experience them. These occur frequently because the opening to the urinary tract is so close to the opening of the vagina which is close to the opening to the anus. The anus is highly contaminated. Infection-causing organisms can easily spread from the anal opening to the vaginal opening and on to the bladder opening. Sometimes contamination happens through wiping after toileting. This is the reason little girls should be taught to wipe from front to back. Most often, however, these urinary infections are contracted during sexual intercourse.

Because cystitis or urethritis is so common in new sexual relationships, we have sometimes suggested that honeymooners take prescribed medication along, particularly if they are going far away from home where consultation with their local physician would be difficult. The pain of cystitis can hit suddenly and be unbearable. Yet it can be relieved by medication almost as quickly as its onset.

We were in Hawaii on vacation several years ago when Joyce developed a bladder infection. This progressed, in a matter of a few hours, from frequent urination to extreme pain. We attempted calling her gynecologist to have a prescription called in to the local pharmacy, only to discover that there were no pharmacies open on that side of the island after 5 P.M. on Friday until Monday morning. In addition, no physician licensed outside of the Hawaiian Islands was allowed to prescribe. While Cliff attempted to locate a physician who would give us a prescription, found a pharmacy that was open, and made a two-hour drive to get the needed remedy—Joyce soaked in a hot tub and drank water and cranberry juice, trying to get some relief. Not much relief was gained until after the medication was taken. Then within an hour the intense pain was totally relieved.

There is a dilemma with the physician prescribing a medication for cystitis before a urinary culture is taken. For Joyce's situation and for much of "honeymoon cystitis," that solution works fine. It's a once- or twice-in-a-lifetime infection that is easily corrected with antibiotics and doesn't reoccur. Not all women have it that easy.

There is a different type of bladder infection called interstitial cystitis, referred to as painful bladder syndrome. It has been researched and written about by a woman urologist, Dr. Larrian Gillespie. She was frustrated by the typical medical approach to women who suffer from chronic painful bladders. What she discovered is that these women do not show bacteria present in their urine as do the women whose cystitis is easily relieved by antibiotics. In fact, when antibiotics are given to these women without first taking a urine culture to determine if bacteria are present, the antibiotics actually make the situation worse. The antibiotics "wipe off" the protective surface of the bladder and are one of the causes of interstitial cystitis, a disease in which the membrane lining of the bladder is destroyed. Because the protective lining is absent, the urine burns the bladder surface, like an acid burn, and eventually the bladder is no longer able to expand and contract. This obviously causes pain.

In fact, the symptoms for interstitial cystitis are the same as those of a bacterial cystitis: frequency of urination, burning pain, and cramps. The difference is the urinary tests show no bacteria, so antibiotics are not the treatment.

Dr. Gillespie has used Rhimo50 (a steroid), an experimental drug approved by the FDA only for this purpose, and sodium bicarbonate (baking soda) to reverse the acidity and allow the bladder cells to regenerate. Other treatments are currently being tested.

When all medical treatment has failed to relieve what seems to be chronic bladder infections, we recommend a "home remedy" and find it very effective. It grows out of clinical reports. Women have reported to us that after years of medical treatment, another woman told them about this remedy. They tried it and it worked! We cannot take credit for the idea. It was brought to us from the personal experience of the women who have come to us for help. Since reading the research by Dr. Gillespie, we assume it works because it restores the natural flora of the entrance to the bladder. It counteracts the infectious agents or irritations in the vagina. And it restores the acid-base balance of the woman's genitals. But these are only guesses. We claim no well-researched, scientific basis for this recommendation. Use it only with medical consent or when all other medical help has failed to correct the problem. We use the same approach for vaginitis when there is no infection present. And we find chronic bladder pain and vaginal irritation are often reported as occurring together. All these problems come to our attention because they lead to sexual dysfunction. Since we have been recommending this, we have also seen it recommended for vaginitis by Sylvia Close, a midwife who wrote from England.

This is the plan:

1. Eliminate or severely reduce sugar and artificial sweeteners in your diet. Unprocessed honey may be used in limited amounts.
2. If you are a sugar craver (many of these women are) or have hypoglycemic-type symptoms such as lightheadedness between meals, then eat fresh fruits (apples are best) and natural cheese, or other protein between meals and a protein at bedtime.
3. Increase fresh fruits and vegetables. In fact, try to stick with fresh foods in general so that you eliminate chemical additives that are irritating to some people.
4. Take an all-purpose vitamin-mineral supplement that is high in the B vitamins.
5. The key recommendation is the use of natural *unsweetened* plain yogurt. Apply it between the labia (lips), to the opening of the vagina, and insert it on a tampon in the vagina. It needs to be applied at least daily. Several times a day is even more effective. In addition, eat plenty of natural unsweetened yogurt. It helps restore the normal bacteria and the acid-base balance throughout the body. If you can't tolerate the taste, stir in a little unfiltered frozen apple juice concentrate and some cinnamon or fresh fruit.

We had been very hesitant about giving such unfounded recommendations until we received a desperate letter from a woman who had heard us interviewed on Dr. James Dobson's "Focus on the Family" radio broadcast.

She had been married five years and had never had sexual intercourse without contracting bladder pain. During those five years, she had continuous and excruciating bladder pain and even blood in the urine. She had consulted her family doctor first, then several urologists, several gynecologists, and finally the top urologist in her state. She and her husband followed a prescribed routine before and after every incidence of sexual intercourse. Their genitals and hands had to be freshly washed with soap and water, she was to urinate before and immediately after sexual intercourse, he was to use a condom to prevent the transfer of organisms from him, and she was to take antibiotics for a certain amount of time after each intercourse. She was now on continuous antibiotic treatment, but with no success. The physicians didn't have anything more to recommend. Her marriage was stressed even though her husband was extremely understanding and cooperative. Her feelings about sex and herself were so negative that the relationship was suffering.

By the time we responded to her letter with a telephone call, she was suicidal. She was in terrible pain, hopeless and helpless, feeling guilty for not wanting sex with her husband.

We validated that all the traditional medical approaches had been tried and were being utilized. Then to give some hope, but not feeling that confident, we suggested our plan. By the way, we also determined that she was a sugar craver and had been told to cut down on sugar by her physician because of some hypoglycemic tendencies. She had recently had a glucose tolerance test.

Three months or so later we received a note thanking us for saving her life and marriage. She said she had been infection- and pain-free for three months. She had begun using our program immediately after the call. She had not discontinued any of the medical prescriptions. Sex was now a part of her life that she positively anticipated. She saw herself as a "normal woman" for the first time.

It was that experience that nudged us into deciding to share with you this "home remedy" plan for persistent, unsuccessfully treated bladder infections. To the best of our knowledge, it can do no harm, even though medically it is uncomfortable for us to publicize a program that has no scientific validation.

Bladder infections with painful urination and sometimes painful intercourse are not a "cross you have to bear." Bring Dr. Gillespie's information to your physician, call her in Los Angeles, California, try our plan. Keep seeking the help you need until you find it. If you encounter your first bladder infection, make certain your physician does a urine culture before he starts you on antibiotics. Once you start antibiotics, the urine culture will not be accurate. The urine sample can be taken and antibiotics started (in the case of severe pain) before the results of the culture are determined. If there are no bacteria present in the urine, the antibiotics should be stopped and other treatment pursued.

Genital Infections

In their natural state the genitals are clean. The penis in the man and the vagina in the woman are primarily free of disease-producing microorganisms. The clear, colorless, odorless secretions keep the genitals comfortably moist. There are bacteria present in the vagina, but these are friendly bacteria that help the body fight off infections. Sometimes women are found to have a few pathogens, disease-producing microorganisms, present but with no other indications of infection. It is believed that the genitals can become contaminated from the anus or by other means. But when a person is in a healthy state, the pathogens may be warded off or lie dormant.

Genital infection may be caused by a fungus, a virus, or bacteria. The infection occurs because of an increase in the disease-producing microorganisms present in the genitals. These pathogens are most often sexually transmitted, although they may also invade the area after surgery or trauma. A person is more likely to acquire a genital infection when the environment of the genitals becomes unfavorable. For some reason the acid-base balance changes, the friendly bacteria of the vagina are destroyed, or the mucous membranes are sluggish. The conditions that make a person susceptible to genital infections include taking the contraceptive pill or douching and altering the normal vaginal environment, taking antibiotics and destroying the friendly bacteria, or being generally run down or in ill health.

Can genital infections be avoided? Prevention can be enhanced by good health habits. A healthy body is a great protection against infections.

Learning to lower the stress in your body is a help. Taking charge of your life so that it works for you and learning to use relaxation techniques for those times when life gets the best of you emotionally are both beneficial. Time management, scheduling, prioritizing commitments are all a part of reducing stress. It helps to alternately tense and relax muscles until you can let your body feel limp as a rag doll. Then fill your lungs with air, breathe in through your nose and blow out in short breaths through your lips until you can't blow out any more. Or you can breathe slowly and deeply.

Understanding nutrition and its effect on the body is a wide-open field of study. Follow a diet that is varied and loaded with fruits and vegetables and other fresh foods such as the whole grains and complex carbohydrates. Eat foods low in sugar and additives. There is controversy as to the best source of protein, whether those be only plant sources (like soya and nuts) or animal sources (meats and dairy products). A balance of both is probably best. Avoiding red meats high in saturated fats is believed to have long-term benefit for the body.

Careful hygiene is another protective measure. Being freshly washed before sexual intercourse reduces the possibility of contamination of the genitals from the anal opening. Girls and women need to learn to wipe from front to back, as was mentioned earlier. Since germs grow fastest in a warm, moist atmosphere, it is best to wear underwear that allows circulation of air (cotton rather than synthetics) and keeps the genitals clean and dry. Drying thoroughly after bathing is critical. Sometimes a blow-dryer set on low heat can be used to dry the genitals. Urinating before and after intercourse has been recommended as a technique to keep the genitals clear of infection since urine is sterile and acid, thus discouraging infections that like an alkaline environment. Condoms used for sexual intercourse can provide a barrier against invasive microorganisms. Avoidance of anal sex is highly advised, since the rectum is full of germs that can cause infection of the genitals.

Since most genital infections are sexually transmitted, one method of prevention is *sexual abstinence*. Since that is not ideal for most of us, the next best prevention method is a monogamous relationship.

Vaginal irritation or vaginitis joins bladder infections in causing havoc in sexual relationships. Sometimes these irritations may be caused by infection, other times by aging, allergic responses, or acid-base imbalances that are difficult to correct. Whatever the cause, the physical discomfort of vaginitis—the burning, itching, and tenderness—make sexual activity undesirable. That is why this is the most common genital "infection" reported in our offices. When infection can not be isolated, but the symptoms persist, we recommend the plan listed for cystitis on page 245 earlier in this chapter. The use of plain, unsweetened yogurt is surprisingly soothing and healing. Apply it immediately for irritation.

Most often the infectious causes of vaginitis are Trichomonas (a parasite), Candida albicans (a fungus), and Hemophilus vaginalis (a bacterium). Symptoms include a change in the consistency, color, and smell of the vaginal discharge, as well as itching and burning sensations.

A physician's diagnosis is needed. The treatment depends on the invading microorganism.

Viral infections are the cause of genital warts and herpes. Both are highly contagious. The warts occur in men and women and are sexually transmitted. Even though they are painless, they are itchy and irritating. All sexual partners of the affected person should be treated. The blisterlike sores of herpes can occur on the vulva or cervix of the woman and on the penis of the man. When they are caused by the Herpes Simplex Virus Type I (the cold sore virus), they are relatively harmless. The more serious virus is the Herpes Simplex Virus Type II which affects the whole body and never seems to leave it. It can be a debilitating disease, in addition to causing incredible genital pain. The person suffers from general symptoms similar to any other viral infections, like the flu. Once a person is infected with herpes, the symptoms recur throughout life. Medications can be given to control the severity of the symptoms, but at this point there is no cure. It is essential that a pregnant woman report herpes to her physician. Herpes in a pregnant mother may cause damage to the developing fetus, transmit herpes to the newborn infant, and risk viral encephalitis, which can be fatal to the infant.

The age-old bacterial infections of gonorrhea and syphilis may seem to have disappeared with the national concern for herpes and AIDS. But like termites in a house, they fester and destroy the lives of their victims when not treated. Fortunately, antibiotics are effective when treatment is sought. Gonorrhea, referred to as the clap or drip, is an extremely serious bacterial infection; it is transmitted by an infected person during sexual intercourse. The symptoms of a burning sensation on urination and a greenish, smelly discharge can occur within three weeks of being infected. The dilemma is that 75 percent of infected women are asymptomatic carriers. They show no signs of being infected, yet can transmit the disease to their sexual partners. The infection is not always limited to the genitals. It can travel into the uterus and the uterine tubes in the woman, and throughout the body in both men and women causing cardiac infections, brain infections, arthritis, and skin lesions. Should a woman be infected and untreated when her baby is born, the baby's eyes are subject to infection with the gonorrhea organism.

Before AIDS, *syphilis* was considered the most serious of all sexually transmitted diseases. It is transmitted from one person to another by direct skin contact. Ten to ninety days after contact, a chancre develops somewhere on the genitals, or on the cervix of the woman, or elsewhere in the body. This is the first or primary stage. If untreated, syphilis passes through secondary, latent, and tertiary stages. The secondary stage is characterized by a rash on the feet and hands, anorexia, fever, and sore throat. The disease circulates to every part of the body through the bloodstream.

The latent stage begins when the secondary stage symptoms recede. This is a hidden stage which can last as long as twenty years. It can be diagnosed by a blood test, treated, and stopped.

The tertiary stage is irreversible. The person is no longer infectious but the disease may have affected any or all of the vital organs of the body. Thus, the person may have brain damage, heart disease, spinal cord damage, and blindness. This damage may demonstrate itself with severe mental disturbance, lack of coordination of voluntary movement (the syphilis shuffle), and general paralysis. If a pregnant woman is infected with syphilis, her unborn baby is at a great risk of being infected.

What about AIDS? It is one of the major health care issues of our time, and the disease is on the increase. Until a cure is found, more and more people are going to be affected by it. Research will be continually supplying us with new information.

Acquired Immune Deficiency Syndrome (AIDS) slipped into medical awareness about six years ago. The rapid increase in the number of cases and the frightening fatality rate continue to surpass the scientific data available. What we know now is that the body's normal defense system against disease or invading foreign organisms is not working. In fact, the immune system is attacking the person's own body rather than fighting off the invasion of infectious organisms and malignancies.

The virus HTLV-III has been identified as the cause of AIDS. However, not everyone exposed to this virus develops AIDS. Thus it is believed that for one to develop AIDS other damage to the immune system must be present. For example, those with parasite infections and drug and alcohol abuse are at greater health risk. Nevertheless, anyone exposed can develop AIDS.

We know that transmission of AIDS occurs through direct contact of body secretions, especially blood or semen. Sexual contact is the primary method of transmission. In this country, about three-fourths of AIDS patients are homosexual or bisexual men. Nevertheless, transmission does occur heterosexually, commonly male to female, as well as homosexually. The risk increases with the number of sexual partners. The AIDS virus is also transmitted by blood-to-blood contact, such as through shared needles in IV drug abuse and through use of blood product or blood transfusions coming from infected donors. Seventeen percent of AIDS patients are intravenous drug abusers. The third way AIDS is transmitted is from mother to child during pregnancy and childbirth. There is no evidence at this time that the disease can be contracted through casual contact.

Once people are exposed to the AIDS virus, they may or may not develop AIDS. Not everyone who tests positive for the AIDS antibody (which shows they have been exposed to the AIDS virus) will develop AIDS. Some develop an AIDS-related condition, referred to as ARC. These people have swollen glands and constant low-grade fever, but they do not have life-threatening conditions. ARC is really a milder form of immune deficiency. About one-fifth of persons with ARC develop AIDS. AIDS is severe immune deficiency, so that the person develops opportunistic infections—infections that a healthy person would be able to fight off. These infections can be bacterial, viral, fungal, and protozoal. It is the multiple infectious diseases that cause death for the victims of AIDS. The outlook is dreadful.

How can we protect ourselves against AIDS? It is natural for us to be anxious about a life-threatening disease which is connected with our sexuality. Sometimes when we are afraid we fail to get the facts clear. It is important to know that the AIDS virus is not spread through the air. It requires direct contact with body secretions or blood. We cannot breathe it in. That is why casual social contact with an ARC or AIDS victim is not of concern. The research also shows that AIDS is not likely, although it is possible, to be communicated through saliva as in kissing. If the victim should have blood in the saliva, that would be dangerous. Obviously, direct contact should be avoided with blood, urine, semen, feces, and open wounds.

The only way to be certain of not being infected sexually is to avoid the exchange of any bodily fluids (semen, urine, saliva, feces, or blood) or contact of body fluid with mucous membranes of someone who might have been exposed to the AIDS virus. How can we be sure of protecting ourselves from someone who has been exposed? One way that certainly reinforces biblical teaching is to have sexual contact only with one person and to know that you are that person's only sexual partner. Even in that monogamous marriage, anal intercourse is highly discouraged unless a barrier like a condom is used. Another way is to use a barrier in all sexual contacts so as to avoid exposing your body to any secretions that might be contaminated with the AIDS virus. Condoms have been shown to effectively block transmission of the AIDS virus. Use a rubber glove for any manual genital stimulation.

Because AIDS may not develop until six months or up to five years after exposure, the only way to be sure that we are not involved with someone carrying the AIDS virus is to have the person get an antibody test for AIDS. There is, however, much controversy about who should be tested. A marriage relationship in which neither spouse has ever strayed or been involved sexually before marriage should be safe.

For Further Study

American Medical Association. *Sexually Transmitted Diseases.* Pamphlet.

Bennett, Jo Anne. AIDS: Epidemiology Update, *American Journal of Nursing,* vol. 85, no. 9, September 1985, 968–972.

Close, Sylvia. *Sex During Pregnancy and After Childbirth.* Wellingborough: Thorson's Publishers Limited, 1984.

Corsaro, Maria, and Carole Karzeniowsky. *STD—Sexually Transmitted Diseases: A Common Sense Guide.* New York: St. Martin's Press, 1980.

Gillespie, Larrian. *Eurology.* vol. 3(1), July 1984. 25–30.

Keeling, Richard P., M.D., "AIDS on Campus: What You Should Know." *Reports,* The Journal of the Association of Universities and Colleges, vol. 28, no. 2, March/April 1986, 24–28.

Sexual Addictions in the Family

The setting is a lovely middle-class home with a family of five. The children are all doing well in school. The mother is involved in the church and community. Father is a successful executive. One Sunday, mother went to church by herself because father said he wasn't feeling well. The kids were all gone for the weekend. Mother decided not to stay for the class that she usually attended after the morning worship service and so arrived home an hour earlier than expected. She walked into the bathroom to find her shocked husband dressed in women's clothes with a raving red wig, makeup, and jewelry. A piece of her died right at that moment. Shock, horror, and despair blasted both of them.

A missionary home on furlough from Africa is arrested for exposing himself to some teenage girls at the local public swimming pool. He has been a "faithful servant" for the past twenty years, a loving family man, and a caring and concerned minister of the gospel. His career is virtually ruined.

A seminary student writes from the Midwest concerned that we are the only people with whom he can talk because we are far away and don't know him. He is planning on a life of service in the church, but is plagued by a habit over which he cannot gain control. Once a week he acts on the compulsion to pick up a prostitute. He doesn't always complete the act, but he takes it to the point of being with the woman without clothes on in her room. How can he continue to "serve God" while he is carrying on in this manner?

A wife discovers a cache of pornographic photos and magazines stored in the garage. They range over a twenty-year period, are well worn and carefully filed. It had always seemed to her that her husband was a prude. He had been so vocal about his disdain for this type of material and the people who used it.

A gospel singer, who has had a very effective ministry, sits in tears as she tells about her inability to stop the habit of getting involved sexually with strange men in every city to which she travels. She grew up in a home with relatively little warmth and care. A sensitive and concerned youth pastor had recognized her talents and encouraged her to pursue them. As she did, she became well known and went on the road, but "the road" only led her deeper and deeper into a habit that had begun at age eighteen, almost by accident. She is now convinced that there is no way that she can break the habit, and is living in continual fear that she will be discovered. She is torn apart inside by the inconsistency of her public ministry and message, and the real life that she leads.

The wife of a local church leader sobs out her story of pain and despair as she tells how her husband, who is superintendent of the primary Sunday school department in a large evangelical church, has been discovered to be molesting his own three- and five-year-old daughters. Always so caring and loving with children, he seems like such a sensitive man. He gives so much of himself to the children under his care and is such a loving father, adored by everyone including his own children. Now the wife is in a heart-wrenching dilemma as to what she should do. One side of her says she should leave him to protect her children from him. The other side feels that she would be taking a very important and special person away from her children and herself. The economic factors only make it worse. What should she do?

Each of these true stories represents a world of dilemmas now thought of as sexual addictions. In the past we have always referred to these as perversions, deviations, self-gratification, or sin. They may be all of those, but for getting control of the behavior it is helpful to understand them as addictions. Usually those engaged in these behaviors despise themselves and their activities. They feel they can't gain control of the behavior. They cannot stop what they are doing. It is as if they are driven to it, acting as it were on remote control. It is similar to the alcoholic who has to have a drink or the drug addict who must get a fix.

The New York Times (Tuesday, 16 October 1984) reported this new understanding of addictive sexual behaviors. This view is being voiced by many authorities. About six years ago, we came to the conclusion from our own practice that these behaviors should be looked on as addictions. The repetitive pattern and lack of cure convinced us. An individual would get control of the behavior, and then a year or two later find himself right back into it. We observed the "out of control" quality of the behavior, and the desperation that was felt by the individual as he tried to get control. A few years later we discovered the book, *The Sexual Addiction,* by Patrick Carnes (CompCare Publications, Minneapolis, 1983). The author had developed a detailed theory for both understanding and working with the sexual addict in the same way that AA works with the alcoholic. He found the treatment to be effective.

The 1984 *New York Times* article quotes a number of others who are coming to this same conclusion. The findings of both Dr. Mark Schwartz from Tulane University in New Orleans and Dr. John Mahoney from Johns Hopkins Medical School are consistent with our own clinical experience, and confirm the addictive pattern of these sexual deviations.

The Pattern of Sexual Addictions

Sexual addiction is similar to an alcohol or drug addiction. The sexual addict develops a dependence on the sexual gratification. The dependence becomes so powerful that it supersedes family, job, and even self-esteem. The sexual addict is "hooked." He leads a secret and double life—in many ways a distorted life. He convinces himself that his behavior is justifiable.

The New York Times article summarizes the key criteria of a sexual addiction:

"Having a sexual preoccupation that interferes with a normal sexual relationship with one's spouse.

"Feeling compelled to have sexual relations again and again within a short period of time.

"A compulsion to engage in sexual behavior that leaves one feeling anxious and depressed or guilty and ashamed.

"Taking large amounts of time from family or work to engage in sex and to look for sexual adventure.

"Being driven to sex as a means to hide from the troubles of one's life."

In the 1982 autumn issue of *Leadership* magazine, an anonymous pastor wrote an article entitled, "The War Within: An Anatomy of Lust." In the article he outlined his struggle over a ten-year period with pornographic magazines, movies, videos, topless and bottomless bars, and peep shows. While he didn't use the word addiction, he described it similarly to others who outline the addictive process. The distorted thinking, the rationalizations, the blame on others, and the delusions that this pastor describes as part of his painful pilgrimage all fit closely with Carnes' understanding of sexual addictions.

The sexual addict goes through a clear cycle. Carnes lists four stages in the cycle. First he talks about *preoccupation.* The individual begins to be obsessed with the desire for the addictive behavior, finding it difficult to think about anything else. One man told us that as he moved into his addictive pattern, he was carried along by a power over which he had no control. Totally possessed or engulfed by the preoccupation, he *had* to make the obscene phone call.

After this comes the *ritual* step. This step can help determine whether or not a behavior is an addiction. These rituals are predictable thought patterns and actions that precede or prepare for the actual behavior. The rationalizations are part of this ritualistic process.

The third step is the *behavior* itself. The addict is compelled through the behavior to the point where he is satiated. This may come after a certain level of arousal or after masturbation has taken place. One patient had a compulsion to have sex with several different women a day. He found that once a woman had her first orgasm he was looking for a way out of the situation even before he climaxed. It was the woman's orgasm that was his addiction. Once he had been able to give her an orgasm, he felt free of the drive to be with her.

Carnes' fourth step is *despair.* After the compulsive behavior is completed, relief is felt. Then the self-depreciating, bitter, hopeless despair comes raging through the addict's total being. He tries to move back into normal life and responsibilities. There is great resolve never to do this again. There is prayer for forgiveness, plans for how it will be stopped the next time the temptation is present, and an avalanche of self-deprecating messages. There is renewed determination that this will never occur again. When the obsessive thoughts begin again the next day, a week later, or two months later, he feels trapped. It is impossible to get out. The anonymous pastor talks about the hundreds of prayers that he had said as a way of attempting to break the addictive cycle. None of them seemed to do any good.

We are continually using the masculine pronoun. While there are women who get caught in the web of sexual addiction, men are the main ones who find themselves enmeshed in it. So to simplify the writing we'll refer primarily to the male gender.

The Types of Sexual Addictions

As defined by Carnes, there are three levels. The first level is those behaviors that do not go against another person's will though at a deeper level they may violate. The second level would be those acts that violate another person's rights and have legal implications. On the third level are those addictions that include physical violation. Let's talk about each of these.

Level one: These are addictive heterosexual relationships. The habit of needing to conquer, possess or subdue a man or a woman on a frequent basis is seen as an addiction. The person may be married and have a happy family, but be driven to be sexually involved with total strangers without any kind of relationship. This driven behavior will eat away at the addict's marriage, open him up to contracting sexually transmitted diseases, and set up incredible emotional turmoil. The stress heightens as his victims "fall in love" with him, and he seeks to find a way out. A Christian leader, well-respected in his church community, was so driven by his compulsion for other women that he was unable to find the time to make the arrangements with his various women. So he corralled his secretary into setting up these appointments for him. This obsessive need to conquer sexually may be acted out within a marriage. The man limits himself to his wife, but makes excessive demands on her for a sexual experience three, four, even five times a day.

Prostitution is another first level addiction. The excitement is often gained from the thrill of getting connected with the woman, negotiating where, what activity, and for how much, and paying the money. The risks are high—not only in terms of arrest and disease but also to career and reputation. Yet for some, this is an outlet they are unable to control.

Homosexual contacts would be similar. Usually these are brief contacts that occur in public places, with no development of a relationship. Again, there is a high risk of disease and discovery as well as all the shame and guilt that accompanies the activity.

Preoccupation with pornographic material in either magazines, movies, videos, or live form is one of the most common forms of sexual addiction. The common rationalization is that the activity hurts no one. Yet the victims feel that gnawing sense of guilt inside themselves. The time taken away from their wives and children to indulge their addiction is engrossing. The money spent is also an issue. Most devastating are the lies and deceit necessary to carry on the habit. Many people occasionally look at a pornographic magazine and don't get hooked. They are not driven, controlled by, or secretive about it. Their interest in the material does not fit the addictive cycle.

Cross-dressing or transvestism, although often not thought of as similar to the addictive behaviors, does have the same cyclic addictive qualities. Transvestism is the habit of dressing in the clothes of the opposite sex. This is usually a man dressing in women's clothes for the purpose of sexual arousal, many times masturbation to ejaculation. The pattern generally begins by early adolescence, age twelve to fourteen. The young boy finds himself attracted to trying on female garments, especially panties, bras, girdles, nylons, slips, and shoes. Most boys go through a time of innocent curiosity about women's make-up, garments, and so on. Usually this is at an earlier age.

The addiction occurs when the secretive activity sets off arousal while the person is experimenting. He responds to the arousal with self-stimulation, which seals the habit. It is important to recognize that this is not a gender identity problem; it does not mean that the person is homosexual. Yes, some homosexuals do dress in women's clothing to attract other men, but the transvestite dresses privately or with a woman partner solely for the purpose of genital arousal. These men are strongly attracted heterosexually. As the habit develops, the man is compelled to act out his obsession regularly. Some men keep a suitcase of clothes in the trunk of their car, at the office, up in the attic, or in the garage so they can indulge the addiction as it grips them.

Some men desire their wives or other partners to participate in the sexual activity with them. They want to make love in the women's clothes or have the woman participate in dressing them. This habit may have developed as the addict was a little boy being dressed up as a girl by his older sisters. If arousal occurred in those experiences, it may have hooked him. For one man, this was a one-time event that occurred when he was twelve years old. His fifteen-year-old sister and her friends decided to dress him in their clothes. It was very arousing for him, but also embarrassing. This combination of the arousal with the uncomfortable feelings seemed to be the hook.

Even though these level one addictions do not go against anyone's will, they certainly leave the victim with an internal battle as he attempts to reconcile his behavior with his Christian faith and view of himself. His exposure always brings trauma to his loved ones.

The *level two* addictions, as Carnes points out, are violators of another person's rights and have legal implications. The first of these is exhibitionism. The exhibitionist deliberately exposes his sexual organs with the intention of evoking a response from the observer. He may wear clothes that easily allow the genitals to be exhibited, flashing from under a coat, exhibiting through a window or at a public beach. It has been our finding that the Christian people, especially the Christian leaders involved in exhibitionism, have been raised in tightly restrictive homes. One would least expect them to be involved in this kind of activity. They are not violent, and in fact, they will shun violence. They experience themselves as inadequate sexually and are attempting to bolster their view of themselves by eliciting a shocked response from their female observers.

Voyeurism is the habit of obtaining gratification by observing others in the nude or engaged in sexual activity. It is natural for anyone to take a second look if he walks by a window and sees a provocative scene. This is not voyeurism. Voyeurism is the compulsion to get sexual gratification from peeping into windows. One traveling evangelist told us that he would often spend three to four hours a night searching for windows in his home town. He could follow a ritual that had been established. When he was traveling, he would have to establish a new ritual. The purpose is to find some location where the sexual activity can be observed without the onlooker being detected, usually bringing sexual arousal, self-stimulation, and ejaculation for the "peeping Tom."

This habit may begin inadvertently. One man, now in his mid-thirties, told us that he had been walking home from school late one night after basketball practice and through a window observed two sisters changing clothes. As they continued their activity he became more engrossed and aroused. This began an almost daily habit that has been most difficult to break. He had stopped the "peeping" for several years at a time, but then suddenly found himself back in the habit. The risks were great, the possibility of arrest and shame high. After a close shave with the law, the voyeurist may get control for a while. He is usually not considered dangerous or violent.

Obscene or indecent phone calls are also illegal, inappropriate, and offensive sexual behavior. Occasionally adolescents will, on a lark, make offensive phone calls. We would not call that an addiction. But there are those adults who become habitual callers, getting their sexual arousal from making phone calls that become more and more sexually explicit. The caller may ask questions or describe sexual behavior while he stimulates himself. The hope is that the listener will not hang up the phone, and perhaps even talk to him. While this kind of a "service" is now available for a fee in many of the larger cities, it doesn't bring the same gratification as is found when the caller imposes himself on an unwilling victim.

A man in his late twenties came to us controlled by his drive to make obscene phone calls. He had done it so much during his seminary years that he had been discovered and arrested. He had stopped for a short time and then fallen back into the process again; he hated himself for it. He recognized how much it violated his beliefs and commitment, and yet he was unable to stop himself. At one point he had gone to a healing meeting and had "the demon" cast out of him. This lasted for several months and then the habit returned. He was not able to get control until he faced the reality that this indeed was an addiction, and needed to be treated as such. He recognized that the desire, the impulse, would always be there but he could gain control of the behavior.

The last form of level two addictions is the fetish. A fetish is an attachment to an object for sexual arousal and release. Stealing may become part of a fetish or remain an innocent activity that involves the use of some article of clothing, such as men's or women's shoes. The addiction will have developed in a similar way to cross-dressing. During childhood or early adolescence, the person developed a sexual attachment to an object as a source of sexual response. for that connection controls the person.

The *third level* of sexual addictions includes those behaviors that clearly violate another individual by force and violence. This would include such things as: child molestation, incest, rape, and some forms of sado-masochistic behavior. The victim is a necessary part of the sexual arousal. Please refer to the previous chapter on abuse for details on these most painful addictions.

These addictions are not limited to the evil, wicked world. They are happening to Christians. Emotional trauma that is experienced later in life seriously affects the sexual adjustment of these victims. Many such stories are shared in the previous chapter.

The Sexual Addict

The sexual addict may be the successful businessman, popular pastor, caring father, attractive male, or the friendly neighbor next door. There is a tendency to label the addict as a sick pervert who needs to be locked up. We meet them face to face in our everyday world. These people don't look different, but they come out of a world of deprivation and pain. As you hear their stories, their addictive behavior makes sense. This does not excuse them or rid them of the responsibility, but it helps us love them.

We think, for example, of the man who was continually told by his father how inadequate he was. He was not enough of a man. He would never amount to anything. It was too bad that he wasn't like his masculine brothers and cousins. As an adult, this person frequented homosexual video and peep shows. In these settings, he would look for a homosexual to stimulate him to orgasm. He would leave having confirmed all the disgrace that had been heaped on him in his growing years.

This feeling of inadequacy is typical of almost all the addictions listed. There is an overwhelming sense of inadequacy. These men feel that they are not worthwhile people. They are despicable, not worthy of love, and not able to have their needs met. The hope behind this addictive drive is to at least get their sexual needs met. They experience sex as their most basic need and the only source of fulfillment in life. Carnes noted that these basic dimensions of the self-concept are foundational for each person who is addicted. He also

...ological and spiritual dimen-
... our capacity to integrate. For
... with God, their relationship with
... The anonymous writer of the "lust"
... Beatitudes the message is, "Blessed are
... shall know God." As people become more
...their addiction, they also move further and further
... in the article, the anonymous pastor suggests ten
ste... ...help one fight the battle against addiction.

1) ...gnize and name the problem." This is difficult but necessary.

2) "Stop feeding lust." Don't keep putting yourself in situations that trigger your patterns. For example, if your long walks in the evening are your opportunity to look in windows, walk in broad daylight. If you need your wife along on business trips to keep you from visiting prostitutes, then take her along.

3) "Demythologize it." When someone is hooked on a sexual addiction, a myth will generally develop around that activity. Face the reality that the shock people experience when you expose yourself to them or telephone them is really disgust and surprise, not sexual arousal.

4) "Confess its real price." Be realistic about the cost in terms of time, energy, money, relationships, anxiety, guilt, and worry, in relationship to yourself, your spouse, your family, your friends, and God.

5) "Trace its history." Whenever we are dealing with a habit pattern that we are trying to break, it is important to understand how it got started. Become aware of all the little steps along the way that led to this point. Write those out. Add to them as further thoughts come to mind.

6) "Study sex in perspective." Keep in mind that the misuse of sex is an immoral, destructive, dirty activity but sex itself is a wholesome, God-ordained activity. The marriage bond is used throughout the Scriptures to symbolize God's relationship to His people. (For a detailed account of this, see *The Gift of Sex*.)

7) "Build fantasies on God's ideal." As one of our friends put it, "Don't commit adultery in your mind, commit marriage." Guide your fantasies away from the obsession and in the direction of your spouse or hoped-for spouse.

8) "Work on some positive addictions." As an addictive person, get yourself hooked on a constructive habit. That can be jogging, writing poetry—or feeding canaries! It really doesn't matter as long as it builds and enhances both you and your relationships.

9) "Recognize the humanity of your victims." Whether these are the girls you are watching through the peep-shows or the girls you are violating, be aware that they have human needs and feelings. You are either invading their privacy or hurting their person.

10) "Obsession comes out of a legitimate set of anxieties, follow them to their authentic source." Get a deep understanding of what is behind your obsession. It may be a need for affection, self-esteem, a father-figure, or a mother in your life. The better you understand what is behind your obsession, the more control you will gain. In addition, be accountable to someone for your addictive behavior.

Sexual addictions are a serious dilemma in our society and in the church. They drain productive energy, distort reality, and destroy lives. Sexual addicts need our help and understanding just as much as do schizophrenics or cancer patients. We invite you to be open, loving, and understanding—but tough in your demands for control. We want to send a message of hope to those who struggle with these troublesome desires that rage so out of control.

For Further Study

Anonymous. "The War Within: An Anatomy of Lust." *Leadership.* Autumn 1982.

Carnes, Patrick, Ph.D., *The Sexual Addiction.* Now Retitled: *Out of the Shadows.* Minneapolis: Comp Care Publications, 1983.

Carrera, Michael. *Sex: The Facts, the Acts, and Your Feelings.* New York: Crown Publishers, Inc., 1981. "Erotica" and "Fetishism."

Subject Index

AA (Alcoholics Anonymous), 255, 263

A Baby? Maybe: A Guide to the Most Fateful Decision in Your Life by Elizabeth Whelan, 8, 14

Abortion, 18, 19, 48, 55, 59, 139, 140
  spontaneous, 62

Abstinence, 19, 27, 161, 163, 164, 248
  vaginal 60

Adam and Eve, 12

Adolescence, 4, 44, 122, 123, 125, 127, 178, 209, 260

Adoption, 4, 44, 45, 42, 49, 50, 51, 52, 53

Adulterous, 226

Affection 40, 41

Agreement regarding parenthood, 8

AIDS (Acquired Immune Deficiency Syndrome), 154, 157, 242, 249–52

Alcohol, 130, 166, 199, 214, 216, 226, 233

Alcoholism, 199, 255, 262

"Am I Normal?" (film) 144

American Journal of Obstetrics and Gynecology, 46

Anal intercourse, 248, 251

Anal opening, 248

Anderson and Cole, 204

Anemia, 199

Anger about infertility, 47, 48

Anorexic, 161

Anus, 243, 247

ARC (AIDS-related condition), 251

Arousal, 36, 40, 50, 80, 81, 93, 169, 175, 179, 180, 181, 188, 193, 197, 201–203, 213, 214, 218, 256, 258, 259, 260, 261
  after prostectomy, 213

Aroused, 188, 197

Artificial insemination, 34, 35, 36

Barbach, Loni, 94

Betrayal of Innocence: Incest and Its Devastation by Susan Forward and Craig Buck, 233, 235

Bible, 119, 127, 128, 160, 163, 165, 167, 187, 239, 262, 264
  Bible study, 40, 263

Biblical affirmation of sexual pleasure in marriage, 143, 146

Bingham, Edmundson, and Stryker, 145

Birth control, 13. 16–29, 34, 47, 48, 50, 53, 66, 123, 145, 154, 156, 157, 162
  barrier methods, 13, 20
  concern about, 13
  in family planning, 5
  natural methods, 26
  reversible methods, 27
  surgical methods, 27

Bisexual, 250

Bladder infections, 243, 244–46, 248
Boas, Prof. Dr. med. C. Van Emde, 134
Bonding, 57, 101, 102, 103
Brain tumors, 199
Breasts, 57, 65, 66, 121, 146, 176, 195, 203, 214, 218
Breast-feeding, 52, 66, 67, 68, 70, 93, 102
Brecher, Edward M., 215, 218
Brockway, Dr. Jo Ann, 199
Buck, Craig, 233

Cancer, 24, 199–200
Candida albicans, 248
Cardiovascular disease, 198
Career, 3, 6, 7, 14, 49, 258
Carnes, Patrick, 255–57, 259, 261
Castrated Woman, The by Naomi Stokes, 212
Celibacy, 164
Cerebral palsy, 199
Cervical cap, 20, 22
Cervix, 21–27, 32, 33, 35, 60, 65, 249
Challenges by Bingham, Edmonson, and Stryker, 145
Chemotherapy, 200
Childbearing years, 14
Childbirth, 52, 55
Childlessness, 11, 12, 42, 44, 45, 46, 47, 48, 49, 52, 53
Children
  choice to have, 4, 10, 47
  planning for, 5
  unwanted, 3, 154
Children: To Have or Have Not: A Guide to Making and Living with Your Decision by Diane C. Elvenstar, 8
Choices by Bingham, Edmonson, and Stryker, 145
Christ, 48, 103
Christians, 119, 125, 128, 129, 157, 159, 162, 163, 164, 165, 174
  single, 153, 154, 158, 166, 167, 168, 257, 259, 261
  difficulty using family planning, 19
Christianity, 133
Church, 16
  Mormon Church, 17
  Roman Catholic Church, 17, 26
Climax, 193
Clitoris, 119, 147, 182, 218
Coitus, 55, 134
"Color Purple, The" (film), 231

Communication, 37, 118, 121, 126, 143, 146, 182, 195, 201, 202, 226
  poor pattern, 91
  skills, 38
Conception, 25, 31, 33, 35, 36, 38, 39, 40, 41, 45, 46, 50, 70, 207
Condom, 13, 18, 20, 245, 248, 251, 252
Contraception, 17, 18, 25
  postcoital, 25, 26
  risk, 26
Counselor, 195, 196, 263
Cross-dressing, 258
Curiosity, 95, 102, 137, 143, 225
Cystitis, 243, 244, 248
  bacterial, 244
  interstitial, 244

"Dear Diary" (film), 144
Delivery, 52, 59, 60, 65, 67, 102
Denial
  of adolescent sexuality, 124
  of infertility, 47, 48
  of sexual abuse, 229, 230, 240
  of single sexuality, 160–61
Depression, 36, 38, 62, 64, 67
Deviations, 254
Dialators, 181, 182
Diabetes, 198
Diaphragm, 13, 18, 20, 21, 22
Disorders, 198
  endocrine, 198
Divorce, 3, 8, 48, 92, 97, 154, 155, 156, 158, 189, 217
Dobson, Dr. James, 119, 125, 131, 245
Douching, 20, 22, 32, 61, 248
Drugs, 130, 199, 200, 233

Egg, 18, 23, 27, 28, 32, 209
Ego
  development, 131
  identity, 126
  strength, 123
Ejaculation, 28, 31, 32, 33, 34, 35, 40, 57, 66, 98, 121, 147, 176, 197, 209, 213, 214, 259
  five to ten seconds warning, 19
  premature ejaculation, 32, 82
  retarded ejaculation, 32, 197
  retrograde ejaculation, 212
Elvenstar, Diane C., 8
Endocrine system, 199

Endometriosis, 35, 49
Episiotomy, 65, 67, 69
Erection, 32, 37, 82, 89, 121, 156, 173, 174, 175, 178, 192, 197, 198, 208, 213, 214, 216, 217
Erectile dysfunction, 212
Estrogen, 23, 26, 148, 209, 210, 212, 215
  estrogen replacement, 210, 212
Exhibitionism, 259, 262
Expectation, 5, 49
  to have children, 5
  that older couples are less sexual, 216
Experience of Love, An by Ingrid Trobisch and Elizabeth Roetzer, 26
Experimentation, 203, 258
  in marriage, 81, 216
  of children, 137, 225
  of adolescents, 176

Fallopian tubes, 27, 32
Family planning, 16
Fear
  of the unknown, 6
  about having children, 14
Feces, 251
Femininity, 38, 46, 211
Fertility, 30, 31, 41, 45, 47, 212
Fetish, 260
Fetus, 61
Finances, 4, 6, 14, 44, 188
Forgive and Forget by Dr. Lewis Smedes, 238
For Yourself: The Fulfillment of Female Sexuality by Loni Barbach, 94
Forward, Susan, 233, 235
Foster, Richard J., 164
Fulfillment, 12, 37, 41, 50, 53, 85, 136, 146, 156, 158, 159, 162, 168, 169, 193, 226, 261
  of reproductive role, 62

Gender identity, 90, 143, 258
Genital organs
  naming, 105, 106, 143
  after childbirth, 65
  considered "dirty," 174
Genital self-discovery, 104, 105
Genital warts, 248, 249
Gift of Sex, The, 35, 50, 51, 80, 94, 127, 132, 141, 178, 181, 196, 201, 202, 264
Gillespie, Dr. Larrian, 244, 246

God, 11, 12, 14, 17, 37, 40, 42, 45, 51, 54, 95, 110, 119, 127, 128, 129, 130, 154, 156, 160, 161, 162, 164, 165, 168, 169, 191, 192, 194, 254, 263, 264
Gonorrhea, 249
Graffenburg, Dr., 18
Grandparents, 14, 188
Grief process, 64, 193, 194
  in infertility, 48, 49
G-spot, 18
Gynecological exam, 180
Gynecologist, 33, 143, 243, 245

Harlowe's Monkey Experiment, 178
Heart disease, 24, 198
Hebrew culture, 12
Hemophilus vaginalis, 248
Herpes, 154, 157, 242, 248, 249
Heterosexuality, 96, 97, 99, 225, 250
  addictive heterosexual relationships, 257
Homosexual contacts, 258
Homosexuality, 48, 96, 97, 98, 99, 228, 250, 258, 261
  response to abuse, 228
"Homosexual stage," 98
Hormonal
  abnormalities, 62, 67, 115
  changes, 56, 211
  cycle, 24
  pregnancy prevention, 23
Hormones, 23, 123, 198, 199
Hot flashes, 209–210
How to Make Love to the Same Person for the Rest of Your Life: And Still Love It, by Dagmar O'Connor, 50
Hygiene, 248
Hysterectomy, 49, 211, 212

Identity, 56
Illness, 190, 191–205
Impotence, 32, 82, 175, 176, 177, 178, 197, 213, 214, 215, 216, 219
  after prostetectomy, 213
Impregnate, 13, 36
Impregnation, 31, 32, 33, 34, 39, 40
Inability to reproduce, 15, 16
Incest, 223, 224, 225, 228, 233, 235, 237, 239, 261
Income, 6
Infant, 4, 51, 52, 66, 67, 89, 101, 102, 103, 104, 130, 143

Infertility, 31, 34, 35, 37, 38, 39, 41, 42, 44, 45, 46, 47, 48, 49, 51, 52, 53
Inhibitions, 94, 187, 188, 189, 216
In-laws, 185–89
Intercourse
  pain during, 65, 67, 82, 177, 178, 198, 246
  preparation for first, 142, 146, 179
  refraining from, 19
  teenage, 136, 144
  unprotected, 26
Intimacy, 37, 38, 39, 40, 57, 58, 63, 77, 78, 101, 103, 122, 126, 158, 159, 163, 164, 168, 188, 192, 193, 195, 196, 201, 203, 204, 206, 226, 234
Intrauterine Device (IUD), 18, 23

Kinsey Reports, The, 215
Kolodney, Robert C., 197

Labia, 70, 147, 182
Labor, 52, 55, 59, 60, 61, 65, 102
Leadership magazine, 256
Leman, Kevin, 145
Libido, diminishing, 212
Life crisis, 45, 201
Lifestyle, 6, 45
"Little Darlings" (film), 126
Liver disease, 199
Long, W. H., 207, 209, 215
Love, 40, 93, 103, 195, 261
Love-making, 13, 37, 39, 41, 60, 65, 162, 190
Love, Sex, and Aging, Consumer Union Report, edited by Edward M. Brecher, 215, 218
Lubricant, 21, 65, 66, 179, 181, 203, 215, 219
  Albolene and Allercreme, 65, 181
  KY jelly, 181

Madonna syndrome, 68
Mahoney, Dr. John, 255
Male climacteric, 212
Male Sexuality: A Guide to Sexual Fulfillment by Bernie Zilbergeld, 95
Malignancies, 199
Make Anger Your Ally by Dr. Neil Warren, 92
Manhood, 46
Marriage
  conflict in, 6
  consummation, 32, 173, 176–78, 180, 183, 184

  delayed until later in life, 11, 142
  links sexuality and spirituality, 140
  encounters, 38
Masculinity, 38, 97
Mastectomy, 195
Masters and Johnson, 99, 197, 202, 209, 215, 217
Masturbation, 26, 40, 94, 110, 118, 119, 123, 144, 156, 167, 175, 208, 217, 256
Maturity, 46, 127
Medications, 25
Menarche, 209
Menning, Barbara Eck, 47, 49
Menopause, 12, 209–12
Menstruation, 25, 26, 28, 31, 45, 121, 144, 146, 147, 209, 211
  menstrual periods, 31, 49, 55, 66, 94, 209
  menstrual cramps, 25
Mental health, 46
Minerals, 24
Miscarriage, 34, 55, 61, 62
Mitchell, Eileen, 46
Molestation, 99, 113, 114, 143, 179, 223–25, 229, 232–34, 236–40, 254, 261
Money, Sex, and Power by Richard J. Foster, 164
Motherhood, 46, 67
Multiple sclerosis, 196, 199
Muscular dystrophy, 199
Mutual respect
  in sexual relationships, 95
  in the family, 138
Mutual stimulation, 125
Myasthenia Gravis, 199

Needs, 3, 63, 102, 125, 156, 158, 165, 201, 202, 261, 265
Nervous system, 199
Neurological disorders, 199
Neurotransmitters, 198
The New York Times, 255
Nipple erection, 174, 197
Non-demand pleasuring, 79, 80, 140, 201
Nonsexual affection, 40, 57
Nudity, 112, 218

Obscene or indecent phone calls, 260
O'Connor, Dagmar, 50
Offspring, 4
Old Testament, 18, 46
Option to have children, 5

Oral contraceptives, 24
  side effects, 24
Oral stimulation, 61, 175, 203, 218, 224
Orgasm, 37, 41, 55, 56, 58, 59, 60, 61, 119,
  125, 147, 158, 159, 192, 197, 206, 208,
  219, 256, 261
Orgasmic, 30, 36, 61, 82, 167, 179, 197, 203,
  218
Ostomy, 196
Ovary, 27, 211
Ovulation, 23, 27, 33, 34, 35, 40, 66, 121,
  147
Ovum, 32

Paintbrush, 182
Parenting, 4, 6, 53, 103, 127
  education, 11
  perpetuation of society, 11
Parenthood, 7, 46
Pathogens, 247
Pelvic
  examination, 36, 180
  exercises 69, 70
  surgery, 22
Pelvis, 198
Penile prosthesis, 213
Penis, 19, 28, 65, 105, 119, 121, 147, 174,
  179, 180, 182, 198, 203, 204, 214, 219,
  247, 249
Performance anxiety, 178
Peritoneum, 27
Perversions, 254
Pill, The, 13, 18, 23, 24, 25, 34, 135, 156,
  247
  combined, 23
  mini-pill, 24
  triphasic, 23
Pituitary problems, 198
Placenta, 61
Planning children, 5
Playing "doctor," 111
Pleasure, 39, 40, 41, 46, 50, 65, 70, 78, 79,
  80, 95, 102, 103, 109, 111, 119, 144, 175,
  177, 179, 181, 182, 206, 208, 213, 214
  after prostectomy, 213
  pleasure oriented sex, 36
Poliomyelitis, 199
Pope John Paul II, 17
Pornographic materials, 154, 158
Positions, 32, 33
  during pregnancy, 58
  knee-chest, 33
  missionary, 33
Postpartum period, 65, 67
Prayer, 40, 68
Preadolescence, 115, 120, 123
Pregnancy, 22, 27, 34, 36, 40, 41, 45, 51, 55,
  56, 57, 58, 59, 60, 61, 62, 64, 67, 70,
  139, 140, 156, 162, 218
  expectations, 4
  multiple, 60
  prevention, 18
  risk, 22, 26
  and sexually transmitted diseases, 249-51
  teenage, 122, 126, 127, 145 unwanted, 16,
  157
Pregnant, 5, 13, 14, 16, 17, 22, 37, 47, 50,
  51, 53, 58, 61, 109, 249
Premarital counseling, 7
Premarital sex, 48, 122, 156
Premenstrual
  tension, 25, 28
  cramps, 25
Pressure, 36, 37, 127, 133
  to have children, 5
Privacy, 85, 187
Procreation, 4, 46, 219
Progesterone, 23, 210
Prostatectomy, 212, 213
Prostate gland, 28, 198, 212
Prostatic surgery, 212-13
Prostitute, 253
Prostitution, 228, 257, 262
Puberty, 34, 56, 93, 118, 123, 139, 142, 144,
  156, 209, 211, 223
Pubic
  bone, 22
  hair, 147
Pubococcygeus (PC) muscle, 69, 70, 78, 179,
  210, 219
PC muscle exercises (Kegel exercises), 180,
  210, 215

Five R system, 107-10
Radiation therapy, 199, 200
Rape, 25, 176, 179, 225, 226, 261
Rebellion, 130, 138
Refractory period, 214
Relationship
  monogamous, 61, 242, 248, 251
Renal (kidney) failure, 199
Reproduction, 16, 46, 144, 208

Reproductive life program, 16
Reproductive organs, 49
  disease of, 198
Reproductive system, 139
Reproductive years, 30, 209
Resistance to having a baby, 6
RESOLVE Inc., 38, 47
Responsibility
  for care of sick child, 194
  for sex education, 128
  for the baby, 67
  for your own sexual pleasure, 80, 202
  of married couples for in-laws, 188
  parental, 4, 14
Rewards of having children, 4
Rhythm (or Billings) method, 13, 18, 26
Roetzer, Elizabeth, 26
Role
  parental, 6, 7
  sexual, 90
Rosenfeld, David C., M.D., 46

Sado-masochistic behavior, 261
Sanctified, 153
Sane Sex Life and Sane Sex Living by H. W.
  Long, 207
Satir, Virginia, 124
Scrotal stimulation, 218
Schwartz, Dr. Mark, 255
Self-concept, 233, 237
Self-esteem, 36, 38, 46, 58, 255, 265
Self-image, 230, 234
Self-stimulation, 95, 105, 111, 119, 125, 159,
  167, 209, 219, 259
Semen, 250, 251
Seminal fluid, 19, 20, 21, 28, 212, 214
Sex-talk, 81
Sex education, 89, 93, 101, 106, 108, 110,
  120, 131, 134, 136, 137, 138, 139, 140,
  141, 142, 143–49, 223
  by adolescent peer-counselors, 142, 145
  for married couples, 143
  for parents, 132, 134, 141, 142
  for the single adult, 142, 146
  in Christian schools, 140
  in the church, 140
  in the schools, 136
  premarital classes, 142, 146
Sex for Christians by Dr. Lewis B. Smedes,
  163

Sexual abuse, 113, 114, 224–41
Sexual Addiction, The by Patrick Carnes, 252–
  55, 259, 261
Sexual addictions, 253
Sexual desire, 36, 37, 57, 58, 67, 161
Sexual development, 103
Sexual drive, 57, 115, 123, 125, 190, 193, 198
Sexual dysfunctions, 197, 198, 199
Sexual enjoyment, 36
Sexual feelings vs. sexual behavior, 128
Sexual identity, 92, 96, 97, 99
Sexual intimacy, 35, 37
Sexual play, 21, 125, 126
Sexual problems, 25, 81, 82, 143, 180, 199
  problem solving, 129
Sexual therapist, 32, 82, 103, 197, 263
Sexual therapy
  for retarded ejaculation, 32
  for impotence, 32
  for unconsummated marriages, 32
Sexually transmitted diseases, 20, 61, 128, 145,
  154, 157, 242, 257, 258
Sexuality
  adolescent, 122
  after sterilization, 28
  and spirituality, 140
  older-adult, 209
Shedd, Charlie, 156
Single person, 153, 154, 155, 157, 158, 159,
  164, 166, 167, 168
Single parents, 3, 91, 92
Smedes, Dr. Lewis B., 163, 238
Sperm, 18, 19, 20, 27, 28, 32, 33, 34, 35, 36,
  212
  sperm count, 33, 34, 35, 212
  longevity, 27
Spermicide, 20, 21, 22, 23, 32
Spinal cord injuries, 199
  Northwest Regional Spinal Cord Injury Cen-
  ter, 199
Spiritual Life, 40
Sponge, The, 21
Spontaneity, 35, 36, 79, 187
Stages of development, 4, 10, 46, 101
Sterilization, 27, 28
Stewardship of children, 10
Stillbirth, 61, 63, 64
Stokes, Naomi, 212
Stress, 6, 11, 33, 35, 36, 40, 55, 61, 62, 64,
  69, 92, 161, 190, 191, 192, 193, 194, 195,
  201, 202, 203, 204, 240, 247, 257, 263

Suicide, 119
Surgery, 27, 34, 212, 213, 247
  pelvic, 22
  prostatic, 212, 213
Syphilis, 249, 250

Ten Commandments for Parents Providing Sex Education by Prof. Dr. med. C. van Emde Boas, 134
Tergi, Igno, M.D., 27
Testes, 28, 212
Testicles, 33, 34, 35, 121, 147
Testosterone, 146, 147, 212
Textbook of Sexual Medicine by Robert Kolodney, William H. Masters, and Virginia E. Johnson, 197
"Then One Year" (film), 144
Therapy, 50, 201, 238
  group, 238
  sexual, 32, 91, 165, 177, 178, 185, 186, 192, 197, 202, 206, 213, 217, 263
Therapeutic situation, 92
Thyroid dysfunction, 198
Timing, 14
Toddlerhood, 104, 143
Toxic Shock Syndrome, 21
Transvestism, 258, 259
Trichomonas, 248
Trobisch, Ingrid, 27
Tubal ligation, 27

Urethra, 28, 210
Urethritis, 243
Urinary bladder, 212
Urinary tract, 243
  infections, 198

Uterine tubes, 249
Uterus, 21, 33, 35, 59, 65, 199, 212, 239
  retroverted/tipped, 33
  sagging, 22

Vagina, 18, 19, 20, 21, 22, 23, 26, 27, 31, 32, 61, 65, 70, 105, 121, 174, 178–82, 199, 210, 214, 217, 219, 243, 247, 248
Vaginal
  lubrication, 89, 156, 174, 192, 197, 198, 203, 204, 215
  mucus, 26, 34
  muscle, 174, 181–83
  obstructions, 22
  outlet, 179
  wall, 215
Vaginismus, 32, 178–81
Vaginitis, 244, 245, 248
Varicocele or varicose vein, 33, 34
Vas deferens, 28, 212
Vasectomy, 28
Vault cap, 23
Vibrator, 203
Vimule cap, 23
Virginity, 157, 160, 237
Voyeurism, 259, 262
Vulva, 121, 198, 249

Warren, Dr. Neil, 92
Weight change, 22, 24, 58
Wet dreams, 121, 167
Widows and widowers, 155, 217
Whelan, Elizabeth M., 8
Whitman, Dr. Frederick J., 96
Withdrawal method, 18, 19
Womb, 51

Zilbergeld, Bernie, 95

Scripture Index

Genesis
2:24   191

Song of Solomon
                                 83

1 Corinthians
7:3–5   19
7:5   83
7:8–9, 32–38   83

Ephesians
6:1–3   191